OXFORD

geog.gcse

teacher's handbook

- starters and plenaries • objectives and outcomes
- answers

< anna king >< catherine hurst >< john edwards >< chris stevens >

< susan mayhew >< jack mayhew >< david smith >

OXFORD
UNIVERSITY PRESS

Great Clarendon Street, Oxford OX2 6DP

Oxford University Press is a department of the University of Oxford.
It furthers the University's objective of excellence in research,
scholarship, and education by publishing worldwide in

Oxford   New York

Auckland   Cape Town   Dar es Salaam   Hong Kong   Karachi
Kuala Lumpur   Madrid   Melbourne   Mexico City   Nairobi
New Delhi   Shanghai   Taipei   Toronto

With offices in

Argentina   Austria   Brazil   Chile   Czech Republic   France   Greece
Guatemala   Hungary   Italy   Japan   Poland   Portugal   Singapore
South Korea   Switzerland   Thailand   Turkey   Ukraine   Vietnam

Oxford is a registered trade mark of Oxford University Press
in the UK and in certain other countries

Authors: Anna King, Catherine Hurst, John Edwards, Chris Stevens,
Susan Mayhew, Jack Mayhew, David Smith

British Library Cataloguing in Publication Data

Data available

ISBN-13: 978-0-19-913467-0
ISBN-10: 0-19-913467-7

10 9 8 7 6 5 4 3 2 1

Printed in Great Britain by Ashford Colour Press, Gosport.

Contents

About this course

geog.GCSE is a complete course for GCSE geography. It is suitable for all GCSE specifications, and offers excellent support for the Secondary Strategy.

The course components

The course consists of the students' book, the teacher's handbook, and the teacher's resource file, which comes with a CD-ROM.

Find out more about the course components by looking at these panels.

The students' book

- A single book for the course
- Chapters divided into two-page units
- Chapter openers give the big picture – the big ideas behind the chapter – and the goals for the chapter
- Aims of unit given in student-friendly language at the start of each unit
- Activities at the end of each unit
- Glossary covering key vocabulary

The teacher's handbook

- Chapter overviews
- Help at a glance for each unit
- Ideas for starters and plenaries for each unit
- Outcomes for each unit
- Answers for Activities
- Glossary covering key vocabulary

The teacher's resource file

- Photocopiable decision-making exercises, enquiries, role-plays, and fieldwork, with assessment criteria and grade information in student-friendly language
- Photocopiable exam-style questions at Higher and Foundation tier, with assessment criteria and grade information in student-friendly language
- Opportunities for teacher, self-, and peer assessment
- Photocopiable self-assessment forms – one for each chapter
- Outline maps
- Course and lesson planners
- All material on CD-ROM, with all material provided as editable Word files
- Photocopiable glossary covering key vocabulary

geog.GCSE provides a wide range of materials. The students' book is the core of the course. It combines a rigorous approach to content with an engaging style.

You can decide how to use the support materials. The whole package provides a comprehensive and flexible course for GCSE geography – which we hope you will enjoy using.

Using this teacher's handbook

This *geog.GCSE teacher's handbook* aims to save you time and effort! It offers full support for *geog.GCSE* students' book, and will help you prepare detailed course and lesson plans.

What it provides

For each chapter of the students' book, this teacher's handbook provides:

1 a chapter overview

2 help at a glance for each unit, including ideas for starters and plenaries and answers for Activities

It also has a glossary at the back, covering the geographical terms the students will meet.

Find out more about the two main components, below.

1   The chapter overview

This is your introduction to the corresponding students' chapter. Look at its sections.

> Sets out the objectives and outcomes for the chapter, and the corresponding unit numbers.

> Sets out the key ideas within, and behind, the students' chapter. The students' version of this is given in their chapter opening unit.

> Gives information to help you with the chapter starters, in the chapter opening units of the students' book.

> Gives a very brief summary of what's covered in the students' chapter. Together with the chapter opening unit in the students' book, it will help you give students a roadmap for the chapter.

2 Help at a glance for each unit

These pages give comprehensive help for each unit of *geog.GCSE* students' book.

Starts with a brief walk through the unit, to show you how it develops.

Summarises ideas covered in the unit, plus underlying ideas where appropriate.

Full answers to the Activities in the students' book, to save you time.

New vocabulary introduced in the unit. See the glossary at the back of this teacher's handbook.

A breakdown of the skills practised. It will help you identify where students may need extra support.

Expected outcomes for the unit. They tie in with the expected outcomes for the chapter.

Suggestions for a starter.

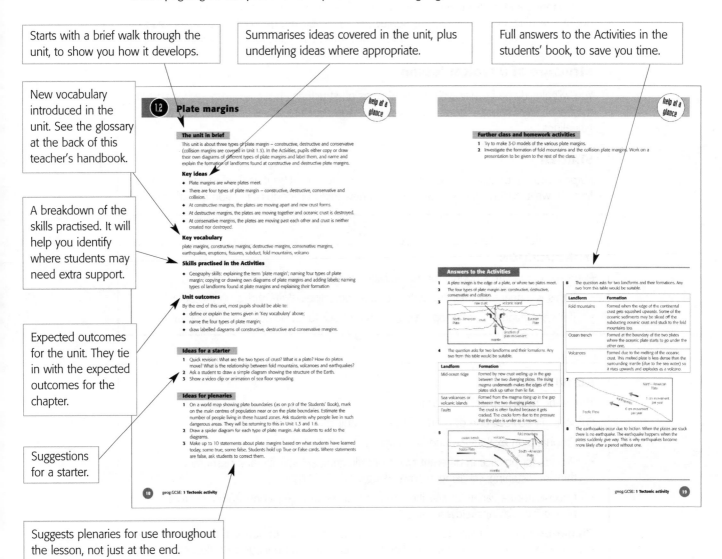

Suggests plenaries for use throughout the lesson, not just at the end.

Planning for high-quality lessons

Well-planned and well-structured lessons are a key requirement, for delivering high-quality teaching and learning in any subject, at any level. The *geog.GCSE* course aims to make it easy to plan, structure, and deliver, high-quality lessons for GCSE geography.

Structure of a typical lesson

You will already be familiar with the guidelines on structuring lessons, promoted as part of the Secondary Strategy. This shows a typical lesson structure, as recommended in those guidelines:

STARTER

Purpose: To capture students' attention and focus the class. Use it as the lesson hook, or to find out what students know already about a new topic, or for quick revision of earlier work.

INTRODUCTION

Purpose: To prepare students for the activities ahead.

- If this is a new topic, tell students the topic objectives. Write these on the board.
- If it's a continuation of a topic, you can refer back to an objective as appropriate.

ACTIVITIES

This is the main body of the lesson.

Purpose: To achieve one or more of the topic objectives.

- Emphasis on exploration and investigation.
- Provide for practice in different types of skill: geographical, literacy, numeracy, thinking, listening, speaking, teamworking, and ICT skills.
- Choose from a variety of activities: reading, answering questions, enquiries, role play, game playing, fieldwork, and ICT.

Plenaries: note that plenaries can be used as staging posts throughout the activities, to gain feedback, check understanding, link to earlier work, and encourage reflection on what is being learnt, and how.

FINAL PLENARY

Purpose: To round off and review what has been done, and to assess what has been achieved against the topic objectives. This is where you help students to:

- check, and crystallise, their understanding
- generalise, for example from an individual case study
- set work in context, and make links to work already done, or to be done in the future
- reflect on how they have learned, as well as what
- check how well they have achieved the topic objectives (self-assessment).

HOMEWORK

Purpose: To confirm, give practice in, and extend, what has been learnt in the lesson.

- The homework can lead on from the final plenary, and be the basis for a starter for the next lesson.

Planning around *geog.GCSE*

Now see how the components of *geog.GCSE* provide material for each part of your lesson.

STARTERS

- The *Help at a glance* pages in this teacher's handbook have suggestions for lesson starters.
- See further notes about starters in this teacher's handbook.

OBJECTIVES

- The opening lines of each unit in the students' book give the purpose of the unit, in student-friendly language. The goals for each chapter are given in its opening unit.
- See also the objectives and outcomes given in this teacher's handbook.

ACTIVITIES

Using the students' book

- The text in the students' book provides the core information students need. Some lends itself to reading aloud, but try 'quiet time' too.
- You can let students work through the text uninterrupted, or break it up with Activities. (These generally follow the order of the text).
- The questions give practice in literacy, thinking, and geography skills.
- Some are ideal a whole-class questions with verbal response. Others can be worked through by students working alone, in pairs or in small groups. Some questions are open-ended questions that challenge students to show what they can do.
- For students who finish early, you could ask them to select and write definitions of key vocabulary from the unit, to make revision notes about the lesson, or to draft a question for an 'Ask the expert' session at the end of the lesson. You could also get them to start an activity from this file.

Using the teacher's resource file

- This file has two main types of activities you can base lessons on:
  - exam-style questions at Higher and Foundation tier, with assessment criteria and grade information
  - decision-making exercises, enquiries, role-plays, and fieldwork, with assessment criteria and grade information.

Plenaries

- The *Help at a glance* pages in this teacher's handbook give suggestions for plenaries, for use throughout the lesson as well as at the end.
- See further notes about plenaries in this teacher's handbook.

Homework

- Some of the Activities in the students' book could be used for homework, particularly certain open-ended questions and those identified as research activities.
- You could use the exam-style questions or longer activities from the resource file.
- At the end of a chapter, students could complete the self-assessment form, and identify parts of the topic they need to re-visit or get extra help on.

More about starters and plenaries

Planning your starters and plenaries

Effective starters and plenaries need to be planned for. With planning, you can ensure that they'll help you to meet your lesson objectives, and that you won't have to rely on sudden inspiration in the classroom. But even where they are planned, you may want and need to modify them as you go along, in response to your students.

Our suggestions for starters and plenaries

The kinds of activities you feel comfortable with, for starters and plenaries, will depend on your teaching style, and the individual class. So the suggestions for starters and plenaries in this book are just that: suggestions! You may want to use some as described, or adapt them. Or they may provide inspiration for new ideas of your own.

The starters

- Most of these are intended for use with the students' book closed, before students have looked at the new unit. But they lead seamlessly into the work in the students' book.
- In some cases you may want to combine two starters to give a more extended one.
- A number of starters require the use of an atlas, and can be an excellent way of giving your students atlas practice that's fun.
- Other starters require both physical and mental activity – for example creating a graffiti wall on the board. This is a good way to get everyone involved.

The plenaries

- There are suggestions for plenaries for use throughout the lesson, not just at the end.
- They have been chosen for a variety of purposes: to encourage feedback; assess understanding; promote reflection; build bridges with material already covered (or still to be covered), with other subjects, and with the real world; help crystallise what has been learnt; and see whether it applies to other situations.
- Some of the plenaries are single questions. You will find that you can readily combine some to make more extended plenaries.
- Some need more preparation than others. You might not want to choose these for every class, but it's a good idea to ring the changes, and keep your students surprised.
- Together with the Activities, the *Ideas for plenaries* section is a rich resource to help you deliver fresh, exciting and effective lessons.

Resources for starters and plenaries

Images

Many of the starters, and some plenaries, require images – mostly photos. These can be printed, on OHTs, or displayed from a computer via an interactive whiteboard or projector.

The Internet is an excellent source for geographical photos and other images. (Try a google image search, for example, with different sets of key words.) You can download the ones you need in advance, rather than hunt during class. Please check with the appropriate people in your school regarding copyright issues.

Building a resource library

Some resources, such as photos, can be used over and over. You may want to create your own resource library. Laminating printed photos, and other resources (such as the True/False cards) will extend their lives and save you time and effort in the future.

Using the chapter openers in the students' book

The chapter openers

The chapter openers in the students' book are in effect the starters for new topics – and you can return to them as an end-of-topic plenary.

Below is a typical chapter opener.

Large photo to hook your students' attention (we hope!). The opening photos usually relate to specific material within the chapter.

Gives the big underlying ideas for the chapter. These provide the context for new learning. At the end of the chapter they can be reviewed, to help crystallise the learning.

Sets goals for the students, in the form of questions they should be able to answer by the end of the chapter.

Chapter starter questions, to get your students thinking. The Chapter overviews in this book give information about the photos, and some background for the starter questions. (Look in the final sections.)

Invites students to revisit the goals at the end of the chapter. Note that *geog.GCSE teachers' resource file* has a students' self-assessment form for each chapter, which refers to these goals.

Using the chapter openers

As you can see, the chapter openers can do quite a lot of useful work, so it's worth spending some time on them.

- 'The big picture' can be read aloud, and discussed.
- You can work through 'Your goals for this chapter' in advance, to find out what students know already. Most will probably be able to answer at least a couple of questions.
- Then the next step is to give students a mental roadmap for the chapter, using the corresponding **Chapter overviews** in this book.

This resource file contains vital support material for *geog.GCSE* students' book, to help you plan and deliver an effective GCSE geography course.

- It offers a wide range of photocopiable learning activities and exam-style questions.
- All materials are also provided on the accompanying CD-ROM, in pdf format.
- All materials and forms, and the planning documents, are also provided on the CD-ROM as Word files, so that you can adapt them.

Learning activities

There's a learning activity for each chapter – a decision-making exercise, enquiry, role-play, or piece of fieldwork.

Some of these activities will take several hours to complete. Some are for individual work, while others provide opportunities for students to work in pairs or small groups; some provide opportunities for whole-class work and feedback.

Most of these activities come with assessment criteria and grade information for all or part of the activity, written in student-friendly language. You can choose whether to show this to your students before or after the activity, or not at all. It can be used for teacher, self-, or peer assessment.

The assessment criteria form allows you to record the mark achieved, to comment, and to identify areas for improvement. It also allows the student to take part in this process.

The form can then form part of the student's assessment portfolio.

There are teacher's notes for each activity, giving the aims of the activity, and advice on how to set up and run it.

Exam-style questions

There are two exam-style questions for each chapter, and there's a Higher and Foundation tier version of each question. The marks available for each part of the question are given. Assessment criteria and grade information is given for each question, written in student-friendly language. It can be used for teacher, self-, and peer assessment.

These questions could be used in class or for homework, or as end-of-topic 'tests'. You could put several together to create a mock exam.

The reflection activity allows you to record the mark achieved, to comment, and to identify areas for improvement. It also allows the student to take part in this process.

The form can then form part of the student's assessment portfolio.

Self-assessment forms

There's a self-assessment form for each chapter. Designed to be used at the end of the chapter, it allows individual students to review and analyse their own work.

The table relates to the text 'Your goals for this chapter' laid out at the start of each chapter in the students' book.

Glossary

A glossary covering key vocabulary is provided. You could use the Word file to create worksheets.

Outline maps

Maps of the British Isles, Europe (political), and the World (political) are provided.

Planning documents

The course and lesson planning documents are provided as Word files to help you plan and record your own courses.

The planning documents are provided as templates on the CD-ROM, for you to use and adapt. They are provided only on the CD-ROM; hard copy versions are not reproduced on this file.

Tectonic activity

The big picture

These are the key ideas behind this chapter:

◆ The Earth's crust is broken into segments called plates.

◆ Plates move as a result of convection currents in the Earth's mantle.

◆ Plates can move towards each other, away from each other or past each other. All these movements cause earthquakes and some cause volcanic eruptions.

◆ Places where earthquakes happen and volcanoes erupt are dangerous places to live, but people do still live in these areas.

◆ The effects of earthquakes and eruptions are usually worse in LEDCs than in MEDCs, and responses to these violent events also differ between LEDCs and MEDCs.

◆ Seismologists might attempt to predict earthquakes – but these are just probabilities of an earthquake happening. It is possible to predict volcanic eruptions by monitoring, so people can be warned about the eruption.

Note that the students' version of the big picture is given in the students' chapter opener.

Chapter outline

Use this, and the students' chapter opener, to give students a mental roadmap for the chapter.

1   **Tectonic activity** As the students' chapter opener, this is an important part of the chapter; see page 11 of this book for notes about using chapter openers

1.1   **The structure of the Earth** How the Earth is made up, where plates are and how they move

1.2   **Plate margins** Constructive, destructive and conservative margins

1.3   **Collision margins** How people cope with living in the Himalayas – earning a living, and living with danger

1.4   **Earthquakes** Why they happen; the Richter scale, and what seismologists do

1.5   **Kashmir earthquake – an LEDC case study** The earthquake in October 2005 – causes, effects and responses

1.6   **Los Angeles earthquake – an MEDC case study** The earthquake in January 1994 – causes, effects and responses

1.7   **Volcanoes** What they are; volcanic hazards; composite and shield volcanoes

1.8   **Volcanoes continued** Why volcanoes occur and erupt; how eruptions can be predicted

1.9   **Montserrat – an LEDC case study** The eruption on Montserrat – causes, effects and responses

1.10   **Mount St. Helens – an MEDC case study** The eruption in 1980 – causes and effects

chapter overview

Objectives and outcomes for this chapter

Objectives	Unit	Outcomes
Most students will understand:		Most students will be able to:
• What the earth's plates are made of, and how they move.	1.1	• Explain that plates are made of crust, and that crust can be either oceanic or continental; draw a diagram to show how plates move as a result of convection currents in the mantle.
• What happens at plate margins.	1.2, 1.3	• Draw diagrams of constructive, destructive, conservative and collision margins; explain why each cause earthquakes and some cause volcanic eruptions.
• What causes earthquakes, and how they are measured.	1.4	• Explain what causes earthquakes; explain what the Richter scale is and that it is a logarithmic scale.
• That there are similarities and differences in the effects of earthquakes in LEDCs and MEDCs.	1.5, 1.6	• Classify effects into primary and secondary; identify similarities and differences between effects in LEDCs and MEDCs.
• That MEDCs generally respond faster and more efficiently to events such as earthquakes.	1.5, 1.6	• Explain why MEDCs can generally respond faster.
• Why people continue to live in areas at risk from earthquakes and volcanic eruptions.	1.3, 1.6	• List four reasons why people continue to live in danger zones.
• What volcanoes are; why they erupt and the hazards they can cause.	1.7	• Explain what volcanoes are and why they erupt; list the hazards they can cause.
• How scientists predict eruptions and attempt to predict earthquakes.	1.4, 1.8	• Describe how scientists monitor volcanoes to predict eruptions, and the methods used to attempt to predict earthquakes.
• That there are similarities and differences in the effects of, and responses to, volcanic eruptions in LEDCs and MEDCs.	1.9, 1.10	• Compare and contrast the eruptions in an LEDC and an MEDC.

These tie in with 'Your goals for this chapter' in the students' chapter opener, and with the opening lines in each unit, which give the purpose of the unit in a student-friendly style.

Using the chapter starter

The photos on page 6 of the *geog.GCSE* students' book are of the Kashmir earthquake of 8 October 2005. The aerial photo was taken on 9 October 2005 and shows the devastated town of Balakot in Pakistan. The photo of children and tents was taken on 12 November 2005 in India-controlled Kashmir.

The Kashmir earthquake measured 7.6 on the Richter scale. It caused severe damage to towns and villages, and roads and bridges; it killed 79 000 people and left thousands injured and homeless. Rebuilding started quickly, but as winter ended people were still living in tents.

Every year, on average, earthquakes kill about 10 000 people. There are thousands of quakes every day. People feel only a small number.

On average, a large earthquake happens somewhere every year; a quake that causes severe damage happens on average once every five years. The deadliest-ever earthquake happened in China in 1556 – it killed 830 000 people.

In a mild earthquake, the ground rumbles like it does when a large lorry goes by. In a more severe quake, the ground shakes. They last just seconds.

We're getting better at predicting earthquakes – scientists use creepmeters to check for shifts along faults, tiltmeters to measure changes in the slope of the land, and satellites to detect changes in the positions of tectonic plates. But accurate prediction isn't possible yet.

The structure of the Earth

The unit in brief

This unit introduces students to the structure of the Earth and plate tectonics. In the Activities, students draw and label a diagram to show the structure of the Earth; explain why plates move; and consider the differences between oceanic and continental crust. They also use a map of plate boundaries to identify different plates.

Key ideas

- The Earth is made up of layers – the core, mantle and crust.
- There are two types of crust – oceanic and continental.
- The crust is broken into plates.
- Convection currents in the Earth's mantle cause the plates to move.

Key vocabulary

core, mantle, crust (oceanic and continental), plates

Skills practised in the Activities

- Geography skills: drawing and labelling a diagram to show the structure of the Earth; using a map of plate boundaries
- Thinking skills: explaining why plates move; identifying differences between continental and oceanic crust; looking for evidence from a map

Unit outcomes

By the end of this unit, most students should be able to:

- define the terms given in 'Key vocabulary' above;
- draw a diagram to show the structure of the Earth;
- explain the differences between oceanic and continental crust;
- understand why plates move.

Ideas for a starter

1 We know what it's like on the surface of the Earth, but what is it like inside? What is the structure of the Earth? Write students' ideas on the board. Say you'll come back to them later. (See plenary 3.)

2 The Earth's crust is made up of plates – which move. Ask students what evidence we have for this.

3 Brainstorm to find out all the earthquakes and volcanic eruptions that students are aware of. Mark them on blank outline maps of the world.

Ideas for plenaries

1 On a blank outline map of the world, mark on the major fold mountains, volcanoes and earthquakes. How closely do they correspond and match up to the map of plates?

2 Ask students what features they think are formed by a) plates moving together b) plates moving apart, and c) plates rubbing past each other? Tell them you will be returning to this in the next two units.

3 Return to students' comments on the board from starter 1. Ask students to say which can be ticked, and which need be crossed out and corrected. (Note: there may be some you haven't met in the unit.)

4 Ask students to sum up what they have learned today in less than 40 words.

Further class and homework activities

How do we know about the layers within the Earth? Investigate this and report back at the beginning of the next lesson.

Answers to the Activities

1 Students' diagrams should look like a one-dimensional version of the artwork on page 8 of the students' book. They should label the inner core, outer core, mantle and crust (oceanic and continental); and should provide further information on each (for example, temperature, composition).

2 Tectonic plates move because they are dragged along by the mantle that they float on. The mantle moves due to convection currents driven by heat from the core.

3 Oceanic crust is basaltic, 5-10 km thick, dense. Continental crust is 25-100 km thick, and less dense.

4 a The UK is on the Eurasian Plate.

   b The USA is on the North American Plate.

   c Because of the spreading (constructive zone) in the mid-Atlantic.

   d Accept any of: Eurasian and Pacific, Nazca and South American, Eurasian and African, Eurasian and Indo-Australian.

   e Pacific and North American or African and Indo-Australian.

5 Evidence could include: the fossil record, geological strata, living plants and animals that are of the same families, mountain ranges, magnetic reversals in the rock record.

6 The theory directly preceding plate tectonics was the continental drift theory of Alfred Wegener. He thought that the continents drifted about but he could give no mechanism for this. Many scientists did not believe in Wegener's theory. Some believed that mountains were formed by the Earth shrinking and shrivelling up like an old apple.

The unit in brief

This unit is about three types of plate margin – constructive, destructive and conservative (collision margins are covered in Unit 1.3). In the Activities, students either copy or draw their own diagrams of different types of plate margins and label them, and name and explain the formation of landforms found at constructive and destructive plate margins.

Key ideas

◆ Plate margins are where plates meet.

◆ There are four types of plate margin – constructive, destructive, conservative and collision.

◆ At constructive margins, the plates are moving apart and new crust forms.

◆ At destructive margins, the plates are moving together and oceanic crust is destroyed.

◆ At conservative margins, the plates are moving past each other and crust is neither created nor destroyed.

Key vocabulary

plate margins, constructive margins, destructive margins, conservative margins, earthquakes, eruptions, fissures, subduct, fold mountains, volcano

Skills practised in the Activities

◆ Geography skills: explaining the term 'plate margin'; naming four types of plate margin; copying or drawing own diagrams of plate margins and adding labels; naming types of landforms found at plate margins and explaining their formation

Unit outcomes

By the end of this unit, most students should be able to:

◆ define or explain the terms given in 'Key vocabulary' above;

◆ name the four types of plate margin;

◆ draw labelled diagrams of constructive, destructive and conservative margins.

Ideas for a starter

1 Quick revision: What are the two types of crust? What is a plate? How do plates move? What is the relationship between fold mountains, volcanoes and earthquakes?

2 Ask a student to draw a simple diagram showing the structure of the Earth.

3 Show a video clip or animation of sea floor spreading.

Ideas for plenaries

1 On a world map showing plate boundaries (as on p.9 of the students' book), mark on the main centres of population near or on the plate boundaries. Estimate the number of people living in these hazard zones. Ask students why people live in such dangerous areas. They will be returning to this in Unit 1.3 and 1.6.

2 Draw a spider diagram for each type of plate margin. Ask students to add to the diagrams.

3 Make up to 10 statements about plate margins based on what students have learned today, some true, some false. Students hold up True or False cards. Where statements are false, ask students to correct them.

Further class and homework activities

1 Try to make 3-D models of the various plate margins.

2 Investigate the formation of fold mountains and the collision plate margins. Work on a presentation to be given to the rest of the class.

Answers to the Activities

1 A plate margin is the edge of a plate, or where two plates meet.

2 The four types of plate margin are: constructive, destructive, conservative and collision.

3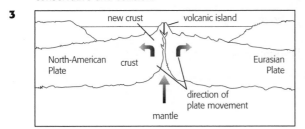

4 The question asks for two landforms and their formations. Any two from this table would be suitable.

Landform	Formation
Mid-ocean ridge	Formed by new crust welling up in the gap between the two diverging plates. The rising magma underneath makes the edges of the plates stick up rather than lie flat.
Sea volcanoes or volcanic islands	Formed from the magma rising up in the gap between the two diverging plates.
Faults	The crust is often faulted because it gets cracked. The cracks form due to the pressure that the plate is under as it moves.

5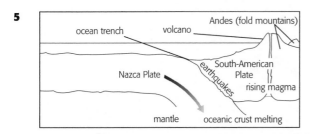

6 The question asks for two landforms and their formations. Any two from this table would be suitable.

Landform	Formation
Fold mountains	Formed when the edge of the continental crust gets squashed upwards. Some of the oceanic sediments may be sliced off the subducting oceanic crust and stuck to the fold mountains too.
Ocean trench	Formed at the boundary of the two plates where the oceanic plate starts to go under the other one.
Volcanoes	Formed due to the melting of the oceanic crust. This melted plate is less dense than the surrounding mantle (due to the sea water) so it rises upwards and explodes as a volcano.

7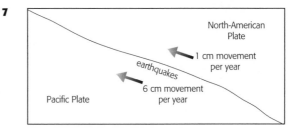

8 The earthquakes occur due to friction. When the plates are stuck there is no earthquake. The earthquake happens when the plates suddenly give way. This is why earthquakes become more likely after a period without one.

The unit in brief

This unit is about collision margins – what they are, and how people in the Himalayas cope with living in a collision zone. In the Activities, students draw and label a diagram to show a collision zone; use a writing frame to produce notes on fold mountains; answer an exam-style question about the economic activities in a fold mountain area; and consider why people continue to live in areas at risk from earthquakes, like the Himalayas.

Key ideas

◆ At collision margins plates are moving together to form fold mountains.
◆ In the Himalayas, people make a living from farming, mining and tourism.
◆ Big earthquakes can happen about once every 25 years in the Himalayas.
◆ People continue to live in the Himalayas because they feel that the benefits outweigh the risks.

Key vocabulary

collision margins, recurrence interval

Skills practised in the Activities

◆ Geography skills: drawing and labelling a diagram of a collision zone; describing economic activity in a fold mountain area
◆ Literacy skills: using a writing frame to make notes about fold mountains
◆ Thinking skills: explaining why people live in the Himalayas

Unit outcomes

By the end of this unit, most students should be able to:
◆ define or explain the terms given in 'Key vocabulary' above;
◆ draw and label a diagram to show a collision zone;
◆ describe the economic activities that occur in a fold mountain area;
◆ explain why people continue to live in the Himalayas.

Ideas for a starter

1 Presentation on collision margins.

2 Recap on the structure of the Earth. Students to draw diagrams with labels.

3 Recall the types of margins discussed so far.

Ideas for plenaries

1 Consider some of the problems in living of a collision zone such as Nepal. Consider population increasing – deforestation – increased run off – soil erosion – terrace collapse – decreasing agricultural production, etc. Draw a linked boxes model to show these developments.

2 How might these developments lead to flooding down in the valley?

3 Put someone in the hot-seat and others ask questions about the structure of the Earth and plate margins.

4 Can you think of any solutions to the problems outlined above in Nepal? Discuss with a neighbour and then with the whole class.

Answers to the Activities

1 Students' diagrams should be similar to the one at the top of page 12 of the students' book.

2 Students' work may vary, because they use their own words to complete the notes, but the general information should be:

Fold mountains are ranges of mountains formed at plate margins. They are formed at destructive margins when the edge of the continental crust gets squashed up by the pressure of the subduction. Also bits of oceanic sediment may be scrapped off the seabed at the subduction zone and squashed onto the fold mountains. They are also formed at collision margins, because two continental plates are squashing together and, as they are the same density, neither sink. So they get squeezed upwards and make fold mountains.

3 Students should choose to write about the Himalayas. This question should be marked out of 6 and should include locational detail as well as detail about economic activities.

Locational detail should include:

- the name of the mountain range (probably the Himalayas);

- the location of the range (in this case Asia, mainly in Nepal, Bhutan and China).

Economic activities should include:

- farming (in the case of the Himalayas, mostly pastoral with some fodder crops, and some rice and vegetable crops. The animals are cows or buffalo used for meat and milk, for carting and pulling, and as a source of manure. 80% of the population is involved in farming. Terraces should be mentioned as a way of dealing with the thin soils and steep slopes.)

- mining (for the Himalayas this should include gold, diamonds, copper ore and slate, all mined by the open-cast method. Pollution and erosion from the mine pits should be described for the highest marks.)

- tourism (a big source of income for the region, with almost 1 million visitors a year. The attractions are the landscape and the Buddhist temples.)

Students may lose marks in the case study questions of their exams due to lack of detail. Therefore, it's important for them to build up detail in their books, so they can revise fully at the end of the course.

4 People continue to live in the mountains because: they may have an income from farming, mining or tourism; they don't perceive the risk; they have confidence in the training they've received about how to cope with an earthquake; they have confidence in the emergency equipment stored in each village; or their religious beliefs mean that the mountains are sacred to them.

The unit in brief

This unit looks at earthquakes. It investigates what they are, why they happen, how they are measured and whether they can be predicted. In the Activities, students explain how earthquakes happen at different types of plate margins; explain the meaning of terms to do with earthquakes; make notes about earthquake prediction and produce a longer piece of writing on people's reactions to earthquake warnings.

Key ideas

◆ Earthquakes are caused by plate movement and friction.

◆ Earthquakes near the Earth's surface cause more damage than those deeper within the Earth.

◆ Earthquakes are measured on the Richter Scale.

◆ It is not possible to predict exactly when or where an earthquake will happen.

Key vocabulary

focus, epicentre, Richter Scale, logarithmic scale, magnitude, seismologist, seismometer, recurrence interval

Skills practised in the Activities

◆ Geography skills: drawing a diagram to show why earthquakes happen at destructive margins; defining geographical terms

◆ Literacy skills: using a writing frame to make notes about earthquake prediction; making notes and producing long piece of writing on people's reactions to earthquake warnings

◆ Thinking skills: explaining why earthquakes happen at different types of plate margin

Unit outcomes

By the end of this unit, most students should be able to:

◆ define or explain the terms given in 'Key vocabulary' above;

◆ explain how earthquakes happen at different types of plate margin;

◆ describe how earthquakes are measured;

◆ understand how scientists attempt to predict earthquakes.

Ideas for a starter

1 Ask students what the types of plate margin we have learned about so far are.

2 Ask students what type of tectonic activity can occur at all types of plate margins.

3 Ask why we don't get earthquakes in the UK (although we can have earth tremors).

Ideas for plenaries

1 Get a copy of a newspaper report describing an earthquake. Read the first section and ask the students to continue the story.

2 On a blank outline map of the world, mark the actual locations of the major earthquakes over the last 25 years. Describe and explain the pattern produced.

3 Tell your neighbour the three main things you learned today.

4 Introduce the idea that earthquakes tend to have more devastating effects in LEDCs than in MEDCs, and generally cause much greater loss of life. Say you will return to this in Units 1.5 and 1.6.

Further class and homework activities

Work with two other people and write the script of a television or radio programme featuring one significant earthquake.

Answers to the Activities

1 The basic cause of earthquakes is friction.

2 Earthquakes happen at collision zones because there is friction between the plates and the mantle, and the plates and the fold mountains above them. The plates do not move smoothly; each jolt of movement is an earthquake.

3 Students' diagrams should look similar to the artwork at the top of page 14 of the students' book. They should show the friction, the arrows of direction of movement of the two plates and the subduction zone.

4 There are earthquakes in California because it is on a conservative margin. That mean two plates are sliding past each other and there is friction between them.

5 Magnitude = the size of the earthquake

Focus = the site of the earthquake

Epicentre = the place on the surface above the focus

Recurrence interval = how often an earthquake of a given magnitude happens

Seismometer = instrument for measuring movements of the earth

Seismologist = scientist who measures and studies earthquakes

6 a Earthquakes are measured using the Richter scale.

 b It is a logarithmic scale.

7 Students' work may vary as they use their own words to complete the notes, but the general information should be: laser beams to measure small movements of faults; monitoring radon gas;

checking water levels in wells; using seismometers; calculating recurrence intervals and watching animal behaviour.

Students may think that each of the methods is or is not accurate, the important thing is that they justify their opinions. The same applies to their notes on warnings.

8 a Students' ideas may include that:

◆ people may evacuate to a safer place in order to save their lives and avoid injury

◆ people may panic and there may be accidents and injuries or traffic jams, making rescue harder if the earthquake happens

◆ people may take their valuables with them if they evacuate in order to protect them

◆ people may buy emergency supplies of food and water, batteries and first aid kits in order to maximise their chances of survival, but causing increased prices or shortages

◆ people may ignore the warnings if they are too vague in terms of time or place

◆ if warnings are given and do not prove to be true, people may disregard future warnings

 b Students' essays should include a clear introduction laying out what predictions of earthquakes are based on, and describing in brief the methods used. There should also be a clear and well-explained discussion of a range of likely effects of predictions, covering local and regional scales, and a clear well-argued conclusion deciding one way or the other whether prediction is a good thing.

Kashmir earthquake – an LEDC case study

The unit in brief

An LEDC case study of the earthquake in Kashmir in October 2005 is included in this unit. It explains why the earthquake happened, what the effects were, and how people responded. In the Activities, students classify the effects of the earthquake and explain why it happened; complete a spider diagram to show responses to the earthquake and identify which types of aid are most effective in the short and the long term.

Key ideas

◆ The earthquake happened at the collision zone where the Indian and Eurasian Plates are moving together.

◆ Primary effects happen immediately and cause injury and death.

◆ Secondary effects happen later and include disease and respiratory infections.

◆ Long-term effects can be social, environmental and economic, and include the fact that 3.3 million people lost their homes and had to spend the winter in temporary shelters.

◆ Immediate responses included providing food and emergency help for survivors.

◆ It was too soon to judge the long-term responses when this unit was written.

Key vocabulary

primary effects, secondary effects, long-term effects, immediate responses, long-term responses

Skills practised in the Activities

◆ Geography skills: completing a spider diagram of responses to the earthquake

◆ Thinking skills: classifying the effects of earthquakes; explaining why the earthquake happened; identifying different types of aid

Unit outcomes

By the end of this unit, most students should be able to:

◆ explain the terms given in 'Key vocabulary' above;

◆ explain why the earthquake happened;

◆ understand the difference between primary, secondary and long-term effects;

◆ give examples of different types of responses to the earthquake.

Ideas for a starter

1 Recap on the vocabulary used in the chapter so far. Students each write down three terms and their definitions. The rest of the class can check them.

2 Show a selection of photos following an earthquake in an LEDC. Ask students to identify what has happened, and the effects this will have.

3 Mind movie time! You are in a remote village in Kashmir in October 2005. You have just got up and the ground starts to shake. It carries on for 60 seconds. What can you see, hear and feel? What is happening? Tell us.

Ideas for plenaries

1 Make a graffiti wall of what students have learned today.

2 One of the major problems in Kashmir was to do with accessibility. Brainstorm how this problem could be overcome in future?

3 Show video footage or news reports of the aftermath of the earthquake.

4 Ask students to prepare a 20-second news bulletin about the earthquake, giving the key facts about what happened and why, the effects and responses. Ask a few students to read theirs out.

Further class and homework activities

1 Contact NGOs and find out what they have done to help in this disaster.

2 Investigate the Los Angeles/San Francisco earthquakes of the past. Prepare a talk for the next lesson.

Answers to the Activities

1 a and **b** The effects of the Kashmir earthquake were:

Primary: 60 seconds of shaking; buildings collapsed; signs fell off walls; windows shattered; furniture fell over; roads cracked; bridges collapsed; 79 000 died; 100 000 were injured; 3.3 million homes were destroyed; landslides; schools collapsed, killing students

Secondary: fires were caused by broken gas pipes; diseases were caused by sewage polluting water, and by decomposing bodies; the effects of exposure (respiratory diseases and hypothermia)

Students may lose marks in the case study questions of their exams because of lack of detail, so it is important to build up detail in their books so they can revise fully at the end of the course.

2 The earthquake happened because it is on the collision zone of the Indian and Eurasian plates.

3 People live in this area because they are farmers and can grow crops in the fertile valleys and herd animals here, and can make money from tourism.

4 a Short-term responses should include:

◆ local people, army and local emergency services rescuing those trapped

◆ Indian Red Cross supplying 21 500 blankets, 300 kitchen sets, and medical supplies

◆ helicopters ferrying the injured to first aid stations and hospitals

◆ the border between India and Pakistan being opened to let supplies cross

◆ tents being given by charities

◆ Pakistan Airways carrying supplies for free

◆ military hospitals being opened for civilians

◆ rescue teams arriving from other countries

Long-term responses should include:

◆ water supplies being repaired in the town of Muzzaffarabad

◆ The Red Crescent building pre-fabricated homes and schools

◆ schools being rebuilt

◆ teachers being trained in counselling

◆ new sanitation systems

◆ new stricter building laws so that new buildings can survive an earthquake

b Students may argue for any type of short-term aid, however the best answers will need to give reasons, including reasons why the other types are less effective. Students should consider the effects of the aid locally and regionally, and any positive or negative feedbacks from the aid locally or regionally and over time.

c Students may argue for any type of long-term aid, however the best answers will need to give reasons, including reasons why the other types are less effective. Students should consider the effects of the aid locally and regionally, and any positive or negative feedbacks from the aid locally or regionally and over time. There is an opportunity for students to research here to find out what has happened recently in this area.

Los Angeles earthquake – an MEDC case study

help at a glance

The unit in brief

This unit includes a case study of an earthquake in an MEDC – the Los Angeles earthquake of 1994. It covers the effects of the earthquake, what caused it, responses to the earthquake and why people continue to live in an area prone to earthquakes. In the Activities, students answer the question 'Why do people live in LA?'; write a factfile about the earthquake and explain why it happened; classify responses to the earthquake; answer an exam-style question and compare the Los Angeles and Kashmir earthquakes.

Key ideas

◆ The earthquake happened along the conservative margin where the North American and Pacific Plates are moving past each other.

◆ People continue to live in the area for a number of reasons – economic, technological, perception (they don't see uncommon events like earthquakes as big risks) and social.

◆ Responses to the earthquake include short, medium and long-term responses.

Key vocabulary

economic, technological, perception, social

Skills practised in the Activities

◆ Geography skills: answering an exam-style question; comparing the Los Angeles and Kashmir earthquakes

◆ Literacy skills: writing a factfile about the Los Angeles earthquake; producing a long piece of writing

◆ Thinking skills: giving reasons why people live in Los Angeles; explaining why the earthquake happened; classifying responses

Unit outcomes

By the end of this unit, most students should be able to:

◆ define or explain the terms given in 'Key vocabulary' above;

◆ explain why the earthquake happened;

◆ give reasons why people continue to live in the area, despite the risks;

◆ give examples of short-, medium- and long-term responses to the earthquake;

◆ compare the effects of, and responses to, earthquakes in LEDCs and MEDCs.

Ideas for a starter

1 Recap on plate boundaries. How are the plates moving in California? What type of plate margin is this? What is the name of the plate margin here?

2 Ask students what they know about California. What you are trying to elicit is that although it is an MEDC it can have, and has had in the past, major earthquakes.

3 Show images of the destruction caused by the earthquake in San Francisco in 1906.

4 Prepare a wordsearch to check students' understanding of key terms covered so far in this chapter.

Ideas for plenaries

1 Use Activity 5 as a plenary comparing the earthquake in Los Angeles with the Kashmir earthquake. Do earthquakes in MEDCS and LEDCS have different effects?

2 Ask students if there is a case for having an international emergency task group ready to go when natural disasters strike.

3 People continue to live in areas at risk from earthquakes. Should we continue rebuilding settlements in earthquake hazard zones?

4 Choose a student to be in the hot seat. Another student asks him or her a question about earthquakes. Then nominate two different students (4-6 pairs in total). There's one golden rule – questions cannot be repeated.

Further class and homework activities

Collect information about other earthquake examples and make suitable wall displays.

Answers to the Activities

1 Possible reasons could include:

- *economic:* People work in the area and can't afford to, or don't want to, lose their jobs by moving. LA is a rich city with, for most people, a good lifestyle, and well paid jobs.

- *technological:* People feel secure that prediction will give them enough warning, and, even if it doesn't, that technology will mean their homes are safe and the emergency services will be able to cope.

- *perception:* People don't see relatively uncommon events like earthquakes as big risks. Regular things like car accidents and crime are often seen as being more likely to happen to you, so are more 'dangerous'.

- *social:* People have their families, friends, schools, favourite places where they live and don't want to lose them.

Students need to write about at least three reasons.

2 a The factfile should include:

Date: 7 January 1994

Time: 4.31 a.m.

Magnitude: 6.7 on the Richter scale (there are other scales so it is important to put Richter)

Location: Northridge (LA)

Focus 18.4 km deep

Duration 15 seconds

Primary effects: shaking, some areas lifted 50 cms, apartment blocks collapsed, 14 died, highways collapsed, cracks in road, landslides

Secondary effects: fire from broken gas mains, 22 000 homeless, final death toll 57, $15 billion damage

b It happened due to friction at the conservative margin between the Pacific and North American Plates.

4 a This is point marked. 1 mark for each point made. Possible answers could include:

- loss of life and injury from falling items or fireball or crushing

- loss of belongings from crushing or fire

- lifestyle changes in terms of loss of jobs, homes, communities where re-homing has happened

- change in culture in terms of more risk awareness and preparation

b This is point marked. 1 mark per point.

- Managing the risk is done by the recovery and reconstruction plan (more emergency crews, more emergency shelters, plans for banks to re-open, practice for emergency and medical staff, stricter building codes)

- Public being given leaflets on how to respond

- Public training in emergency practices

5 b The essay should be detailed and contain specific information about each case study. The essay should be clearly structured with an introduction giving background of the locations, dates and causes of the two quakes. The body of the essay should detail the primary and secondary effects, deaths and injuries and the similarities and differences in each. Students need to consider the short- and long- term responses in each case, and explain why they are different. Students should include reference to LEDC and MEDC considerations.

The unit in brief

This unit introduces volcanoes. It deals with what they are and looks at composite and shield volcanoes. In the Activities, students produce a presentation about volcanoes as an ICT activity. They can include extra research of their own, and make the presentation to the whole class or to a small group.

Key ideas

◆ Volcanoes can produce a range of hazards, including ash clouds, pyroclastic flows, and mudflows (lahars), as well as lava.

◆ The shape and explosiveness of a volcano depends on the type of lava emitted.

◆ Composite volcanoes occur where the lava is acidic, and are found along destructive plate margins.

◆ Shield volcanoes form where the lava is basic, and occur along constructive plate margins and where there are hotspots.

Key vocabulary

pyroclastic flow, ash cloud, lava, mudflow (lahar), composite volcano, acid lava, crater, magma, shield volcano, basic lava, hot spots

Skills practised in the Activities

◆ ICT skills: the activity in this unit asks students to produce a presentation about volcanoes, including what a volcano is, where they are found and why, and what composite and shield volcanoes are like

Unit outcomes

By the end of this unit, most students should be able to:

◆ define or explain the terms given in 'Key vocabulary' above;

◆ give examples of some of the hazards that volcanoes produce;

◆ understand that the shape and explosiveness of a volcano depends on the type of lava emitted;

◆ explain what composite and shield volcanoes are like and where they occur.

Ideas for a starter

1 Show photographs or video clips of volcanoes erupting. Ask students to identify different types of eruptions and reasons for the variation.

2 Students work in pairs to create a spider diagram, showing what they already know about volcanoes.

3 Recap on the primary and secondary effects of an earthquake.

Ideas for plenaries

1 Plot the location of the major volcanoes on a world map showing plate boundaries. Ask students to describe and explain the pattern.

2 Compare your map in 1 with one showing world population density. Why do many people live in volcanic regions?

3 Ask students to think about whether volcanic eruptions can be predicted. What could be measured, or monitored, to help with prediction?

4 Students who did starter 2 can return to their spider diagrams and add anything else they have learned in a different colour. They can then try and classify, or group, the information, e.g. cause, effect (primary or secondary) location etc. They could classify by underlining in different colours, and add a colour key.

Further class and homework activities

Make a 3D model of a volcano and display it to the rest of the class.

Answers to the Activities

1 Good presentations should include: a definition of volcanoes; an explanation of constructive and destructive margins, and hot spots; descriptions and explanations of composite and shield volcanoes; some individual research, such as the names of some examples.

To keep students involved during other presentations, and to enable them to share good ideas between them and to feed back constructively to each other, they could assess each other using a grid like this (add rows as necessary):

Student	Did the presentation include ... (tick or cross)	Things that were good	Things that could be improved on next time
	◆ what volcanoes are ◆ how they happen ◆ two types of volcano ◆ some individual research		

The unit in brief

This unit tells students more about volcanoes – why they form, and how volcanic eruptions can be predicted. In the Activities, students complete a paragraph about volcano formation, consider which methods used for predicting eruptions are best, and find out how Mount Fuji's popularity as a tourist attraction in Japan contributes to the area's economy.

Key ideas

◆ Volcanoes form when magma is forced up through the crust.

◆ Volcanoes form at destructive and constructive margins, and at hotspots.

◆ at destructive margins, the melted crust is less dense than the rest of the mantle.

◆ at constructive margins, plates move apart and magma rises to fill the gap.

◆ at hotspots, a strong upward convection current in the mantle forces magma through the crust.

◆ Volcanoes are monitored so that scientists can predict when they are likely to erupt.

Key vocabulary

destructive margins, plug, constructive margins, hotspots, seismometer, tiltmeter, global positioning system (GPS)

Skills practised in the Activities

◆ Geography skills: finding out about Mount Fuji and explaining how tourism contributes to the economy of the area

◆ Literacy skills: completing a paragraph on the formation of volcanoes

◆ Thinking skills: giving examples of how eruptions can be predicted, and considering which methods are best

Unit outcomes

By the end of this unit, most students should be able to:

◆ define or explain the terms given in 'Key vocabulary' above;

◆ understand how volcanoes form at destructive and constructive margins, and at hotspots;

◆ give examples of the methods used by scientists to monitor volcanoes.

Ideas for a starter

1 Draw a sketch diagram of a volcano on the board. Ask students to label it.

2 Ask students at which types of plate margin we find volcanoes. Tell them that some volcanoes do not fit this pattern, and where are they situated.

3 Write words such as composite volcano, shield volcano, acidic land, basic land, destructive margin, constructive margin, hotspot and their meanings on separate sheets of paper. Students hold the sheets up. The rest of the class match them.

Ideas for plenaries

1 Brainstorm to find out how many volcanic eruptions students know about. Plot their locations on a blank outline map of the world.

2 What do students know about the effects of eruptions? Are they likely to be different in LEDCS and MEDCS? (They will return to this in Units 1.9 and 1.10).

3 make 10-15 statements, based on what students have learned about volcanoes so far, some true, some false. Students hold up True or False cards. Where statements are false, ask students to correct them.

Further class and homework activities

1 Investigate a major eruption such as Mt St. Helens and note the sequence of events that led to the eruption.

2 Make a documentary showing the events that led to the eruption. Plan your interviews and try to organize a camera to record the programme. Try to achieve a balance between factual information and opinion. Try to include graphics and explanation.

3 Investigate the Soufriere Hills volcanic eruption on the island of Montserrat. Be ready to lead the lesson next time.

Answers to the Activities

1 The missing words are: volcanoes; magma; margins; apart; gap; gentle; hot spots

2 a There are various ways to predict eruptions. These are:

♦ seismometers measuring tiny earthquakes

♦ satellite images detecting heat underground

♦ tiltmeters detecting bulges in the volcano

♦ GPS to detect movement in the volcano's surface

♦ monitoring gas emissions (the more sulphur dioxide given off, the closer it is to the eruption)

♦ listening for sounds like gurgles and belches

b Students should consider things like how much warning is given (the magma starts to move only days before an eruption – is this enough time to evacuate?) and accuracy (listening for sounds is still rather vague).

3 Students' research should find out these basic facts (as well as some of their own):

♦ Mount Fuji is a dormant volcano.

♦ It last erupted in 1708.

♦ It is 3500 metres high.

♦ It is a composite volcano.

♦ 200 000 people climb it each year.

♦ It is a tourist attraction because of the views from the top, especially of the sunrise.

♦ It is sacred in ancient Japanese culture.

♦ It supplies jobs to about 250 000 people.

Students should consider the types of jobs that would be created due to tourism (direct and indirect), and the more able could extend their ideas to consider the multiplier effect.

The unit in brief

An LEDC case study of the volcanic eruption on Montserrat is included in this unit. It explains what happened once Chances Peak began erupting in 1995, why it started erupting and gives examples of both the immediate and long-term responses to the eruption. In the Activities, students draw a timeline to show the main events in Montserrat and produce a table of the effects of the eruption. They explain why the eruption happened, sort responses into short and long term, and think about why people have returned to Montserrat.

Key ideas

◆ Chances Peak began erupting in July 1995, and people began to be evacuated from the danger areas in August 1995.

◆ The eruption was caused by the subduction of the North and South American Plates under the Caribbean Plate.

◆ Immediate responses included monitoring the volcano and evacuating people.

◆ Long-term responses included continuing to monitor the volcano, people returning to the island and a redevelopment programme funded by the UK.

Key vocabulary

immediate responses, long-term responses

Skills practised in the Activities

◆ Geography skills: describing the location of Montserrat; producing a table of the effects of the eruption

◆ Thinking skills: drawing a timeline to show the events in Montserrat; explaining why the eruption happened and why pyroclastic flows are dangerous; sorting the responses into short and long term; thinking about people's attitude to risk

Unit outcomes

By the end of this unit, most students should be able to:

◆ explain the terms given in 'Key vocabulary' above;

◆ draw a timeline of the events in Montserrat;

◆ understand what caused the eruption;

◆ identify short- and long-term responses to the eruption.

Ideas for a starter

1 Recap different types of volcano.
2 Ask students to use the Atlas to find the location of Montserrat. Is it an MEDC or an LEDC?
3 Mind movie time! You are in Montserrat but have to leave because the volcano has been erupting. What has happened, how do you feel? Tell us.

Ideas for plenaries

1 Ask students to write a 20 second news bulletin of the eruption and its aftermath. Ask a few students to read theirs out.

2 Ask students to work a with partner and write interviews and responses from people living in different parts of the island.

3 Students work in pairs to test each other on key terms and definitions about volcanoes.

4 Sum up what you have learned today in less than 40 words.

Further class and homework activities

Design the sort of tourist brochure which could bring people back in the future. Check holiday brochures to see if, after more than 10 years, tourists are returning to the island.

Answers to Activities

1 a Montserrat is an island in the Caribbean.

b The time-line should be as follows:

July 1995
Dust and ash start to erupt from the top of Chances Peak.
Scientists measure the emitted gases and changes in the shape of the volcano.
Seismographs measure tiny earthquakes.

August 1995
An evacuation begins to the north of the island.

April 1996
Everyone has to leave the capital Plymouth.

June 1997
Hot ash, gases, mud and rocks (pyroclastic flows) cover the south of the island. 19 are killed.

2006
There are still some eruptions, and the south is still unpopulated.

2 The completed table should look like this:

3 The North and South American Plates are being subducted under the Caribbean Plate. The melted plate, mixed with sea water is less dense than the rest of the mantle. So the melted magma rises upwards. The dissolved gases are released when the magma gets higher up. That's because the pressure is less high in the crust. The released gases pushed out the dust and ash from previous eruptions.

4 a A pyroclastic flow is a mixture of burning gases, dust, ash and rocks flowing from the volcano down the flanks.

b It is very hot and flows very fast, so it cannot be outrun and it can start fires.

6 Students will come up with their own ideas about why people are returning. These could include:

◆ wanting to continue their lives from before;

◆ dissatisfaction with their lives in the new place (USA, Antigua or UK);

◆ wanting to rejoin family or friends.
The fact that people are returning means that they have judged the risk either to be falling or to be outweighed by the benefits of returning.

Effects on people	Effects on the environment	Effects on the economy
evacuation from homes, loss of jobs, living in halls and schools and churches, loss of community, loss of property, loss of farmland, change in status, some people leave the island so this leads to a new lifestyle, having to start again with very little, families may be broken up	the southern part of the island has been covered with ash, there is air pollution from gases and ash	loss of tourist income, loss of farmland so people have to buy their food and also lose the income from selling their produce, loss of property and jobs

The unit in brief

This unit includes an MEDC case study – the eruption of Mount St. Helens in the USA in 1980. It looks at the causes and effects of the eruption. In the Activities, students draw a timeline to show the events at Mount St. Helens; complete a mind map about the eruption; produce a table of the effects (both short and long term) of the eruption; and compare the eruptions in Mount St. Helens and Montserrat. They also produce revision notes for the whole chapter.

Key ideas

◆ The eruption in 1980 was preceded by earthquakes, which began two months before the volcano blew.
◆ Mount St. Helens is located over a destructive margin.
◆ The volcano produced a pyroclastic flow, mudslides and ash clouds.
◆ Immediate responses included warning people to evacuate the area.
◆ Long-term effects included government funding for rebuilding industry and as compensation; the local economy has benefited from tourism; there is an increased risk of flooding.

Key vocabulary

pyroclastic flow

Skills practised in the Activities

◆ Geography skills: producing a table of effects; comparing the Montserrat and Mount St. Helens eruptions; producing revision notes for the chapter
◆ Literacy skills: producing a long piece of writing
◆ Thinking skills: drawing a timeline of events at Mount St. Helens; completing a mind map about the eruption; explaining

Unit outcomes

By the end of this unit, most students should be able to:
◆ explain the term given in 'Key vocabulary' above;
◆ draw a timeline of the events at Mount St. Helens;
◆ make a table of the effects of the eruption;
◆ explain why so few people were killed or injured when the volcano erupted.

Ideas for a starter

1 Locate Mount St. Helens in an atlas.
2 Name the plate margins in the area.
3 Describe the likely activity taking place underground before the eruption.

Ideas for plenaries

1 Visit a number of websites and collect information and pictures of this eruption. Make a wall display of your information.
2 Write a newspaper story outlining how the eruption took place over a period of time.
3 What do you think the authorities learnt from the way they managed this disaster?
4 What are the major generalisations in this unit of work? Make a note of them and discuss these with your class.
5 Make sure you know all the vocabulary and are comfortable in using it. Make a word game and give it to your neighbour to test them.
6 Volcanoes and earthquakes and their associated disasters may happen at any time. Be ready to collect information on any new events which take place and have a current events part of your notice board for collecting new materials.

Answers to the Activities

1 The time line should include the following information:

20 March –	earthquake under the mountain	
25 March –	47 earthquakes	
26 March –	local people are warned that they might have to evacuate the area	
27 March –	the mountain releases gas and steam	
3 April –	a bulge appears in the side of the mountain, and keeps growing	
12 April –	the bulge is measured and is found to be 100 metres high	
30 April –	a 30-km danger zone is set up around the volcano	
10 May –	several more earthquakes	
18 May –	the volcano erupts	

2 There are volcanoes in the Cascade Range because it is on the margin of the Pacific and North American Plates.

3 Students' mind maps will vary. They might include the following information:

pyroclastic flow: flattened and burnt trees over 360 million square km; moved at 300 km/hr; killed 7000 animals and 12 million salmon; 61 people died

mudslides: formed when hot magma melted snow; flowed down river valleys at 35 metres per second

ash cloud: went 24 km up into the sky; planes were diverted; formed a layer 15 cm deep when settled; settled layer made roads unusable and ruined crops and farm machinery; cost of damage caused by ash was $175 million

shape of the mountain: bulge grew inside as magma built up; after the eruption the mountain side had been blown out and the top had collapsed – it was 365 metres lower

4 There was a low number of deaths and injuries because: there were few people living and working in the area; scientists issued warnings so people knew about the danger and many chose to leave; the authorities put a 30-km danger zone around the volcano that people weren't allowed to enter.

5 The completed table should look something like this:

Short-term effects	Long-term effects
Pyroclastic flow erupted from the top and side, moving at 300 km/hr	Aid of $951 billion to the area from the government to rebuild industry and compensate people
Trees flattened and burnt over 360 km²	The volcano is a tourist attraction so the economy is now wealthier than before
7000 animals killed	Increased risk of flooding due to the new landscape
12 million salmon in a fish farm killed	
61 people killed	
Melted snow caused mudslides moving at 35 m/sec	
Smoke, ash and dust made a cloud 24 km high, diverting planes	
The ash made a layer 15 cm deep, leading to road closures and ruining crops and farm machinery	

6 a Similarities in processes: both eruptions involved gas, steam, and ash, meaning both eruptions featured a pyroclastic flow; both eruptions led to ash clouds and ash deposits.

Differences in processes: the volcano on Montserrat is still active.

Similarities in effects: Both eruptions caused deaths and injuries – though there were more deaths at Mt St Helens than on Montserrat; both eruptions caused widespread damage to farmland/vegetation.

Differences in effects: The Montserrat eruption had a greater impact on the local people and economy – it destroyed the island's capital city, and more than half the island's people have left.

Differences in short- and long-term responses: Tourism to Montserrat, the LEDC, has declined and the island has lost this vital source of revenue – but Mt St Helens, in the MEDC, is now a tourist attraction and the local economy is wealthier than it was before the eruption. Both areas received aid and compensation – although the Mt St Helens area received more from the US government than Montserrat got from the UK and USA.

b The essay should be detailed and contain specific information about each case study. The essays should be clearly structured with an introduction giving background on the location, dates and causes of the two eruptions. The body of the essay should detail the primary and secondary effects, deaths and injuries, and the similarities and differences in each. The students need to consider the short- and long-term responses in each case and explain why they are different. Students should include reference to LEDC and MEDC considerations.

Rocks and landscape

2

The big picture

These are the key ideas behind this chapter:

◆ There are many different types of rocks, but they are grouped into three categories – sedimentary, igneous and metamorphic.

◆ The classification of rocks into sedimentary, igneous and metamorphic is based on the way each type of rock was formed.

◆ Different rock types produce their own distinctive landforms and landscapes.

◆ The land use of an area depends on the underlying rock.

◆ Certain types of land use – such as quarrying – can cause conflict.

Note that the students' version of the big picture is given in the students' chapter opener.

Chapter outline

Use this, and the students' chapter opener, to give students a mental roadmap for the chapter.

2   **Rocks and landscape** As the students' chapter opener, this is an important part of the chapter; see page 11 of this book for notes about using chapter openers

2.1   **It's just a rock isn't it?** Sedimentary, metamorphic and igneous rocks, and how they were formed

2.2   **Granite** How it was formed, and how it affects the landscape

2.3   **Dartmoor – a granite area** Dartmoor's physical landscape, and its human uses

2.4   **Limestone** How it was formed, its properties, and limestone features found in the Yorkshire Dales

2.5   **Making a living in the Yorkshire Dales** Economy and employment in a limestone area

2.6   **Ingleton quarry** People have conflicting views over quarrying – one of the economic activities in the Yorkshire Dales National Park

2.7   **Chalk** How it was formed, how it affects the landscape and land use on the North and South Downs

2.8   **Clay** How it was formed, how it affects the landscape and land use around Lough Neagh in Northern Ireland

Objectives and outcomes for this chapter

Objectives	Unit	Outcomes
Most students will understand:		Most students will be able to:
● That sedimentary, igneous and metamorphic rocks are formed in different ways.	2.1, 2.2, 2.4, 2.7, 2.8	● Give an example of igneous and sedimentary rocks, and explain how they were formed.
● How granite affects the landscape.	2.2, 2.3	● Describe the landscape of a granite area, and explain how the landscape has been formed.
● How land is used in a named area of granite.	2.3	● Name a granite area; describe the land use in the named area.
● How limestone features are formed.	2.4	● Give four examples of features found in limestone areas; explain how they were formed.
● That some of the employment and human activity in limestone areas can bring problems, and create conflict.	2.5, 2.6	● Explain the pattern of employment in the Yorkshire Dales; list the problems that tourism can cause; explain why activities such as quarrying can create conflict.
● How chalk affects the landscape.	2.7	● Describe a chalk landscape; name a chalk area and say how it is used.
● How clay affects the landscape.	2.8	● Name a clay area and describe the landscape; say how the land is used in the named area.

These tie in with 'Your goals for this chapter' in the students' chapter opener, and with the opening lines in each unit, which give the purpose of the unit in a student-friendly style.

Using the chapter starter

The photo on page 28 of the *geog.GCSE* students' book is of Bowerman's Nose on Dartmoor.

Bowerman's Nose is a natural feature, made of weathered granite.

But with a bit of imagination, Bowerman's Nose looks like a human face. And it's a face with a story … According to legend, Bowerman was a hunter on Dartmoor. He was chasing a hare one day when he and his hounds accidentally ran into a coven of witches, overturned their cauldron, and disrupted their ceremony. The angry witches decided to punish Bowerman the next time he went hunting. One of the witches turned herself into a hare – she caught the attention of the hounds, and led them on an exhausting chase. The hounds collapsed first, then Bowerman fell. The witches then turned them all to stone – Bowerman became Bowerman's Nose, and the hounds are the rocks on Hound Tor, about a mile away.

Bowerman's Nose is located on the northern slopes of Hayne Down, close to the village of Manaton. It features in many books, calendars, and postcards.

Granite is a hard rock – it is slow to erode. Granite, and Dartmoor, are covered in units 2.2 and 2.3.

It's just a rock isn't it?

The unit in brief

This unit introduces the three main types of rock – sedimentary, metamorphic and igneous – and explains how they were formed. In the Activities, students sort information about different types of rock, and find out how different rocks are used.

Key ideas

◆ The three categories of rock are sedimentary, metamorphic and igneous.

◆ Sedimentary rocks have been laid down in layers. Examples include limestone, chalk, clay and sandstone.

◆ Metamorphic rocks have been altered by extremes of heat and/or pressure. Examples include schists and marble.

◆ Igneous rocks are a result of volcanic activity and come from magma. Basalt and granite are examples.

Key vocabulary

sedimentary, igneous, metamorphic

Skills practised in the Activities

◆ Literacy skills: writing up uses of rock types.

◆ Thinking skills: sorting information on different rock types; finding out about how rocks are used.

Unit outcomes

By the end of this unit, most students should be able to:

◆ define the terms given in 'Key vocabulary' above;

◆ explain how sedimentary, metamorphic and igneous rocks are formed;

◆ give examples of sedimentary, metamorphic and igneous rocks;

◆ give examples of how different types of rocks are used.

Ideas for a starter

1 Bring samples of different types of rock into the classroom and allow the students to handle them and write down their observations. Give them a checklist – colour, hardness, layers, crystals etc.

2 Discuss the geology of the local area. Use a geology map – there may be one in the Atlas – to help. Are there any quarries in the area that students know of? If so, what is the rock used for?

3 Ask students why Geographers need to know about the characteristics of rocks. Try to name some areas of study where the geology is important to understanding the geography of the area.

Ideas for plenaries

1 Ask students to try to work out rules to identify each type of rock (sedimentary, igneous, metamorphic).

2 Use photographs of a range of rocks to test out students' rules of identification.

3 Ask students to name some physical features which may be caused by the difference in resistance of one rock to another.

4 Ask students how different rocks are used. How do their qualities determine their use?

Answers to the Activities

1

Sedimentary	limestone made from shells and skeletons of sea creatures squashed together
sandstone	made from sand that has been squashed together
Igneous	basalt cooled lava from volcanoes
granite	magma which has cooled inside the Earth's crust
Metamorphic	marble made from limestone that has been subjected to heat and pressure
schist	made from basalt or shale that has been pressurised

2 Limestone: building, and in the manufacture of glass, steel, cement, chemicals, paper, ceramics, paint, plastics

Sandstone: building, paving stones

Basalt: statues (sculpture), jewellery, ornaments, road foundations

Granite: road stone, sculpture, building, paving stones, tombstones, ceramics (china clay)

Marble: building, furnishing material (e.g. kitchen worktops), statues, tombstones

Schist: building, especially gardens, collected by collectors

Students should also note that each rock type creates a specific type of scenery which, in many places, is economically 'useful' because it attracts tourists, e.g. limestone/Yorkshire Dales, granite/Dartmoor.

The unit in brief

This unit is about granite. It explains what granite is, how it was formed and the landscape features it produces. In the Activities, students produce a mind map about granite which helps to pull all the information from the unit together, and complete a paragraph about frost-shattering.

Key ideas

◆ Granite is an igneous rock formed when magma cools within the Earth's crust.

◆ Granite intrusions include dykes, sills and batholiths.

◆ Dartmoor, Bodmin Moor and Land's End are part of a huge batholith. The exposed rocks are called tors.

◆ Granite is weathered by frost-shattering.

Key vocabulary

granite, igneous, magma, granite intrusions (dyke, batholith, sill), tor, joints, frost-shattering, blockfield

Skills practised in the Activities

◆ Thinking skills: producing a mind map about granite; completing a paragraph about frost-shattering

Unit outcomes

By the end of this unit, most students should be able to:

◆ define or explain the terms given in 'Key vocabulary' above;

◆ name different types of granite intrusions;

◆ describe how tors are formed;

◆ explain how granite is weathered.

Ideas for a starter

1 Ask students what they know about granite. What type of rock is it? What are its qualities? Where is it found?

2 Study the rock sample used in Starter 1 (Unit 2.1) or pictures of the rock (such as that in Unit 2.2 of the students' book) and try to identify important features.

3 Use the photo on the students' book chapter starter (page 28 of the Students' book). It is Boweman's Nose on Dartmoor (made of weathered granite). Ask students to describe it and suggest why it is sticking up.

Ideas for plenaries

1 Draw a series of diagrams to help explain how frost-shattering (freeze-thaw weathering) works.

2 Describe how tors are formed?

3 Make a graffiti wall of what students have learned today.

4 A quick fire test: call out a student's name and a definition (e.g. for granite, igneous, tor, frost-shattering). The student has 5 seconds to give you the term.

Further class and homework activities

1 Draw a sketch map of Dartmoor and locate as many tors as possible. You may have some OS maps to help you. Collect pictures of the tors and make them into a wall display.

2 Make a study of the area around Edinburgh, in particular noticing the intrusions and the impact they have on the landscape. Look at the location of the castle. Has this got anything to do with igneous rocks. You may have a photograph to work from.

Answers to the Activities

1 Mind map might include:

Granite

location

Bodmin Moor, Land's End, Cornwall, Dartmoor, Devon

formation

molten rock (magma) that cooled below the Earth's crust

jointed rock (lines of weakness)

types of intrusion

vertical: dyke, ridge

dome: batholith

sideways: sill

resistance to weathering and erosion

frost-shattering otherwise a hard, strong rock,

tors

2 Rocks like granite have many joints. This means water can get into the cracks. When the temperature falls below 0 °C the water turns to ice and expands. This forces the joint to get bigger. Eventually pieces fall off, making a blockfield at the bottom of the tor.

The unit in brief

This unit looks at one granite area – Dartmoor. Students will find out about Dartmoor's physical features and about how people use Dartmoor. In the Activities, students answer an exam-style question which asks them to describe the physical features of a granite landscape they have studied, complete a table of land use on Dartmoor, and use a photo to look at some of the pros and cons of china clay mining on Dartmoor.

Key ideas

◆ Dartmoor is the top of an exposed batholith. It is the largest area of exposed granite in the south of the UK.

◆ Dartmoor is used for farming, mining and tourism.

◆ The china clay industry is big business. It's worth £120 million a year to the Cornish economy, and employs 2500 people.

◆ Mining china clay can cause problems for tourists and those who rely on income from tourism.

Key vocabulary

batholith, tor, china clay

Skills practised in the Activities

◆ Geography skills: describing physical features of a granite landscape; completing a table of land use; describing the appearance of a china clay mine from a photo

◆ Thinking skills: suggesting benefits and problems of china clay mining

Unit outcomes

By the end of this unit, most students should be able to:

◆ define or explain the terms given in 'Key vocabulary' above;

◆ know where Dartmoor is;

◆ describe the physical features of a granite landscape;

◆ know the three main types of land use on Dartmoor;

◆ understand how china clay is mined, and that, although it is important for the local economy, it can cause problems for those who rely on income from tourism.

Ideas for a starter

1 Recap – students describe to their partner what granite is like and the landscape features it forms.

2 Ask students where Dartmoor is. With all books closed and no clues on walls, ask students to mark it on an outline map of the UK on the board.

3 What do students know about Dartmoor? Show an image of Dartmoor, or again use the photo on the chapter starter in the Students' book (p.28). What is the landscape like? What is it used for?

Ideas for plenaries

1 Produce a concept map of Dartmoor as a class, including economic information, e.g. tourism, mining and farming.

2 Brainstorm how more people could be encouraged to visit Dartmoor (but note that tourism can create conflict and problems). Students could use these ideas to create a poster for homework.

3 Show a photograph of Dartmoor. Students should produce an annotated sketch of the area.

4 Create an acrostic. Students write GRANITE down the side of a page and make each letter the first letter of a word, phrase or sentence about granite.

Further class and homework activities

Write a visitor guide to the area emphasizing the formation of granite and the development of the tors.

Answers to the Activities

1 Note that students are asked simply to describe the landscape (not to explain it). While some features of the landscape are the result of human activities (e.g. farming), they are still a part of today's physical landscape, so mention should be made of them.

Granite landscape, e.g. Dartmoor

Granite tors, which are resistant to erosion, stand up above the lower land around them. The 160 tors here are large blocks of bare rock, with little or no vegetation growing on them. They are the exposed top of a batholith which formed from volcanic magma that cooled below the Earth's crust, and then the softer overlying material was eroded away. The tors have deep cracks running across and down them. The landscape around the tors, covering an area of 625 square kilometres, is hilly and grass-covered, with almost no trees. The hills are split by deep river valleys with steep sides where the water has eroded into the joints in the rock.

There are few settlements in this landscape. The soil is poor so there are no crops, just grass. Where the land is farmed, it is used for sheep grazing. However, the land is very beautiful and Dartmoor is a designated National Park. It is visited by 10 million people a year.

3 a A china clay mine creates a big, white gash in the landscape, which is visible from a distance. The waste tips are ugly and stand up above the level of the land. The mine needs to build roads for lorries to carry away the clay and these also cut across the landscape.

b The mine provides work for local people and brings in money to the area (£120 million a year).

c The mining activity spoils the appearance of the landscape; dust from the mine hangs in the air and settles on the surrounding land; lorries cause congestion and noise in local villages. These are all likely to deter tourists from coming to the area.

An additional note on this activity: students may be interested to know that the Eden Project, in Cornwall, was built inside an abandoned china clay quarry – the ultimate in 'recycling'!

2

Land use in Dartmoor	Why is it there?	What happens?
sheep farming	The soil is poor and acidic, so it only supports poor-quality grazing (it's not good enough for cows).	Sheep are allowed to roam freely on the moor.
mining	As granite cooled, minerals like copper and tin concentrated into layers, or veins. Some of the minerals are chemically weathered underground and formed china clay – useful for making paper and ceramics.	In the past, these minerals were mined but it's no longer economical to do so. China clay is washed out using water and giant hoses. It's allowed to settle and the clay is extracted. The industry is worth £120 million a year and employs 2500 people.
tourism	Granite creates a very beautiful landscape (Dartmoor is now a National Park), with few roads and settlements.	Many people come to walk, camp, and to see the beautiful landscape and the wildlife here. Some stay in local villages and spend money in the shops, so bringing money and jobs to the area.

The unit in brief

This unit is about limestone. It explains what limestone is, how it was formed, its properties, and where it is found in the UK. It tells students about limestone features which can be found in areas such as the Yorkshire Dales. In the Activities, students produce a mind map about limestone which helps to pull all the information from the unit together, and a table of limestone features.

Key ideas

◆ Limestone is a sedimentary rock consisting mainly of calcium carbonate (which comes from the remains of sea creatures).

◆ Limestone is found in several areas of the UK, including the Yorkshire Dales.

◆ It is usually jointed and quite strong.

◆ Limestone produces a number of landscape features only found in limestone areas.

Key vocabulary

limestone, sedimentary, calcium carbonate, gorges, caves, stalactites, stalagmites, dry valleys, swallow holes, limestone pavements, grykes, clints, dolines.

Skills practised in the Activities

◆ Geography skills: making a table of limestone features

◆ Thinking skills: producing a mind map about limestone

Unit outcomes

By the end of this unit, most students should be able to:

◆ define or explain the terms given in 'Key vocabulary' above;

◆ understand how limestone is formed;

◆ know where limestone is formed in the UK;

◆ understand what properties limestone has;

◆ describe limestone features and explain how they are formed.

Ideas for a starter

1 Recap: What are the features of a sedimentary rock? How were they formed? Can you give some examples of sedimentary rocks?

2 Show photographs of a limestone area such as the area around Malham. Ask students to describe the landscape. Can they name any features? Can they provide evidence that this is a limestone area?

3 Ask students to come up with 5 things they know about limestone.

Ideas for plenaries

1   Use an OS map extract of a limestone area, such as around Malham, and ask students to identify a number of limestone features.

2   Show photos of limestone features, or use those in this unit. Students should draw an annotated sketch from the photographs to show how the features are formed.

3   Use the OS map used in Plenary 1 to get the students to describe to a partner what they would see as they walked the Pennine Way through Malham and beyond the Field Study centre at the head of Malham Tarn.

4   Ask 6 students to describe a limestone feature to the rest of the class. (Students describe one of swallow holes, dry valleys, caves, gorges, limestone pavements, and dolines. They must not name the feature. The rest of the class must guess what the feature is.

Further class and homework activities

Draw a poster encouraging people to visit the area.

Answers to the Activities

1   Mind map might include:

Limestone

location
   Yorkshire Dales
formation
   sedimentary, skeletons and shells of
   sea creatures
resistance
   calcium carbonate – easily dissolved by
   rain and seawater
   jointed – line of weakness
   quite strong – cliffs do not collapse easily
landforms
   dry valley
   scar
   gorge
   swallow hole
   pavement
   gryke
   clint
   doline
   cave
   stalactite
   stalagmite
   resurgence stream

2

Feature	Example (Yorkshire Dales)	Description	Formation	Diagram
Swallow hole	Gaping Gill near Ingleborough	A hole in the ground down through which a stream falls	Water dissolves a joint then flows into it rather than over the land	[Suitable simple annotated sketch]
Dry valley	Watlowes Valley near Malham	A valley with no water running in the bottom (water flows under the ground)	Formed after the last ice age when the ground was saturated so water could not permeate into the underlying limestone	[Suitable simple annotated sketch]
Cave	Below Gaping Gill	A hole under the ground	Created by water dissolving the limestone underground.	[Suitable simple annotated sketch]
Gorge	Trow Gill, near Clapham	A large, steep-sided vertical crack in the landscape	May have been formed by the roof collapse of several caves, or possibly formed by powerful streams flowing as ice melted after the last ice age	[Suitable simple annotated sketch]
Limestone pavement	Malham	Exposed layer of limestone with deep vertical cracks (grykes) cut between the level surface blocks (clints)	Once the limestone was exposed, the vertical joints were weathered away by solution	[Suitable simple annotated sketch]
Doline	North of Malham Tarn	A hollow in the limestone that does not have a stream flowing into it	Either water dissolved limestone near the surface or a cave roof collapsed	[Suitable simple annotated sketch]

The unit in brief

This unit looks at one limestone area – the Yorkshire Dales. Students find out about the economy of the area and the jobs that people do. They discover that while tourism is important to the local economy, it also brings problems. In the Activities, students complete a writing frame to produce a case study of the Yorkshire Dales, and analyse an employment bar graph.

Key ideas

◆ Quarrying, tourism and farming are all important to the Dales economy.

◆ Tourism brings in about £175 million a year, while quarrying brings in £6 million a year.

◆ 20% of people work in farming, compared to 2% nationally.

◆ Tourism brings problems as well as benefits.

Key vocabulary

economy, honeypot

Skills practised in the Activities

◆ Geography skills: explaining patterns of employment

◆ Numeracy skills: analysing a bar graph of employment data

◆ Literacy skills: completing a writing frame to produce a case study about the Yorkshire Dales

Unit outcomes

By the end of this unit, most students should be able to:

◆ explain the terms given in 'Key vocabulary' above;

◆ know the three main types of employment in the Yorkshire Dales and the key facts about each;

◆ understand that although tourism is very important to the local economy, it brings other problems with it;

◆ interpret the bar graph of employment in different sectors.

Ideas for a starter

1 Ask students to find the Yorkshire Dales in an Atlas map and identify the urban areas closest to the Dales.

2 Recap: How does limestone form, what are its main features?

3 Show a photo of a limestone area and ask students to describe the landscape. How do students think people make a living in areas like this?

Ideas for plenaries

1 How attractive do you think the Yorkshire Dales would be for a young person to live and work in?

2 Many young people leave the area every year to go to the large towns on the edge of the Dales. What effect will this have on the local economy? Draw a flow chart to show the likely consequences of this movement.

3 Brainstorm how you can encourage new investment into the area so that the young people stay. List all your ideas. Any which harm the physical environment must then be deleted.

4 Imagine you are a local who is trying to move to a local city rather than stay in the Dales. You'd like to stay but can't afford the housing. Prepare a 2 minute 'chat' for a local phone-in radio show. You must explain your feelings and say what has driven up the price of housing.

5 Create an acrostic. Students write LIMESTONE down the side of a page and make each letter the first letter of a word, phrase or sentence about limestone.

Further class and homework activities

This is the situation in many upland parts of UK. How can we get people to stay and continue to manage the countryside? Try to brainstorm as many ideas as possible and go to the Dales National Park website and see if they have been incorporated in the local development plan.

Answers to the Activities

1 This depends on students' answers, but here is a possible completed writing frame:

Title: Case study – Yorkshire Dales

This area is located in the north of England, on the east side of the Pennine hills.

The geology of the area is largely limestone.

The three main economic activities in the Dales are quarrying, tourism and farming.

Quarrying is important because the limestone that is extracted brings in £6 million a year to the area, from the eight large quarries.

Farming in this area is mostly sheep farming because the soils are thin, making it difficult to grow crops. The area is also hilly, and can be very cold in winter. Farmers work in the traditional way in order to care for the beautiful landscape here.

Tourism is very important too. People come to see the limestone scenery and the pretty villages, and to walk along the footpaths in the area.

Good things about tourism are that it creates jobs (in hotels, bed and breakfasts, restaurants and shops), and brings in £175 million a year to the area.

Possible negative effects of tourism are the result of too many visitors, and conflicts of interest:

- Some places become crowded with people and traffic (honeypots), and local people may resent the visitors.

- Visitors may damage farmland, break down walls, leave gates open, drop litter, disturb livestock.

- Footpaths and limestone pavements are damaged by too many trampling feet and bike tyres.

- House prices are pushed up by 'incomers' buying holiday homes, so local people can't afford to buy in their home towns.

2 a The Yorkshire Dales has a greater proportion of people employed in farming than in the rest of England and Wales – more than 20% compared with about 2% in England and Wales. There is a lower percentage working in all the other sectors – for example, in manufacturing 18% in England and Wales, but only 9% in the Yorkshire Dales – though the proportions of those working in mining and quarrying, and in construction, are similar in both regions. The largest sector of employment, both in England and Wales and the Dales, is in services: 62% in England and Wales, and only a little less (56%) in the Dales.

b There are more people in agriculture in the Dales because there are few resources here for industry (manufacturing) except limestone, which is quarried and used elsewhere. The climate here means winters are cold, and the hills make access difficult. However, it is a good environment for sheep farming.

The reason why there is such a high proportion of people working in services is that tourism, which is very important to the area, creates a need for hotels, guest houses, restaurants, shops and activities that tourists like to enjoy in this attractive environment.

The unit in brief

This unit focuses on Ingleton quarry in the Yorkshire Dales. Students find out that people have different views about quarrying. In the Activities, students produce a fact-file about the quarry, and decide on its future – whether it should carry on, limit production to another three years, or close down now.

Key ideas

◆ Quarrying is important. Only 15 people are employed directly but the quarry has a multiplier effect on the local economy.

◆ Money has been spent to reduce the environmental impact of the quarry, but some tourists will be put off by it. (Tourism brings in far more money than quarrying.)

◆ Limestone is a non-renewable resource. The long-term effect of quarrying on the environment needs to be considered.

Key vocabulary

non-renewable, sustainable, ecosystem

Skills practised in the Activities

◆ Geography skills: drawing the sketch map of the location of the quarry

◆ Literacy skills: producing a fact-file about the quarry; preparing a presentation about the future of the quarry

◆ Thinking skills: deciding on the future of the quarry, based on advantages and disadvantages

Unit outcomes

By the end of this unit, most students should be able to:

◆ define or explain the terms given in 'Key vocabulary' above;

◆ know where Ingleton quarry is;

◆ understand that people have different views about quarrying in the Yorkshire Dales;

◆ understand that there are advantages and disadvantages to quarrying;

◆ draw a sketch map to show the location of the quarry.

Ideas for a starter

1 Recap: What is limestone used for? What are its qualities?

2 How important is quarrying in the Yorkshire Dales. Ask students for facts and figures.

3 Show a photo of Ingleton quarry. Ask students what effect it has on the environment. Why does quarrying cause conflict?

Ideas for plenaries

1 Work out the positive and negative impacts of a quarry in the middle of the national park. You may find it helpful to draw a table with positive and negative columns. Give each impact a value from -5 to +5 and then total up the columns. What does this tell you?

2 Write 50 words for the local newspaper supporting the quarry, as it provides jobs and few other local enterprises do that!

3 How would you attempt to screen the quarry further and prevent some of the worst problems of the development?

4 Write the phrase 'Quarrying in a National Park' in the middle of the board. Create a mind map around the phrase. How many ideas can students come up with in 2 minutes?

Role play the meeting to decide on the future of the quarry. The following roles could be used but you may wish to invent more:

◆ the manager of the quarry

◆ a quarry worker

◆ a conservationist

◆ a national park ranger

◆ a local resident

◆ a tourist

◆ a newly-arrived resident – retired and looking for quiet!!

Prepare your speeches and try to argue the case for one of the three options.

Answers to the Activities

1 Answers will depend on the students' selection of information, but a good answer will include all the arguments for and against the continuation of quarrying activities.

The sketch map should include a careful selection of features around the quarry that need protecting, e.g. waterfalls, footpaths; and ways in which views of the quarry can be or have been improved, e.g. by planting trees. Students need to note other features in the immediate area, and think about potential problems; e.g. the quarry is only a short distance away from the village of Ingleton, so… How visible is it from the village? How much noise does it create?

2 Answers should consider both sides of the argument for each option, clearly stating the specific points for and against. The presentation **c** should present a strong case, with well-supported arguments, for the option that is selected by the student.

Some students could conduct online research on Ingleton quarry – several websites provide useful educational information on environmental activities there.

The unit in brief

This unit is about chalk. It explains what chalk is, how it was formed, what it is used for, and the type of landforms it produces. It introduces the North and South Downs – areas of chalk. In the Activities, students produce a mind map about chalk which helps to pull all the information in the unit together, and answer an exam-style question which asks them to describe the physical landscape of a named area of chalk and explain the main type of land use in the area.

Key ideas

◆ Chalk is a sedimentary rock composed of calcium carbonate.

◆ Chalk is used in making plaster, putty, cement, mortar and so on.

◆ Chalk produces landforms such as dry valleys, steep cliffs and rolling hills.

◆ The North and South Downs are examples of chalk landscapes. Grazing animals protect the downland habitat.

Key vocabulary

chalk, sedimentary, calcium carbonate, porous, dry valley, solution, steep cliffs, rolling hills, downland habitat

Skills practised in the Activities

◆ Geography skills: describing the physical landscape of a named chalk area

◆ Thinking skills: producing a mind map about chalk; explaining the main type of land use in a named chalk area

Unit outcomes

By the end of this unit, most students should be able to:

◆ define or explain the terms given in 'Key vocabulary' above;

◆ know where the North and South Downs are;

◆ understand how chalk is formed, and what it is used for;

◆ know the types of landforms found in chalk areas and how chalk is eroded;

◆ describe the physical landscape of a chalk area.

Ideas for a starter

1 To check students' understanding of the key terms covered so far in this chapter, devise a word game such as where definitions and key terms have to be turned over together and matched. The winner is the student with most pairs.

2 Ask students to draw a sketch diagram to show how sedimentary rock is formed.

3 Where do we find chalk in the UK? Ask students to use an Atlas/geological map to help them locate chalk. Draw the locations on a blank outline of the UK.

Ideas for plenaries

1 Provide students with an OS map of chalk downland and ask them to comment on the shape of the landscape, the drainage, the types and location of settlements, the agriculture and land use.

2 Show photos of downland areas or use those in the students' book. Students should draw and annotate sketches from the photographs.

3 Make a grafitti wall of what students have learned today.

4 Play 'Just a minute' – the topic is 'sedimentary rocks'. Students have the chance to talk for a minute on sedimentary rocks without repetition or hesitation. As soon as a student repeats an idea, or hesitates, the next student takes over until the minute is up.

Further class and homework activities

1 Draw a series of cross-sections from the OS map and mark on the different types of land use. Display them so that the whole class can see. What is the dominant land use?

2 Brighton and Hove Albion FC have planning permission to build a stadium in the South Downs. Watch out for newspaper cuttings and other resources on the issue. Collect these together and display them on a wall display.

3 The chalk downlands of West Sussex have been designated a national park. Investigate this area and say whether you think the area is worth preserving.

Answers to the Activities

1 Mind map might include:

Chalk

location
  Seven Sisters
  North Downs
  South Downs
  White Cliffs of Dover
formation
  sea shells (esp. foraminiferans) squashed under pressure
  sedimentary – calcium carbonate
resistance
  slow erosion by solution
  no joints
  porous – lets water through
farming
  sheep
landforms
  dry valleys
  rolling hills (Downs)
  cliffs
vegetation
  grasses
  herbs
  orchids
  shrubs
uses
  building

plaster
putty
cement
mortar
rubber
blackboard chalk

2 a Students should note that they are asked to describe the physical landscape; they do not have to explain it. (Part b covers land use, i.e. the human impact on the landscape.)

Chalk landscape, e.g. South Downs or North Downs

The landscape is of gently rolling hills with rounded tops. Some of these hills have a steeper slope on one side than the other. Between the hills there are often quite deep valleys with steep sides, but no water flows in these small valleys. The hills are covered with grass and only a few trees. The chalk rock is usually only exposed where it has been eroded by the sea. On the south coast of England, for example, it forms the high, very steep cliffs known as the Seven Sisters. There are sometimes springs at the foot of chalk hills, where they meet an underlying layer of clay or other impermeable rock.

b Sheep farming is the main land use. The soil overlying chalk is thin and generally supports grass, some specialised herbs, and only a few trees. This environment attracts several rare insects and flowers. The grazing animals prevent the growth of shrubs that might otherwise take over and change the landscape. In large areas of the North and South Downs, sheep are deliberately used to graze the hills and preserve the special downland environment. Crops like wheat and barley can be grown in chalk areas, but as chalk downlands are relatively dry, the crops must be drought-resistant.

The unit in brief

This unit is about clay. It explains what clay is, how it was formed, what it is used for and the type of landscape it produces. It introduces the area around Lough Neagh in Northern Ireland – an area of clay. In the Activities, students produce a mind map about clay which helps to pull all the information in the unit together, and answer an exam-style question which asks them to describe and explain the physical landscape of a named area of clay. They also produce revision notes for the whole chapter.

Key ideas

◆ Clay is a fine-grained sedimentary rock, produced as a result of the chemical weathering of other rocks and minerals.

◆ Clay is used in paper making, for the tips of spark plugs, in chemical filters and so on.

◆ Clay is impermeable.

◆ The area around Lough Neagh in Northern Ireland has a clay geology. It is a flat area with bogs and rivers, and is a mixture of farmland (the main land use), grasses, woodland and marshes.

Key vocabulary

clay, sedimentary, slumping, impermeable

Skills practised in the Activities

◆ Geography skills: describing and explaining the physical landscape of a clay area; producing revision notes for the chapter

◆ Thinking skills: producing a mind map about clay

Unit outcomes

By the end of this unit, most students should be able to:

◆ define or explain the terms given in 'Key vocabulary' above;

◆ know where Lough Neagh is;

◆ understand how clay is formed, and what it is used for;

◆ say how people around Lough Neagh make a living;

◆ describe the physical landscape of a clay area.

Ideas for a starter

1 What are the three categories of rock called? Draw three simple pictures on the board to show the formation of sedimentary, igneous and metamorphic rocks. Ask students to identify which is which.

2 Ask students to come up with five things they know about clay.

3 Use a geological map to locate areas of clay. Remember that it is a rock, although we may see it as very fluid and slippery!

Ideas for plenaries

1 Clay is a porous rock when dry but becomes impermeable when it is wet. Provide students with OS map extracts of a clay area and a chalk area and ask them to compare the drainage patterns.

2 What type of improvement might a farmer have to make to a field in a clay area to make it more productive?

3 Show photos of a clay area. Students should annotate a sketch of a photo to describe the landscape and land use.

4 Ask students if they found anything difficult about the work in this chapter. What? Why? What would help to make it less difficult/easier to understand?

5 Do an alphabet run from A-Z with a word or phrase to do with rocks and landscape for each letter.

Further class and homework activities

Investigate the economic uses for clay.

Answers to the Activities

1 Mind map might include:

Clay
location
    Lough Neagh, N. Ireland
    South East England
    Fenlands
    Weald
    London Basin
formation
    chemical weathering
    transportation and deposition by rivers and ice
    very small particles (less than 0.02 mm)
resistance
    weak material
    slumps when wet
    water cannot pass through it easily
landforms
    flat land
    rivers
    bogs, marshes
    Broads
farming
    fruit and vegetables (market gardening)
    cereal crops (wheat)
    dairy cattle
uses
    waterproofing landfill sites
    bricks
    pots
    paper
    chemical filters

2 Here students are asked both to describe and explain the physical landscape.

Clay landscape, e.g. East Anglia

The Fenlands of East Anglia are generally very flat and low-lying. This is because the clay is not strong enough to make steep slopes, because it collapses under its own weight. When it gets wet, it simply slides (slumps) down any slope. The land is very wet, because the clay is impermeable and does not allow water to pass through it easily. In many places it is waterlogged, creating boggy areas. However, several rivers pass through the area, and large parts of the Fens are also drained by artificial channels, so that crops can be grown on the rich soils. Because water does not pass easily through the soil, it is high in nutrients. Except for a few areas that are preserved as wildlife habitats, e.g. the Broads, most of the Fens are now cultivated for fruit and vegetables (market gardening) and, in some drier areas, for wheat. It is easy to use farm machinery on these flat lands. There are few industries, but in some places the clay is extracted, for making bricks for example.

3 Glacial landscapes

The big picture

These are the key ideas behind this chapter:

◆ Glaciers are like frozen rivers which flow very slowly.

◆ Like rivers, glaciers erode, transport and deposit material. They create a range of different landforms as a result of erosion and deposition.

◆ Glacial landforms can be recognised on OS maps.

◆ Upland glaciated areas are used for forestry, farming and tourism.

◆ Tourism creates problems which have to be managed.

Note that the students' version of the big picture is given in the students' chapter opener.

Chapter outline

Use this, and the students' chapter opener, to give students a mental roadmap for the chapter.

Objectives and outcomes for this chapter

Objectives	Unit	Outcomes
Most students will understand:		Most students will be able to:
● What a glacier is.	3.1	● What a glacier is.
● How glaciers change the landscape as a result of erosion, transportation and deposition, and that freeze-thaw weathering plays a part.	3.1, 3.2, 3.3, 3.4	● How glaciers change the landscape as a result of erosion, transportation and deposition, and that freeze-thaw weathering plays a part.
● How to recognise glacial landforms on OS maps.	3.5	● How to recognise glacial landforms on OS maps.
● What types of land use are found in upland glaciated areas.	3.6, 3.7	● What types of land use are found in upland glaciated areas.
● That tourism is important to the local economy, but brings problems too.	3.7	● That tourism is important to the local economy, but brings problems too.
● That there are solutions to the problems that tourists cause, and that people have different views about some of the solutions.	3.8	● That there are solutions to the problems that tourists cause, and that people have different views about some of the solutions.

These tie in with 'Your goals for this chapter' in the students' chapter opener, and with the opening lines in each unit, which give the purpose of the unit in a student-friendly style.

Using the chapter starter

The photo on page 46 of the *geog.GCSE* students' book shows the Aletsch Glacier, Switzerland. The dark stripes are medial moraines, and give a clear impression of the glacier 'flowing' down the valley.

The Aletsch is the largest glacier in the Alps. It is 24 km long; in places it's 1.5 km wide and more than 900 metres deep.

Its start point is at 4000 metres. It covers an area of 120 sq km (45 sq miles). It descends into the valley of the Upper Rhone. At its fastest it moves at about 180 metres a year, or about 50 cm a day.

The weight of the ice has been calculated at 27 billion tonnes. If we melted the glacier, it would give everyone on Earth 1 litre of water a day for six years.

Scientists study the world's ice sheets and glaciers because they can tell us a lot about the history of climate change and the current trend towards global warming.

Like many glaciers, the Aletsch Glacier is retreating under the influence of global warming. In the middle of the 19th century it extended 3 km further down the valley than it does today, and since then its thickness has been reduced by about 100 metres. It is now retreating by up to 50 metres a year.

The unit in brief

This unit is about glaciers. It explains what glaciers are, where they are found, and how they shape the landscape. In the Activities, students produce a mind map about glaciers based on one in the students' book. They can add extra information to it based on their own research. They also explain the process of freeze-thaw weathering and describe the effects of this process on the landscape.

Key ideas

◆ A glacier is a body of ice which moves downhill.

◆ Glaciers are found in big mountain ranges, and wherever it is cold enough. Ice sheets are found in places like Greenland, Iceland and Antarctica.

◆ Glaciers erode by plucking and abrasion.

◆ Moraine is material that is transported and later deposited by glaciers.

◆ Much of the surface moraine results from freeze-thaw weathering.

Key vocabulary

glacier, ice sheet, ice age, melt-water, crevasse, plucking, abrasion, striation, moraine (ground, lateral, medial), freeze-thaw weathering

Skills practised in the Activities

◆ Geography skills: describing the effect of freeze-thaw weathering on the landscape

◆ Thinking skills: producing a mind map about glaciers; explaining freeze-thaw weathering

Unit outcomes

By the end of this unit, most students should be able to:

◆ define or explain the terms given in 'Key vocabulary' above;

◆ understand that a glacier is a body of ice which moves downhill;

◆ know where glaciers and ice sheets are found;

◆ explain how glaciers erode;

◆ name different types of moraine;

◆ explain the process of freeze-thaw weathering.

Ideas for a starter

1 Brainstorm glaciation to find out what students know about the topic already. What do they know about ice ages, glaciers and the effect that glaciation has had on the landscape?

2 Show photos of glaciated landscapes and point out the features created by, or altered by, glaciation. Ask the students to list the features and suggest how they might have been formed.

3 Draw a U-shaped valley on the board. Superimpose a V-shaped river valley over it. Ask students to estimate the depth of ice in a valley glacier, and consider the erosive powers of a glacier as well as how much material a glacier erodes.

3 Mind movie time! You are being lowered into a crevasse in a glacier. What does it feel like? What can you see and hear? Tell us. If you have seen 'Touching the Void', this might help!

Ideas for plenaries

1 Use the map on page 48 in the students' book. Do you live in an area which was once covered in ice or in an area which was unglaciated? Do you know any features which could be of glacial origin? Make a class list.

2 If you live in an unglaciated area do you think your landscape would have been unaffected totally by the effects of ice? What might have affected your area?

3 If you did not use starter 4 ask students to imagine what it would be like being lowered into a crevasse in a glacier. Ask them to think of 10 key words which sum up what it might be like. If they have seen 'Touching the Void', this might help.

4 What might be happening to glaciers as the world warms up due to global warming. What will the consequences be of this?

5 Write down as many words as you can relating to today's work.

Further class and homework activities

Investigate Ice Ages and be ready to report back to the class at the beginning of the next lesson.

Answers to the Activities

1 At this stage students should just re-create, on a large sheet of paper (A3) the basic diagram, with plenty of space around it to add features as they work through the chapter – for example all the landforms they encounter in units 3.2-3.5, and any more that they research in the course of their work on glaciation.

Glaciation can be a large topic; make sure in this unit that students understand the basic processes (how glaciers move), and that they are clear about the differences between the various types of moraine. Through research, they should select one particular area on which there is plenty of information so that in an exam answer they can give named examples. For this reason it is probably best to select an area in the UK (Wales, Lake District, Scotland), which is well covered by Ordnance Survey maps on which the various features created by the processes of glaciation can easily be seen today.

2 a Freeze-thaw weathering is a weathering process that occurs in cold climates where the temperature fluctuates above and below 0 °C, allowing ice to form and melt repeatedly.

b Water fills cracks in the rock. When the temperature falls below 0 °C, the water freezes and expands by about 9%, making the cracks wider. When the ice melts, more water enters the crack and freezes in turn, forcing the crack even wider. Over time, the repetition of this process forces pieces of rock to break off. These pieces of rock can then be carried away by ice or water.

c Freeze-thaw is an important process in cold climates, especially upland regions in many parts of the world, because it breaks up the bedrock and enables further weathering and transportation of material – and eventually the creation of soils in which plants may grow. Therefore, over time, it allows a change in the landscape from solid rock to a place where vegetation can take a hold. In the long term, it provides an environment for other plants and for animals that feed on those plants.

Glacial landforms – erosional features

The unit in brief

This unit looks at some of the erosional features created by glaciers, namely corries, arêtes and pyramidal peaks. In the Activities, students produce a flow diagram to show how corries form, make notes on arêtes and pyramidal peaks, and draw and annotate a diagram of one of the photos on the spread in the students' book to show how either corries, arêtes or pyramidal peaks are formed.

Key ideas

◆ Glaciers create landforms as a result of erosion and deposition.

◆ Corries (cirques or cwms) are formed when ice moves out of a hollow. When the ice melts, a corrie-lake or tarn may be left behind.

◆ If two corries form back-to-back, or side by side, a ridge called an arête forms between them.

◆ When three or more corries cut backwards into a mountain, a pyramidal peak, or horn, develops.

Key vocabulary

corries, cirques, cwms, back wall, lip, corrie-lake, tarn, arête, pyramidal peak, horn

Skills practised in the Activities

◆ Geography skills: drawing a sketch diagram of a photo and adding annotations

◆ Literacy skills: making notes on arêtes and pyramidal peaks

◆ Thinking skills: producing a flow diagram to show how corries form

Unit outcomes

By the end of this unit, most students should be able to:

◆ define or explain the terms given in 'Key vocabulary' above;

◆ explain how corries, arêtes and pyramidal peaks form;

◆ draw and annotate a diagram to show how corries, arêtes or pyramidal peaks form.

Ideas for a starter

1 Recap: Ask students to describe the processes of plucking, abrasion and freeze-thaw weathering?

2 Ask students to name features formed by glacial erosion. What do they know so far about how they were formed?

3 show a video of glacial landforms. Ask students to describe what they see.

Ideas for plenaries

1 Work in pairs. Each pair writes the definition for the key vocabulary in this unit. Their partner has to work out what is being described.

2 Provide photos of upland glaciated areas in the UK. Ask students to annotate them with any glacial features they can identify.

3 Make a graffiti wall of what students have learned today.

4 Sum up what you have learned today in less than 40 words.

Further class and homework activities

Try to work on a model of erosion starting with a high upland area with some small indentations through to cirques and pyramidal peaks then to erosion of the peaks or horns to a low nearly flat area. Try to draw diagrams to support your understanding.

Answers to the Activities

1

Snow collects in a sheltered hollow at the top of a mountain …

↓

It turns to ice and then begins to move downhill, pulled by gravity.

↓

As it moves, it curves or rotates (rotational slippage).

↓

The material in the hollow is loosened by freeze-thaw weathering, and the moving ice plucks and abrades this material away from the sides of the hollow, making the hollow wider and deeper.

↓

Most material is eroded from the back wall, which becomes very steep. Less is eroded at the front, so a lip forms here.

↓

When the ice melts, a lake may form in the hollow behind this lip.

2 An alternative to the sentence beginnings in the students' book would be to ask students to create a four-column table, like the one below. They could eventually make similar notes for all the features described in this chapter. The format of this table could also provide the basis for revision cards on which the information is set out systematically (just one example is included here).

Feature	Looks like …	Formation	Example/s
Arete	A sharp ridge	Two corries form next to each other, leaving a sharp ridge between them	Striding Edge, The Lake District

3 Suitable additional images for drawing and annotating can be found on a number of Internet sites, including a search of Google Images – insert the names of known glaciated locations.

Students might be challenged to see how many different glacial features they can accurately label on a single such image. For example, on the top photograph on page 51 they could also identify and add labels for the corrie lake on the left (ask them to find out its name – the answer, Red Tarn, can be found on the map on page 56), and the steep scree slopes on either side of the arête which have been scoured by glaciers.

The unit in brief

This unit looks at some of the other erosional features created by glaciers, i.e. glacial troughs, truncated spurs and hanging valleys. In the Activities, students draw and annotate a sketch of a photo in the students' book; match beginnings and endings of sentences about erosional features, and consider why there's a lake at Wast Water in the Lake District.

Key ideas

◆ As glaciers move, they erode the sides and floor of the old river valley to form a glacial trough.

◆ The ends of interlocking spurs are eroded, leaving truncated spurs.

◆ When the glacier melts, tributary valleys are left hanging on the valley sides, creating hanging valleys.

Key vocabulary

abrasion, plucking, glacial trough, U-shaped valley, interlocking spurs, truncated spurs, hanging valleys, misfit stream

Skills practised in the Activities

◆ Geography skills: drawing and annotating a field sketch from a photo
◆ Thinking skills: matching beginnings and endings of sentences about erosional features; thinking about the formation of a lake in a glacial trough

Unit outcomes

By the end of this unit, most students should be able to:

◆ define or explain the terms given in 'Key vocabulary' above;

◆ understand and explain how glacial troughs, truncated spurs and hanging valleys are formed;

◆ draw and annotate a field sketch from a photo.

Ideas for a starter

1 Who can remind me how corries, arêtes and pyramidal peaks are formed? Who can draw a diagram on the board to show their formation?

2 If you did not show a video of glacial landforms as a starter for Unit 3.2 you could show it for this unit. Ask students to describe what they see.

Ideas for plenaries

1 Provide students with a word search which includes all the key vocabulary covered so far in this chapter.

2 Students write definitions for the key vocabulary found in the word search.

3 Provide photos of upland glaciated areas. Ask students to identify glacial features. For each feature they identify, describe how it is formed.

4 Make 10-15 statements about glaciers and erosion features based on what students have learned so far, some true, some false. Students hold up **True** or **False** cards. Where statements are false, ask students to correct them.

Answers to the Activities

1 Students must draw an appropriately annotated field sketch

2 A glacial trough is … the eroded valley left by a glacier.

A hanging valley is … a tributary valley that enters a main valley part way up the valley side.

Truncated spurs are … the ends of interlocking spurs that have been cut off by the glacier.

This activity can be extended by asking students to prepare similar definitions for other features they study in this chapter, and then exchanging them with each other. They might also be asked to comment on each other's definitions – it's surprising how many variations there can be in describing just one feature! (All definitions must, of course, be accurate.)

3 Misfit streams are small streams that flow in the bottom of a glacial trough.

[These streams seem small in comparison with the size of the valley that they occupy, and the concept of misfit streams is not always an easy one to grasp. It requires some leap of the imagination to envisage what the valleys would have looked like when they were filled with ice. One way of demonstrating this is to create a three-dimensional model to show how the ice scraped away huge quantities of material both from the sides and the base of previously much smaller valleys.]

4 It will help students to answer this question if they have an Ordnance Survey map of the area (1:50 000 sheet 89, or use the Internet), which shows the contours in the area. Wast Water is the deepest lake in the Lake District (70 metres). During the Ice Age the ice moved down from the high land to the north and west and scoured out this deep, rocky trough which is now filled by a long, narrow ribbon lake. It has a lip at one end and this holds the water within the trough. The south-east side of Wast Water is exceptionally steep, rising from the 70 metres' depth of the lake to 609 metres above sea level, in a distance of about a kilometre.

The unit in brief

This unit is about glacial landforms created by deposition. It looks at terminal moraine, ribbon lakes, drumlins, eskers and kames. In the Activities, students explain what terminal moraines and ribbon lakes are, and try to make the connection between terminal moraine and global warming. They suggest reasons why Keswick developed by Derwent Water; write out true and false statements based on their knowledge of glaciation so far, read them out to the rest of the class for them to decide which are true and false; and make revision cards for all the features they have learnt about in this chapter.

Key ideas

◆ The material deposited by a glacier is called till.

◆ Terminal moraine marks the furthest point a glacier reached.

◆ Where water is trapped behind a terminal moraine in a glacial trough, a ribbon lake will form.

◆ Drumlins are shaped by the movement of the ice.

◆ Eskers are long ridges of material deposited by streams which flow under glaciers.

◆ Kames are mounds of debris which accumulated in crevasses in the ice.

Key vocabulary

till, terminal moraine, ribbon lake, drumlin, esker, kame

Skills practised in the Activities

◆ Geography skills: making revision cards for all the features learnt about in the chapter

◆ Thinking skills: explaining terminal moraines and ribbon lakes; making connections; suggesting reasons why Keswick developed by Derwent Water; writing and identifying true and false statements

Unit outcomes

By the end of this unit, most students should be able to:

◆ define or explain the terms given in 'Key vocabulary' above;

◆ explain how terminal moraine and ribbon lakes are formed;

◆ understand how drumlins, eskers and kames are formed;

◆ suggest why Keswick developed next to Derwent Water.

Ideas for a starter

1 Look out of the window. Until 10,000 years ago the ground was buried under ice. What features did the ice create as it deposited material?

2 Produce a diagram of a valley glacier, then remove the glacier.
   ◆ What features are left behind after the ice has melted ?
   ◆ What effect will the melted water have on the remaining features in the landscape?

Ideas for plenaries

1 Provide photos of glaciated areas which have a number of depositional features. Ask students to identify as many as possible.

2 How do humans use these depositional features?

3 Create an acrostic. Write GLACIAL LANDFORMS down the side of a page. Make each letter the first letter of a word, phrase or sentence about erosional or depositional landforms.

4 Did you find anything difficult about the work on glacial landforms? What? Why? What would help to make it less difficult?

Further class and homework activities

Use reference books to look up significant examples of depositional features.

Answers to the Activities

1 a The terminal moraine is the material that is left behind as a ridge when the ice melts. It marks the furthest point reached by a glacier.

Students should be clear about the distinctions between a terminal moraine, a ground moraine, a lateral moraine and a medial moraine (see Unit 3.1).

b A ribbon lake forms when water is trapped in the glacial trough after the ice has retreated, usually because the outlet is dammed by a terminal moraine. (An example is Wast Water – see activity 4 in Unit 3.3.)

c Currently, many glaciers around the world are in retreat, almost certainly as a result of global warming. This is clear to scientists and other observers, because the glacier's terminal moraine is visible some distance ahead of the glacier's front edge, or 'snout'. This means that the ice is no longer moving forward or even at a standstill, but is in clear retreat – it is melting. Terminal moraines seen in landscapes that are no longer covered by ice represent the point at which the climate changed (got warmer) in the past.

2 Students should consider all the factors involved in choosing an early settlement site, and its situation. Initially these would have been related to the lie of the land and access to life needs (food, water, shelter, defence, materials).

Selecting a site for a settlement on or near a lake is usually a good choice because it provides constant water and a means of defence. Keswick is on a low, relatively level site surrounded by hills, so it would have been easier to build here, and sheltered from extremes of weather. The lower land (which is obviously moraine material) was probably good farming land (moraines often provide good soils), with the hills offering a supply of building materials (wood, stone) and an environment suitable for grazing sheep (and possibly cattle lower down). The trees on the lower slopes of the hills would also have provided wood for fuel. The rising land would provide a dry site for settlement if it was too wet very close to the lake. The fact that this area is on lower land means that it would also have been a focus of routeways through the neighbouring hills.

3 These statements will depend on students' own ideas. Where students recognise that false statements have been read out, they should be encouraged to write out the correct version, rather than just say 'false'.

A couple of examples of possible statements:

A terminal moraine is material that collects at the side of the glacier. (False: this is the definition of a lateral moraine.)

An esker is a long wiggly ridge that formed under the ice. It is made up of material that was carried by a stream running at the base of the glacier. (True.)

Statements should cover not only individual features but also the processes that take place in glaciated areas, e.g. freeze-thaw weathering, plucking and abrasion.

4 This activity also ties in with the work started in Unit 3.2 Activity 2. The following is a list of individual features that should be covered by students who have worked through the chapter on glaciation. They are all visible today in a landscape that was once glaciated, i.e. after the ice has retreated.

arête

corrie/cwm/cirque (and terms back wall, lip, tarn)

drumlin

esker

glacial trough/U-shaped valley

hanging valley

kame

lateral moraine

medial moraine

misfit stream

pyramidal peak (horn)

ribbon lake

striation

terminal moraine

till

truncated spur

The unit in brief

This unit includes a full page extract from an Ordnance Survey map (1:50 000 scale) of the Lake District (the area around Thirlmere, Helvellyn and Grasmere). In the Activities, students use the map to identify glacial landforms and practise a wide range of skills, as detailed below.

Key ideas

This spread is different to most others in the students' book, in that there is no content as such. It includes activities based on the OS map and the large photo of Thirlmere.

Key vocabulary

relief

Skills practised in the Activities

◆ Geography skills: describing how height and steepness are shown on OS maps, and describing the relief of the area shown on the map in the students' book; using six-figure grid references and reading the map to match locations, places and landforms; drawing a cross-section; explaining the location of Grasmere and the A591, using map evidence; using a map and photo together; using the map to give examples of landforms, describing the landforms and explaining how they were formed.

Unit outcomes

By the end of this unit, most students should be able to:

◆ explain the term given in 'Key vocabulary' above;
◆ demonstrate a range of map skills, including:
    ◆ describing relief;
    ◆ using six-figure grid references;
    ◆ identifying landforms;
    ◆ drawing a cross-section;
    ◆ using a map in association with a photograph;
◆ describe landforms and explain how they are formed.

Ideas for a starter

1   Who can name the glacial erosion features we have looked at? Who can name the depositional features we have looked at?
2   Call out glacial landforms and ask students to classify them according to whether they are erosional or depositional.
3   Use Activity 1a and 1b as a starter. You could also ask students – What colour are contours? What is the interval between contours? What is a spot height?

Ideas for plenaries

1   Provide photos of the glacial features shown on the OS map. Ask students to provide grid references for the features shown in the photos.
2   Pick 3 glacial features on the OS map. Describe a walk between the 3 to a partner. Use grid references to explain your route and describe the features you see.
3   Provide students with a table of glacial features and ask them to draw the contour patterns.
4   Tell your neighbour the two key things you have learned today.

Further class and homework activities

1   Design a tourist brochure of the Lake District or another upland area and include information about the glacial features found in the area. Draw diagrams and sketches if possible.

2   Investigate Snowdonia. Collect information from a variety of sources and put together a wall display. Contact the National Park Office and look up websites on the internet.

Answers to the Activities

The map on page 56 of the students' book is a useful resource and reference for many of the activities in this chapter. By giving four- and six-figure grid references, individual glacial features can be identified and pinpointed for students to locate; for example, Red Tarn, a corrie lake/tarn, at 3415.

1 a Height is shown in two ways on OS 1:50 000 maps:

By contours: these are brown lines drawn at 10-metre vertical intervals, numbered at 50-metre intervals. Note also that lake depths are marked by blue contours (as in Thirlmere).

By spot heights: small black dots, numbered to the nearest metre above mean sea level. Note that these are not always at high points – ask students to find some 'low' spot heights, along roads for example. Can they suggest why these are included on a map?

b It is possible to see on a map where land is steep because this is where the contours are very close together, forming a dense brown mass (as around Helvellyn, for example).

c Note that relief describes both the rise and the fall of the landscape. Descriptions should not only cover the higher areas shown on the map, but should also consider the valleys between them. They should also cover the direction in which streams and valleys are running (to find this out students may need to look closely at the contours), and the relative steepness of slopes (again referring to contours – around Grasmere the land is much less steep than around Thirlmere, for example). Plenty of named examples and specific figures (maximum heights of hills, depths of valleys) should be included in the description.

2   342151 = spot height 949 on Helvellyn

321131 = car park

349079 = Alcock Tarn

This activity can be extended to provide useful practice in map reading and identification of specific features on a map – see note above.

3   Brown Cove = corrie

Thirlmere = ribbon lake

Striding Edge = arête

along the eastern edge of Thirlmere = truncated spurs

Red Tarn = corrie lake

Grisedale = glacial trough

along the eastern edge of Thirlmere = hanging valleys

4   Students draw an accurate cross-section of line A–B.

5   The part of Grasmere shown in square 3307 is an area of low, flat land crossed by the River Rothay, which would have been a good site for an early settlement in this otherwise very hilly area: flat land, good water supply, a crossing-point of the river, on a routeway at a point where several routes meet; probably also good soils here for growing crops.

6   The A591 is a relatively direct north-south route which follows the valleys where it can do so, and skirts the eastern shore of Thirlmere. It crosses the line of hills between Grasmere and Thirlmere at a point named Dunmail Raise (238 metres), a relatively low pass between two lines of higher hills. Students should notice that it is also labelled 'Roman Road', which means that the original road was built by the Romans, so the line of the route has more or less been maintained for about 2000 years. Building and maintaining roads in this type of environment is always difficult, and they are generally at as low a level as possible, avoiding steep gradients and extreme climatic conditions.

7   All of the trees planted around Thirlmere are conifers. Thirlmere is in fact a reservoir supplying water to Manchester. It makes use of the existing ribbon lake, and it is important to maintain the flow of clean water into the lake. Trees were planted to stabilise the ground around it and to prevent surrounding rocks and soil being washed into the lake. They also help to prevent evaporation of water from the surrounding land, as more water is trapped in the soil by the tree roots. The slopes here are so steep that the land cannot be used for farming, but planting trees may bring in a small income.

Following the Second World War, there was a deliberate policy to plant fast-growing conifers in the upland regions of Britain, including several large areas of the Lake District. Many such areas are now gradually being replaced by mixed native woodland species.

8 a   From the south of square 3315.

b   North-west.

9   This activity is a continuation of Unit 3.3 activity 2 and Unit 3.4 activities 3 and 4. If they have been updating their revision notes, students should have no difficulty in completing and even adding to this table. Emphasise again how important it is that they memorise at least one named example for each feature (except drumlins, eskers and kames), so that they can quote these in exam questions referring to features and processes of glaciation. The Lake District has numerous examples of most of these features.

The unit in brief

This unit is about how people use the land in an upland glaciated area. Snowdonia is used as the example here. In the Activities, students copy a diagram from the students' book and add facts about using land in Snowdonia. They also use a writing frame to produce their own case study of the hill farm featured in the unit, and draw a sketch map to show the location of the farm.

Key ideas

◆ Snowdonia is an upland glaciated area in North Wales.

◆ 16% of the land in Snowdonia is forested – mainly with coniferous trees.

◆ Merthyr Farm is a hill farm in Snowdonia which keeps sheep and cows.

◆ The climate is too cold, and the soil too thin, for crops to grow.

◆ Farmers have to diversify in order to survive.

Key vocabulary

There is no key vocabulary in this unit.

Skills practised in the Activities

◆ Geography skills: copying a diagram and adding facts about Snowdonia; drawing a sketch map of the location of Merthyr Farm

◆ Literacy skills: using a writing frame to produce a case study of Merthyr Farm

Unit outcomes

By the end of this unit, most students should be able to:

◆ give an example of an upland glaciated area;

◆ describe how people use the land in an upland glaciated area;

◆ understand why, and how, farmers diversify.

Ideas for a starter

1 Show photos of Snowdonia. Brainstorm the type of activities people want to do in this area?

2 Add to the activities produced in starter 1 and others which might take place in an area like Snowdonia and which students might not have thought of such as: hill walking, mountain biking, farming, site seeing, climbing, army training, quarrying etc. Ask students which activities could exist together and which would need to be apart.

3 Ask students to locate Snowdonia on a blank outline map of the UK.

Ideas for plenaries

1 Use an OS map extract of part of Snowdonia and find glacial features and examples of economic activity.

2 How should Snowdonia be developed? Discuss various options: leave the situation as it currently is; increase the subsidies payable on sheep; plant more of the upland areas with coniferous trees. What are the consequences of each one?

3 Should upland areas be left unmanaged so that people are discouraged from visiting? This may only cater for people who will care for the area in a sustainably way. What do you think?

4 Take 2 minutes with a partner to think up one interesting question about how people use the land in an upland glaciated area that we have not covered today.

Answers to the Activities

1

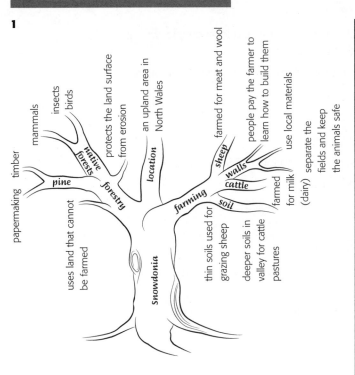

2 Case study: Farming in a glaciated area, at Merthyr Farm

This farm is in Snowdonia, North Wales.

The size of the farm is 140 hectares.

The type of farm is pastoral (grazing animals).

Animals are sheep, for their meat and wool, and cows for their milk.

It is difficult to farm in upland areas because the climate is too cold and the soil is too thin for crops to grow, and the lower slopes get waterlogged due to poor drainage. The grazing on the higher slopes isn't very nutritious for animals like sheep, and the price of lambs and wool has dropped badly so it's hard to make any money from them.

Ways round the problems are to bring in more money by offering bed and breakfast accommodation, providing rental space for caravans, and offering lessons in dry stone walling. The farmer also gets a subsidy from the government for farming in this difficult environment.

3 Students can either use the map in the students' book, or search for maps on the Internet which show the area at different scales. Sketch maps should include features that could influence the farm's activities, e.g. access by road and rail, situation in relation to the sea/National Park and to centres of population (Liverpool), etc.

Following these activities, students might discuss ways in which a farmer like Caerwyn Roberts could further increase his income from the farm, given its site and situation.

The unit in brief

In this unit students find out more about economic activity in an upland glaciated area. The focus here is on tourism in Snowdonia, and the benefits and disadvantages that it brings. In the Activities, students create a mind map about tourism in Snowdonia; write a role play about conflict between local people and tourists; produce a newspaper article on the problems caused by tourism, and suggest some solutions to the problem; find out about Betws-y-Coed – one of the honeypot villages in Snowdonia.

Key ideas

◆ Tourism is vital to the economy of Snowdonia.

- There are approximately 8 million visitors a year.

- 5000 people have jobs related to tourism.

- Tourism brings in approximately £180 million a year to the area.

◆ Tourism brings problems too.

- Footpaths are eroded.

- Jobs may be seasonal.

- There is a high volume of traffic.

- Litter is caused.

- House prices are raised.

- Honeypot villages attract too many tourists.

- Farm animals escape and are worried by dogs.

Key vocabulary

There is no key vocabulary in this unit.

Skills practised in the Activities

◆ Geography skills: finding out about Betws-y-Coed

◆ Numeracy skills: reading pie chart

◆ Literacy skills: writing a role play of conflict between tourists and local people; writing a newspaper article about the problems that tourists cause

◆ Thinking skills: making a mind map about tourism; thinking of solutions to problems caused by tourists

Unit outcomes

By the end of this unit, most students should be able to:

◆ give three reasons why tourism is important to the economy of Snowdonia;

◆ describe some of the problems that tourists cause;

◆ suggest how some of the problems caused by tourists could be solved.

Ideas for a starter

1 Make a graffiti wall of tourist activities in an upland area such as Snowdonia, and the impacts they might have.

2 Show photos which show a range of the effects tourism can have on an area such as Snowdonia.

Ideas for plenaries

1 Provide students with an OS map extract of Snowdonia. Ask them to identify glacial features as well as other tourist attractions (and provide grid references for all).

2 Ask students to create a 30 second soundbite for a local radio programme on the future of Snowdonia. Different students can take on roles of people with different views. Ask several students to read this to the rest of the class.

3 Ask students to draw up a table listing the advantages and disadvantages (problems) that tourism brings to Snowdonia.

4 Question time! Think back over the lesson and write down 3 questions related to what you have learned. The teacher will ask a member of the class to try to answer.

Further class and homework activities

1 Use an OS extract of Snowdonia to plan a touring holiday in which the visitors would stop off at various points and do short walks and visit various features. You should try to plan in photograph opportunities

2 Design a poster advertising the attractions of Snowdonia.

3 Take another national park and investigate it. Compare the problems of Snowdonia with the other area.

4 Go to the following website and investigate tourism within the UK: http://www.staruk.org.uk/ Try to find out how important Snowdonia is to the national tourism pattern.

Answers to the Activities

1 Mind map might include:

Snowdonia

jobs	problems
cafes, restaurants	traffic
B&Bs	litter
hotels	conflicts of use
shops	holiday homes
forestry	honeypots
farming	locations
transport	castles Caernarfon/Conwy/Harlech
visitor centres	towns/villages Dolgellau/Porthmadog
activities	Llaneris/Beddgelert/Bettws-y-Coed
walking 51%	Llyn Peninsula
mountain biking 8%	Cambrian Coast/Nefyn/Aberdaron
school trips 5%	Aberdyfi/Barmouth/Tywyn/Pwllheli
historical attractions 12%	National Park
railway journeys 4%	

2 This can be an individual, group or whole-class activity. Decide first what the exact point of conflict is – some examples:

   ◆ scramble-bikers want to use a public bridleway that goes across a local sheep-farmer's land;

   ◆ ramblers are accused by a local landowner of leaving gates open;

   ◆ car drivers have been caught speeding through a local village.

Make sure that both sides of the argument are fully covered – it shouldn't be so difficult for most students to see the problem from both points of view! Can they offer any solutions to the problems?

3 Students should cover as many points as possible – and perhaps suggest a few more besides. The article should be well-written and presented, ideally as a desktop-published feature, and be written in a style that is interesting to read. It might include a drawing, cartoon or photo with a suitable caption. The article should certainly include reference to at least some of the conflicts looked at in activity 2.

4 Again, presentation here is important. The final document will provide a useful case study for a student's revision portfolio, which they can refer to in appropriate exam answers. The research will also be useful practice in distilling information from the Internet, making useful selection of material and re-presenting it at an appropriate level. Remind them that a map or diagram can often provide as much information as written text. It may be a useful exercise for students to compare their case studies, to share ideas on how similar information can be presented in different ways.

5 By the time students have worked through the previous activities, they should have some clear ideas about how the problems can be tackled – and also how difficult it is to solve some of these problems. The UK National Parks are unique in that the land is not owned by the nation; nor are they managed solely for their landscape and wildlife. They are mainly farmed areas, where people live and work. Consequently, the two aims – to conserve these special landscapes and still maintain a viable way of life for the people who live there – have to be achieved side by side.

Students may find it useful to hold a brainstorming session, in groups or as a class, before they tackle this activity. There are no clear, easy answers, and solutions often depend on local circumstances. It is just such situations that have to be dealt with regularly by local councillors and the National Park Authorities.

The unit in brief

This unit looks at how some of the problems caused by tourists in Snowdonia can be managed, and considers people's views about the management schemes. In the Activities, students complete a table of management solutions to various problems, and make consequence maps for some of the solutions. They also answer two exam-style questions – one on footpath erosion, and another describing the problems caused by tourists in a named upland area and the attitudes of local people to the solutions introduced.

Key ideas

◆ There are a variety of management solutions to the problems caused by tourism in Snowdonia. They revolve around:

- housing;

- traffic and transport;

- encouraging new businesses and therefore creating jobs.

◆ Other solutions tackle litter and footpath erosion, etc.

◆ People have different views about the management schemes.

Key vocabulary

There is no key vocabulary in this unit.

Skills practised in the Activities

◆ Geography skills: completing a table of tourist problems and management solutions; describing problems caused by tourists and commenting on people's attitudes to management schemes

◆ Thinking skills: making consequence maps for management solutions; explaining how footpath erosion can be managed

Unit outcomes

By the end of this unit, most students should be able to:

◆ explain how different solutions can be used to manage the problems created by tourists in Snowdonia, and give at least six examples;

◆ describe people's views about the management solutions;

◆ say why different people might have different views.

Ideas for a starter

1 To check students' understanding of the key terms covered so far in this unit devise a 'pairs' game where key terms and definitions have to be turned over together and matched.

2 Draw a sketch map of Snowdonia on the board. Ask students to identify the glacial features, human uses and tourist attractions in Snowdonia.

Ideas for plenaries

1 Provide students with a cross-word including the key terms from this chapter.

2 Choose a student to be in the hot seat. Another student asks him or her a question about managing tourism in Snowdonia. Then nominate different students (4-6 pairs in total). There's one golden rule – questions cannot be repeated.

3 Go back through the work from this chapter and highlight all the key topics. Take 2 minutes to tell your neighbour the key thinks you have learned in this chapter.

Further class and homework activities

1 Write a short report entitled the management of Snowdonia using the following as a structure:
   ◆ An introduction to the area and an outline to the problems of conflicting use.
   ◆ An outline of the alternative solutions you have considered.
   ◆ An analysis of each solution in terms of the consequences of the actions.
   ◆ An evaluation of the solutions and a recommendation of the final solution or combination of solutions.

2 Put together a brochure for Snowdonia combining information about the physical and human landscapes

Answers to the Activities

1 Some of these problems and their solutions may have been covered in the previous unit, but this is a useful summary table for student revision.

problem	management solution
litter in Betws-y-Coed	imposing fines
traffic jams	3 by-passes planned; only cycles and buses allowed on some roads; more bike hire centres; advertising of local public transport
car parking	new tourist developments within walking/cycling distance of villages; residents-only car parks; park-and-ride schemes
path erosion	lay new stone paths; plant new grass (and see activity 3 below)
house prices	planning permission only for low-cost houses for local people; houses only advertised locally; housing associations build to let to local people
gates being left open	Countryside Code posters to remind tourists
seasonal jobs	local business developments and light industries encouraged (planning permission and special grants, e.g. from the Welsh Development Agency)

2 Students should think right through the consequences of imposing a management solution, including the disadvantages of the 'solution'.

3 Footpath erosion is a serious problem in many areas that attract tourists, especially in upland areas, which are often very wet and easily become muddy. It can be tackled in various ways, depending on the local conditions. Much of this work is carried out by volunteers, although on some National Trust properties, for example, people are paid to do this work.

For 4 marks students must come up with at least 4 clear suggestions on how to manage the problem. For example:
◆ Lay a new path made of stone.
◆ Plant new grass – a path is often reseeded after a new stone path is laid.
◆ Place special mesh below the path surface that will stop the ground being eroded.
◆ Divert the footpath away from areas especially in need of protection.
◆ Build new drainage channels to take water away from the route of the path.
◆ Build new footbridges over streams and marshy areas.
◆ Create boardwalks over the top of exceptionally wet places.
◆ Erect clear notices directing people along the designated footpaths.
◆ Erect information boards explaining to tourists why the measures are necessary. These might also include details of the local wildlife.

4 This activity requires research (and possibly fieldwork if circumstances allow it, especially for part b for which local opinion may be more difficult to acquire). An Internet search of particular places in National Parks, and careful study of local maps, should enable students to prepare a suitable case study to cover a number of likely exam questions like these. Some appropriate examples are the areas around:
◆ Llanberis in Snowdonia
◆ Malham in the Yorkshire Dales
◆ Dovedale in the Peak District
◆ Ambleside in the Lake District.

The problems are common to most of these places – although the attitudes may vary considerably!

4 River landscapes

The big picture

These are the key ideas behind this chapter:

◆ Rivers use their energy to erode and transport material. Deposition occurs when a river lacks enough energy to carry its load.

◆ Rivers change from their source to their mouth. There are characteristic landforms in the upper, middle and lower courses of a river.

◆ The drainage basin cycle is part of the water cycle.

◆ Rivers flood, and there are human and physical causes of flooding.

◆ The effects of flooding are different in MEDCs and LEDCs.

◆ There are a range of hard and soft engineering methods which can be used to try to prevent flooding. The methods used vary in MEDCs and LEDCs often for economic reasons.

Note that the students' version of the big picture is given in the students' chapter opener.

Chapter outline

Use this, and the students' chapter opener, to give students a mental roadmap for the chapter.

4 River landscapes As the students' chapter opener, this unit is an important part of the chapter; see page 11 of this book for notes about using chapter openers

4.1 Introducing rivers The source, middle course and mouth of a river. Erosion, transportation and deposition

4.2 The river's upper course The river channel, V-shaped valleys, interlocking spurs and waterfalls – with the River Tees as a case study

4.3 The river's middle course The formation of meanders and ox-bow lakes and the River Tees as the case study

4.4 The river's lower course Floodplains, river mouths, estuaries and deltas with the River Tees as the example again

4.5 Water – it gets around How water circulates continually between the ocean, atmosphere and land; the drainage basin cycle as part of the water cycle, and hydrographs

4.6 Flooding Human and physical causes of flooding, and changes to the hydrograph

4.7 Flooding in North Yorkshire The causes and effects of flooding in North Yorkshire in 1999 (an MEDC case study)

4.8 Flooding in Mozambique The causes and effects of flooding in Mozambique in 2000 (an LEDC case study)

4.9 Managing floods Hard and soft management methods – each method has problems and may fail

4.10 Controlling flooding in MEDCs and LEDCs How the flood risk is managed in North Yorkshire and Mozambique

Objectives and outcomes for this chapter

Objectives	Unit	Outcomes
Most students will understand:		Most students will be able to:
● How rivers change from their source to their mouth.	4.1	● Describe changes in the river channel, velocity and load.
● That rivers shape the land by erosion, transportation and deposition.	4.1	● Name and describe four methods of erosion, and four methods of transportation; describe how deposition takes place.
● That the processes of erosion, transportation and deposition produce characteristic landforms along a river.	4.2, 4.3, 4.4	● Explain how V-shaped valleys, interlocking spurs, waterfalls, meanders, ox-bow lakes, floodplains, levees, estuaries and deltas are formed.
● How to recognise river landforms on an OS map.	4.2, 4.3, 4.4	● Identify a range of river landforms on an OS map and describe them.
● How the water cycle operates and how the drainage basin cycle is part of the water cycle.	4.5	● Draw simplified diagrams of the water cycle and drainage basin cycle.
● That there are physical and human causes of river flooding.	4.6	● Give four physical causes of river flooding; give three human activities which increase the flood risk; explain why each physical and human factor can lead to flooding.
● What hydrographs are and what they show.	4.5, 4.6	● Explain what hydrographs show.
● The causes and effects of flooding in North Yorkshire in 1999.	4.7	● Classify factors causing flooding into human and physical; explain how they led to flooding; describe the short-term effects; identify long-term effects.
● The causes and effects of flooding in Mozambique in 2000.	4.8	● Give at least two short-term and two long-term causes of flooding; describe the short-term effects; identify long-term effects.
● How floods can be managed, and that MEDCs and LEDCs take a different approach to flood management.	4.9, 4.10	● Describe the range of hard and soft management techniques for managing the flood risk; describe the different methods used in North Yorkshire and Mozambique and explain why they are different.

These tie in with 'Your goals for this chapter' in the students' chapter opener, and with the opening lines in each unit, which give the purpose of the unit in a student-friendly style.

Using the chapter starter

The photo on page 64 of the *geog.GCSE* students' book shows the Grand Canyon of the Verdon River, on the edge of the Alps in Provence, south-east France.

The gorge is 21 km long and in places 700 metres deep. The bottom varies in width from 6 metres to 100 metres. It has been formed by the erosion of the limestone rock by the Verdon River. It is Europe's widest and deepest gorge.

The canyon was only fully explored in the early 20th century. Before then people found the deepest parts too difficult to get to, and just a few local woodcutters went down on ropes.

Now the canyon is a great tourist attraction, with people hiking, climbing, and rafting.

The Verdon River flows for 175 km from its source in the south-western Alps – it's a tributary of the Durance, which in turn is a tributary of the Rhone, which flows into the Mediterranean Sea.

The unit in brief

This unit introduces rivers and what they do – erode, transport and deposit material. In the Activities, students complete a table about the different parts of a river, and a writing frame about erosion, transportation and deposition. They also answer an exam-style question about erosion.

Key ideas

◆ Rivers change from their source to their mouth.

◆ The energy which a river has, enables it to erode and transport material.

◆ Rivers erode by one of four processes: abrasion, attrition, hydraulic action and solution.

◆ Rivers transport their load by one of four processes: solution, suspension, saltation, traction.

◆ Deposition occurs when a river lacks enough energy to carry its load.

Key vocabulary

erosion, abrasion, attrition, hydraulic action, solution, transportation, suspension, saltation, traction, load, bedload, deposition, sediment, velocity

Skills practised in the Activities

◆ Geography skills: completing a table about parts of a river; explaining and describing the processes of erosion

◆ Literacy skills: completing a writing frame about erosion, transportation and deposition

Unit outcomes

By the end of this unit, most students should be able to:

◆ define or explain the terms given in 'Key vocabulary' above;

◆ describe how rivers change from their source to their mouth;

◆ explain how rivers erode;

◆ name the processes that rivers use to transport their load;

◆ know that deposition occurs when a river lacks enough energy to carry its load.

Ideas for a starter

1 Name as many of the world's greatest rivers as you can. Which is the longest river in the world? Use your atlas to help you.

2 Which river is associated with these cities: London; Kolkata; Paris; Cairo; New Orleans; Cardiff; Glasgow; Bristol; New York?

3 Can you name the most important river in the UK? Which is the nearest river to you?

4 Why is a location near a river important? Why was it important in the past?

Ideas for plenaries

1 Work with a partner. Write down all the important terms from this unit. Write the definitions for the items between you.

2 Show students the BBC video of the River Tees. Ask them to produce a sketch map showing the important features, and the changes in the land use of the floodplain, from source to mouth.

3 Imagine you are part of the load of a river. Describe your journey from source to mouth.

4 Stir some soil into a beaker of water and watch as the sediment falls out of the water. What do you see? Is this how rivers work?

5 Draw a spider diagram of all the various uses we make of rivers. In a different colour try to identify any conflicts, problems or issues to do with our use of rivers.

Further class and homework activities

Collect pictures of river landscapes and make a wall display of them. Try to annotate your display to describe the processes taking place in the photographs. Try to arrange them from source to mouth.

Answers to the Activities

1

part of the river	description	velocity	width	depth	particle size
upper	near source; upland stream, hilly area	slow-flowing (friction)	narrow	shallow	large
middle	mid-stream over more level land	faster-flowing	wider	deeper	smaller
lower	near mouth, flowing over flat land	fast-flowing	wide	deep	very small (suspended)

2 Rivers have energy so they can work, which means they can erode, transport and deposit material.

When a river has lots of energy it can erode. Ways it can do this are:

◆ hydraulic action: this means water is forced into cracks in the banks and over time this breaks up the bank into small pieces;

◆ solution: this means material from the bed and banks is dissolved in the water, which also helps to break up the materials in bed and banks;

◆ attrition: this means the materials knock against each other and against the bank and bed, wearing them away;

◆ abrasion: this is the action of the materials carried by the water, which scrape against the bed and banks and also wear them away.

Rivers can transport the material they have eroded as long as they have enough energy. Material can be carried in several ways:

◆ in solution – dissolved in the water;

◆ in suspension – small particles are carried along in the water;

◆ as bedload – heavier material is dragged along the bed;

◆ by saltation – smaller materials bounce along;

◆ by traction – larger materials roll along the bed.

If a river doesn't have enough energy it drops (deposits) its load, or sediment, in order of size. The heaviest material is dropped first, then progressively smaller particles. Any dissolved material is carried out into a lake or the sea.

3 Rivers have high energy when they are flowing fast or when there is a lot of water in them.

4 a Erosion is the wearing away of the land by material carried by rivers and streams. (In a wider context, erosion may also be by wind, waves or ice.)

b Rivers erode in four main ways: abrasion, attrition, hydraulic action and solution. (See 2 above.)

The unit in brief

This unit looks at the river near to its source, and uses the River Tees (introduced in Unit 4.1) as a case study. The river channel, V-shaped valleys, interlocking spurs and waterfalls are covered in this unit. In the Activities, students use an extract from an OS map to draw a cross-section of a V-shaped valley; produce a flow diagram to explain how High Force developed; and answer an exam-style question which asks them to draw and label a sketch diagram of High Force from a photo and complete a paragraph about the formation of waterfalls.

Key ideas

In their upper course, rivers:

◆ flow slowly as they carry a large bedload, and the channel is narrow and shallow;

◆ cut downwards by vertical erosion to create steep V-shaped valleys;

◆ flow around protruding hillsides, creating interlocking spurs;

◆ may have waterfalls. These develop when they meet a band of softer rock after flowing over a harder, more-resistant one.

Key vocabulary

river channel, bedload, V-shaped valley, interlocking spurs, waterfall, gorge

Skills practised in the Activities

◆ Geography skills: drawing and annotating a cross-section of the Upper Tees valley from an OS map extract; drawing and labelling a sketch diagram of High Force from a photo

◆ Literacy skills: completing a paragraph on waterfalls

◆ Thinking skills: explaining interlocking spurs; producing a flow diagram to explain how High Force developed

Unit outcomes

By the end of this unit, most students should be able to:

◆ define or explain the terms given in 'Key vocabulary' above;

◆ draw a cross-section from an OS map and explain how V-shaped valleys develop;

◆ explain how waterfalls develop;

◆ draw a sketch diagram from a photo.

Ideas for a starter

1 Draw a generalized long profile of a river from source to mouth on the board. Ask students to identify the upper course, the middle course and the lower course. What are the main processes – erosion, deposition, transport – taking place at each of the stages?

2 The amount of water in a river channel will vary from time to time across the year. Why? How does the amount of erosion, deposition and transportation vary with the amount of water in the channel?

3 Show photos of a V-shaped valley, interlocking spurs, waterfalls and gorges. Ask the class to name them and suggest how they were formed.

Ideas for plenaries

1 Give students photos of waterfalls. They have five minutes to sketch one with labels and annotations. Students swap and check each other's sketches.

2 Provide students with a suitable OS map. Ask them to follow a river from its source and try to find examples of steep-sided valleys, waterfalls and gorges.

3 Draw accurate cross-sections across the river valley using the OS map. Remember to use the same vertical and horizontal scales.

4 Provide a student with labelled samples of hard and soft rock (e.g. granite and shale). The student has to demonstrate how a waterfall forms.

Further class and homework activities

1 Try to investigate other well-known waterfalls and see if they have formed gorges as well.

2 Try to find examples of river flowing over different rock types. Compare the shapes of the valleys and find out about the relative resistance of the rocks concerned.

Answers to the Activities

1 Students should draw an annotated cross-section of line A-B to explain V-shaped valleys.

2 Interlocking spurs are the alternating hills that stick out into a river's path. A river in its upper course doesn't have the power to erode these hills, so it has to flow around them.

3 Students should produce a flow diagram with sketches similar to the diagrams at the top of page 69 of the students' book, applied to High Force.

4 a An annotated sketch diagram of the photo at the bottom of page 68 of the students' book.

b Missing words: hydraulic action, plunge pool, retreat.

The unit in brief

This unit looks at the middle course of the river, and again uses the River Tees as a case study. Meanders and oxbow lakes are covered in this unit. In the Activities students, use an extract from an OS map to draw a cross-section of a meander; draw a sketch map of a meander now and when an oxbow lake has been created; and answer an exam-style question which asks them to draw a cross-section of the river channel at a meander and explain how the river is eroding the river cliff.

Key ideas

In their middle courses:

◆ rivers erode laterally as well as vertically;

◆ rivers develop large bends, known as meanders;

◆ differences in velocity mean that there is more erosion on one side of the river meander, and more deposition on the other side.;

◆ oxbow lakes form when a river erodes a new channel across the neck of a meander.

Key vocabulary

meanders, thalweg, river cliff, point bar, slip-off slope, oxbow lake, swan's neck meander

Skills practised in the Activities

◆ Geography skills: drawing and annotating a cross-section of the Middle Tees valley from an OS map extract; drawing and annotating sketch maps of meanders; drawing a cross-section of a river channel at a meander, and explaining how rivers erode river cliffs

Unit outcomes

By the end of this unit, most students should be able to:

◆ define or explain the terms given in 'Key vocabulary' above;

◆ draw a cross-section from an OS map, and explain how meanders develop;

◆ explain how oxbow lakes form.

Ideas for a starter

1 Recap the development of a waterfall, and key terms so far in this chapter.

2 Show photos of a river's middle course. Ask students to identify the features they can see and suggest how they were formed.

Ideas for plenaries

1 Provide students with a suitable OS map. Ask them to identify the middle course of a river and features typical of the middle course.

2 Use OS maps to look at the middle section of rivers. Rivers are often used to mark boundaries. Try to find examples of this and you may find examples of where the river has changed its channel position while the boundary is in the former position. What does this tell you about the processes operating in the river?

3 What sort of land use should happen on the floodplain? Give reasons for your answer. What sort of land use should not happen on the flood plain?

4 Tell me two important things you have learned today about meanders, and two important things you have learned today about oxbow lakes. Now tell me another two things about meanders and oxbow lakes.

Answers to the Activities

1 Students should draw an annotated cross-section of line A-B to explain the meander.

2 Students draw two sketches to explain the likely changes to the river meander in the map extract over time, culminating in the creation of an oxbow lake.

3 a Students draw a labelled sketch of the cross-section of a river channel at a meander, similar to the diagram in the bottom left of page 70 of the students' book.

  b The river is eroding at the river cliff because on this side of the river bend the water is flowing at a greater velocity. As a result, it has greater power to erode the bank and bed on this side, which is deeper.

The unit in brief

This unit is about the lower course of a river, with the River Tees still used as the case study. Floodplains, estuaries and deltas are covered in this unit. In the Activities, students complete a paragraph about a river's lower course; draw a labelled diagram of a floodplain and explain how terraces and levées form; and draw and label sketch maps of an estuary and delta from resources in the students book.

Key ideas

◆ In their lower courses rivers flow in a wide, deep channel.

◆ Floodplains are the land on either side of the river.

◆ When rivers flood, the coarsest material is deposited first – forming a levée.

◆ Estuaries are wide, deep river mouths.

◆ Deltas form when a river deposits its load and the sea currents aren't strong enough to remove it.

Key vocabulary

mudflats, floodplain, alluvium, terraces, levées, estuaries, deltas, distributaries, bird's foot delta, arcuate deltas

Skills practised in the Activities

◆ Geography skills: drawing and labelling a diagram of a floodplain; drawing and labelling a sketch map of Tees estuary from an OS map or photo; drawing and annotating a sketch map of the Nile delta from a photo

◆ Literacy skills: completing a paragraph about a river's lower course

◆ Thinking skills: explaining floodplains, alluvium and the formation of terraces and levées

Unit outcomes

By the end of this unit, most students should be able to:

◆ define or explain the terms given in 'Key vocabulary' above;

◆ draw a diagram of a floodplain and explain how terraces and levées form;

◆ draw a sketch map of the Tees estuary from an OS map or photo;

◆ draw a sketch map of the Nile delta from a photo and explain how it has formed.

Ideas for a starter

1 Create a graffiti wall of what students have learned so far about rivers, the work of rivers and landforms.

2 When the river deposits its load does it dump it all in one go? How does it deposit its load? What landforms are created?

3 Ask what do students know about floodplains, estuaries and deltas? Can they give examples?

Ideas for plenaries

1 Which other rivers have deltas? What type are they? How have they formed?

2 Draw a diagram showing how the following change from source to mouth: channel width; channel depth; channel smoothness; size of load; amount of water (discharge); pollution; main types of transport; amount of load, etc.

3 Do rivers slow down, or speed up as they move from source to mouth? Explain your answer.

4 Prepare an odd-one-out to try on a partner using what you have learnt about rivers and landforms so far.

5 Choose a river landform feature and draw an annotated diagram to show how it was formed.

Further class and homework activities

1 Investigate the use of the River Nile and the current concern about the delta of the River Nile.

2 Investigate a local river or stream. Try to collect information to see if some of the ideas in this section actually work on a short stretch of river. (Make sure you're careful. This can be dangerous if you misjudge the nature of the channel and the velocity of the water.)

Answers to the Activities

1 Missing words: flat, industry, marshland, deep, fast, small, mudflats.

2 a A floodplain is the flat area on either side of a river at the lower end of its course, which is often flooded.

b Alluvium is fine material (silt) that is left behind after a river floods. It is carried down by a river when it has sufficient energy to transport it. Alluvium usually makes good soil for farming.

c Terraces form in some places because at one time the sea level was higher than it is today, so rivers did not have to fall so far to reach the sea. When the sea level dropped, rivers had to cut down further to reach the sea, and they left behind the terraces of alluvium that were originally formed in those earlier times.

d Levées are formed when a river floods over its usual channel. As it does so, its flow slows down and it drops (deposits) its load. It deposits the heaviest material first, leaving mounds or levées at the side of the main river channel.

e Students should be able to re-create the drawing on page 72 of the students' book, and label it correctly.

3 Students should outline the main course of the river, the coastline, and general areas of industry along the river, adding the labels and title specified in the activity. Drawing sketch maps of this type is useful practice in selecting material from a detailed map. Sketch maps should not be accurate to the last detail, but nor should they be over-generalised. It is useful, too, to show just a few important named locations. The map can be saved as a useful revision case study exemplar.

4 Labels for a sketch map of the delta should provide explanations, for example:

◆ The fast-flowing river carries a large amount of sediment.

◆ The river slows as it flows towards the sea.

◆ It begins to deposit the sediment (load) as it slows down.

◆ The sea here is fairly calm and the land is quite flat, so the load builds up in the sea to form a delta.

◆ Distributaries form where sediment has blocked river channels.

5 a If sea level rises, the sea would flood over the low-lying delta. The river would have less far to travel to the sea, it would drop its load further upstream, and the delta would retreat.

b If a dam is built upriver, it will mean that less water is flowing in the river bed below it, so it will have less energy to carry a load. Some of the load will also have been trapped by the dam. If there is less load, there is less material to be deposited in the delta. The sea may also begin to erode the materials in the delta, and if there is not enough load to replace it, the delta will retreat.

The unit in brief

This unit is about the water cycle, and how water reaches rivers. In the Activities, students draw and label diagrams of the water cycle and the drainage basin cycle; match definitions and their correct terms and explain what hydrographs show.

Key ideas

◆ The water (or hydrological) cycle is a continuous transfer of water from the oceans, into the atmosphere, onto land and finally back into oceans.

◆ The drainage basin cycle (or system) is part of the water cycle which operates on the land.

◆ Discharge is the volume of water flowing past a given point in a river channel at a given time.

◆ A hydrograph shows the discharge of a river at a given point, over a period of time.

Key vocabulary

evaporation, transpiration, condensation, precipitation, stem-flow, drip-flow, interception, surface run-off, infiltration, throughflow, percolation, groundwater flow, permeable, impermeable, hydrograph, discharge

Skills practised in the Activities

◆ Geography skills: copying and labelling a diagram of the water cycle; drawing and labelling diagram of the drainage basin cycle; matching definitions and terms; describing and explaining hydrographs

Unit outcomes

By the end of this unit, most students should be able to:

◆ define or explain the terms given in 'Key vocabulary' above;

◆ understand that the water cycle is a continuous transfer of water from the oceans; into the atmosphere, onto land and finally back into oceans;

◆ draw a diagram of the drainage basin cycle;

◆ describe and explain what a hydrograph shows.

Ideas for a starter

1 Draw the hot water system in your home. Describe the water's journey around the home.

2 It's raining today (or yesterday or ….). Where does the water come from? Where is it going? Build up the water cycle on the board.

3 Who can remember the water cycle? Can you draw a simple version on the board? How does the drainage basin cycle fit into the water cycle?

Ideas for plenaries

1 Have a set of cards with definitions and different terms to do with the water cycle and drainage basin cycle. Ask one student to read out the definition on the card they have and this is then paired with the correct term from someone else's card. This continues until all the definitions have been paired up. Alternatively this can be played as a card game in which cards are placed face down with the definition on one and the term on another. Students then try to turn over the matching pair. The student with most sets of pairs wins!

2 Describe the journey of a water molecule through the water cycle. Make it an adventure story!

3 Let's look at the global water cycle. How much water is stored in the oceans? How much is stored in the ice caps and in glaciers? Present this as a flow diagram drawn to scale.

4 Ask students to investigate one major flooding event in the UK in the last 5 years. They will need to collect information on the causes and effects of the flooding and be ready to describe the event in the next lesson.

Answers to the Activities

1

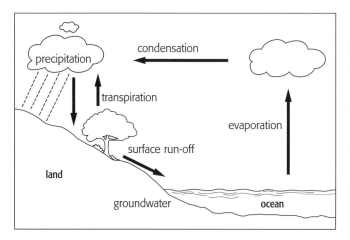

2 Students can draw a simple outline copy of the diagram on page 74 of the students' book, replacing the numbers with the key terms. However, they should be able to explain what each of these terms means, if they are challenged to do so. They will find it useful to create a list of these definitions (see 3 below).

3

precipitation	rain, hail, snow and sleet
stem- and drip-flow	water dripping and falling from plants
infiltration	water soaking into the bedrock
throughflow	water flowing through the soil towards the stream
percolation	water flowing through the saturated bedrock towards the river
groundwater flow	water soaking into the soil
channel flow	water flowing in the river
transpiration	water vapour breathed out by plants
evaporation	water turning into water vapour

4 Discharge is the volume of water flowing past a single point in the river in 1 second. It is measured in cubic metres per second (m3/sec).

5 a A hydrograph shows the discharge of a river or stream over a period of time, in cubic metres per second (m3/sec). Some hydrographs (as here) also show the amount of precipitation falling during the same period, so that relationships between the two features can be seen in graphic form.

 b Peak discharge = 8 m3/sec.

 c Lag time = 10 hours

The unit in brief

This unit introduces flooding. It looks at what causes flooding and how this affects the shape of the hydrograph. In the Activities, students complete a table of factors which increase the flood risk and classify them into natural and human factors; think about why buildings are still being put on floodplains; give examples of what can be done to reduce the flood risk, and explain how hydrographs can be used.

Key ideas

◆ Floods happen when a river receives more water than its channel can hold.

◆ Floods can be caused by a variety of natural and human factors.

◆ An increase in the amount or speed of water reaching a river will affect the shape of the hydrograph.

Key vocabulary

antecedent rainfall, deforestation, impermeable, urbanisation, lag time, rising limb, peak discharge, catchment

Skills practised in the Activities

◆ Geography skills: completing a table to explain how various factors increase the risk of flooding

◆ Thinking skills: classifying flooding factors into natural and human factors; giving examples of ways to reduce the flood risk; explaining the use of hydrographs

Unit outcomes

By the end of this unit, most students should be able to:

◆ define the terms given in 'Key vocabulary' above;

◆ understand why floods happen;

◆ explain how floods can be caused by a range of natural and human factors;

◆ explain how hydrographs can be used to show the effect that land use has on the flood risk.

Ideas for a starter

1 Flooding – what do students know about it? Causes? Effects? Have they ever been in a flood? What was it like?

2 Ask several students to report back to the class on the recent flooding event investigated.

3 Give students a graph showing rainfall over a 24-hour period and ask them to draw a hydrograph. They should then describe what they have drawn.

Ideas for plenaries

1 Draw a systems diagram of the water cycle for students (this can be done in advance). Ask students what happens to the hydrograph when things change e.g. a change of season, vegetation being replanted or removed, a different rock type – permeable to impermeable, land is built on etc.

2 Can students suggest ways in which the flooding hazard can be minimized?

3 Ask students what the effects of afforestation, dredging the channel, deepening the channel, zonation, etc. will be on the flood.

4 You have five minutes to prepare a short report for the local newspaper describing a local flood. Off you go!

5 Ask students to investigate flooding in North Yorkshire in 1999. They will need to present their findings to the rest of the class in the next lesson.

6 Make up 5-10 statements based on the causes of flooding, some true, some false. Students hold up True or False cards. Where statements are false, ask students to correct them.

Answers to the Activities

1

Flooding factor	How it increases the chance of flooding
heavy rain (N)	adds more water to the river
antecedent rainfall (N)	saturates the ground so that later rainwater flows straight over the surface, as run-off, to the river
long spell of hot dry weather (N)	bakes the soil surface so that rain cannot easily soak into it, so rainwater flows over the surface and into the river
steep slopes (N and H)	rainwater runs straight over the surface, with little or no infiltration
impermeable rocks (N)	rainwater cannot percolate through to the groundwater; instead it flows quickly by throughflow and surface run-off into the river
snow melt (thaw) (N)	adds more water to the river
deforestation (H)	soil is not held by tree roots, so water moves quickly over the ground surface, taking soil with it; more soil in the river leaves less space in the channel for water; deforestation also allows water to reach the ground surface more easily, so it is saturated more easily
ploughing up and down (H)	creates channels for rain-water to move along more quickly as it flows down to the river
urbanisation (H)	creates new hard surfaces and drains, so water cannot soak into the ground but is carried quickly over the surface into the river

Key: N = natural factors, H = human factors

2 The basic reason for allowing building on floodplains is one of social pressures. This could lead to a useful classroom discussion: for example, why is the government planning to build hundreds of thousands of new houses and even new towns in the South East and East Anglia? Although the total national population is fairly stable, there is an increasing demand for single-occupancy dwellings: fewer couples are getting married, there is a growing number of single-parent families, and more people are choosing to live alone. This is creating a huge demand for new housing in certain parts of the country. Businesses, too, are demanding more space for expansion and new development. As brownfield (previous use) sites are becoming scarce and are often unsuitable, there is a greater pressure on using less-suitable sites such as those on floodplains.

3 Students should consider both natural and human features: permeable rocks, conservation of natural water meadows (good for wildlife too), contour ploughing, building artificial banks/levées, creating new, straighter channels (to speed flow), building sluice gates and/or dams (to control flow).

4 A hydrograph shows the volume of water flowing past a single point in the river over a period of time. If several hydrographs are recorded over a period when changes are made to the local environment, the hydrographs can be compared and deductions made as to the effect of those changes on the river's discharge. So, for example, if an area has undergone urbanisation or deforestation, the effect of these interventions can be seen on the local streams and rivers by studying a series of hydrographs. Hydrographs may also include rainfall during the same period, in which case it is possible to include this factor in the assessment too.

The unit in brief

This unit provides a case study of flooding in an MEDC – North Yorkshire in the UK – in 1999. It examines the causes and effects of the flood. In the Activities, students produce their own version of the case study by completing a variety of activities, including drawing a location map; explaining how the flood affected people in the short and long term; completing a table to explain how various factors led to the flood, and a writing frame to describe the flood hydrograph at Buttercrambe.

Key ideas

◆ The River Derwent starts in the North Yorkshire moors.

◆ The flooding in 1999 was the worst for 70 years.

◆ A range of physical and human factors led to the flood.

◆ Flooding has immediate and long-term effects.

Key vocabulary

There is no key vocabulary in this unit.

Skills practised in the Activities

◆ Geography skills: drawing a map of the River Derwent basin; completing a table to explain how various factors led to the flood

◆ Literacy skills: completing a writing frame to describe the flood hydrograph

◆ Thinking skills: thinking about and explaining the short and long-term effects of the flood; classifying the flood factors as physical or human

Unit outcomes

By the end of this unit, most students should be able to:

◆ draw a map to show where the River Derwent is;

◆ explain how various physical and human factors led to the flood;

◆ describe the short and long-term effects of the flood.

Ideas for a starter

1 Ask several students to present their findings on the flooding in North Yorkshire in 1999.

2 Recap: the factors affecting flooding, and how they affect the shape of the hydrograph.

3 Show video/news clips of the flooding in North Yorkshire in 1999.

Ideas for plenaries

1 Prepare an interview with a resident who has been flooded in North Yorkshire. Work in pairs so that one can be the interviewer and one the interviewee.

2 Look at the photo on p.79 of the students' book. How high is the flood water? If that amount of water got into your home what would it be like? What damage would it do? What would it be like when the floodwater went down? Who would pay for the damage to be repaired?

3 Is your area at risk from flooding? Why do you think that? If you live near a river how could you check the risk? (Environment Agency website.) Would an OS map give you any ideas?

4 Would flooding in an MEDC cause more damage than in an LEDC?

5 Ask students to investigate reports on floods in Mozambique in 2000. Answers should be explained. They need to prepare a short report for the class.

Answers to the Activities

1   Students' maps should simplify the river network shown on the map. Their writing, in the form of annotations/labels, should describe the relief and drainage patterns of the area, which help to explain why there were floods there in 1999. Further annotations could list other factors, as noted under the heading 'Why?' on page 79. Their annotated map will help students to prepare a useful case study on flooding in an MEDC.

2   Students should think around and through this open-ended question. They could brainstorm in groups, and draw up their ideas as a mind map. Severe floods can create huge problems in the transport and services networks, damaging roads, bridges and railway lines, cutting off electricity, flooding the pipeline systems (water and sewerage) and generally causing difficulties for people who are trying to communicate and to move around. Problems can be both short-term and long-term: in the short term, for example, emergency services need to be able to help people at immediate risk; for longer-term effects, see 3 below. People living in urban areas often receive the most media attention in these situations, but rural communities can be severely affected too; farmers have the additional worry of losing their stock (animals).

3   People may feel insecure, especially if their home has been damaged (will the floods come again?); insurance on homes is likely to increase – does the insurance cover the losses, especially of personal items?; damaged roads, bridges, railways and homes have to be repaired – restoring infrastructure networks may take time, so in the meantime it's difficult for people to continue to work normally; lasting trauma of experiencing the floods; plans for new buildings need to consider the problem of potential floods; continuing programme to keep all waterways clear of rubbish and debris; possible re-routing of part of a river and/or building floodbanks; planting of trees to help absorb water, especially on slopes.

4

Factor	Human (H) or physical (P)?	How did it lead to flooding?
antecedent rainfall	P	meant that the ground was already saturated so any more rain flowed over the surface
heavy rain	P	flowed quickly into rivers and streams, carrying debris with it
snow melt	P	added yet more water to already full rivers
steep slopes	P	help water to flow more quickly into rivers; soil likely to be removed by water
peat removal	H	peat absorbs water, so its removal allowed water to run off more quickly
deforestation	H	tree roots hold water, and leaves/branches protect the soil; if removed, water flows over the surface quickly, removing soil with it
building in the floodplain	H	building creates hard surfaces and covers the soil, so water flows off quickly into drains and then rivers; previous meadows no longer able to absorb water
rubbish	H	blocks drainage ditches, streams and rivers, obstructing the free flow of water, so dams build up and then may burst to cause floods

5   The hydrograph shows the discharge of the River Derwent at Buttercrambe. The pattern for January and February 1999 indicates regular periods of heavy rainfall (3 in January, 1 in February) when discharge was high. The small peaks represent the peak periods of discharge following those storms – the highest peak, in January, was 50 m³/sec. In March there was a rapid and serious increase in discharge. The peak of the discharge during the flood was 150 m³/sec.

6 a   Places lower down a river course have warning of a flood because people higher upstream can communicate that there is a lot of water flowing in the river channel, which will eventually reach those lower down the river basin. All rivers naturally flow downhill towards the sea (or a lake).

   b   Any river gets bigger as it flows downstream because many tributary streams join it as it flows towards the sea. The water of each of these tributaries is added to the volume already in the main river channel.

The unit in brief

This unit provides a case study of flooding in an LEDC – Mozambique in 2000, as a contrast to the MEDC case study in Unit 4.7. It looks at the causes and effects of the flooding. In the Activities, students identify the short-term effects of the flood and think about what the long-term effects might be; prepare a PowerPoint presentation on the floods (what happened and why); and answer an exam-style question which asks them to describe the causes of a flood they have studied.

Key ideas

◆ Six different rivers were affected by the flooding.

◆ Over 1 million people lost their homes and thousands drowned.

◆ Over 80% of the people work in agriculture, and the flood destroyed much of the most fertile farmland.

◆ The floods happened for a mixture of short and long-term causes (some physical and some human).

Key vocabulary

There is no key vocabulary in this unit.

Skills practised in the Activities

◆ Geography skills: describing the causes of a flood

◆ Thinking skills: identifying the short-term effects of a flood; thinking about the long-term effects

◆ ICT skills: making a PowerPoint presentation about the floods

Unit outcomes

By the end of this unit, most students should be able to:

◆ know where Mozambique is and which areas were affected by flooding;

◆ identify the short-term effects of the flood;

◆ explain how human factors contributed to the flooding;

◆ describe the causes of the flood – both short and long-term.

Ideas for a starter

1 Who can remind me what can cause flooding in the UK? Do you think floods in LEDCS have similar causes?

2 Ask several students to present their short report on flooding in Mozambique to the rest of the class.

3 Where is Mozambique? Find it in the atlas. Can you find out some basic information about the country including the climate, natural vegetation and soils?

Ideas for plenaries

1 Organise the class into small groups to write a short report on the flooding in Mozambique. Different groups can work on and introduction to the problem; the causes of the flood; the lessons from the flood.

2 Ask students to produce concept maps of the flooding in Mozambique.

3 Provide students with photographs of the flooding in Mozambique. Ask them to annotate them with causes and effects of the flooding.

4 In Mozambique the water rose 8 metres in 5 days. What did this do to people's homes and livelihoods? What damage did it do? Who would pay for the damage to be repaired?

5 What are the similarities and differences in the causes and effects of flooding on MEDCs and on LEDCs?

Further class and homework activities

Investigate other areas in LEDCs which suffer from flooding e.g. Bangladesh. These websites may be a good starting point:

www.drik.net/

www.irn.org/pubs/wp/bangladesh.html

www.cru.uea.ac.uk/tiempo/floor0/archive/t8art2.htm

www.sdnbd.org/sdi/issues/floods_drainage/article/flood%20control%20in%20 Bangladesh.htm

Answers to the Activities

1 a Short-term effects: thousands of people drowned; homes were flooded, so people had to go to refugee camps; diseases spread quickly; farmland was flooded and destroyed; roads, railways and electricity supplies were all damaged.

b Long-term effects: people have to rebuild their homes, whole communities are possibly destroyed as people are displaced by the flood; farmland is lost, so many people's livelihood is lost; animals are drowned, ditto; roads, railways, electricity and communications are very expensive to rebuild, especially for a poor LEDC; there would be an additional need to prepare for future floods; pressure on the government (economic and political); loss of plant and animal life could change the natural environment.

2 Students can use this presentation to prepare a useful case study of a flood in an LEDC. It's important that they include plenty of detail – perhaps some individual accounts of the experience. They might also compare the effects of a flood in an MEDC (Unit 4.7) and in an LEDC. The latter is likely to recover much more slowly from such an event – why? (Lack of money to implement the necessary programmes to rebuild communities and the infrastructure.)

3 Note that the question does not suggest where the flood may be – so it could be in an MEDC or an LEDC. However, causes are likely to be similar. Students should, where possible, give named examples in their answers. Some common causes:

◆ Heavy rain or other precipitation falling over a long period.

◆ Steep slopes

◆ Destruction of trees in the same region or in upper parts of the same drainage basin (for building, fuel or commercial uses).

◆ Destruction of other natural vegetation (e.g. peat, marshland, flood meadows) in the same region or in upper parts of the same drainage basin (usually so that the land can be used for building or for farmland).

◆ Urbanisation – land is built over, for houses, roads, industry. Water then flows over hard surfaces and more quickly into streams and rivers.

◆ Blocked waterways, usually by rubbish produced by people; lack of waterway maintenance.

The unit in brief

This unit looks at the choices we have for managing floods in terms of hard and soft engineering methods. In the Activities, students look at the advantages and disadvantages of hard engineering methods; draw a mind map of soft engineering methods and use it as the basis for a short essay, and complete a paragraph on hard and soft engineering.

Key ideas

◆ In England and Wales, the Environment Agency has responsibility for looking after rivers and trying to prevent flooding.

◆ Hard management methods include building dams, embankments and flood walls, as well as channelising the river and providing storage areas for extra water.

◆ Soft engineering methods include creating washlands, land-use zoning, afforestation and warning systems.

◆ The choice of methods used depends on a range of factors.

Key vocabulary

hard management, dams, embankments, flood walls, channelising, storage areas, soft management, washlands, land-use zoning, afforestation, warning systems

Skills practised in the Activities

◆ Geography skills: completing a table of the advantages and disadvantages of hard engineering methods

◆ Literacy skills: completing a paragraph on hard and soft engineering methods; writing a short essay on soft engineering

◆ Thinking skills: completing a mind map of soft engineering methods

Unit outcomes

By the end of this unit, most students should be able to:

◆ define or explain the terms given in 'Key vocabulary' above;

◆ give four examples of hard engineering methods and explain the advantages and disadvantages of each;

◆ give three examples of soft engineering methods;

◆ understand how decisions are made about which methods to use to try to prevent flooding.

Ideas for a starter

1 What have you learnt so far about how the flood risk can be managed?

2 Flood management is divided into 'hard' and 'soft' methods. What does this mean?

3 Show photos of a variety of flood management methods – some obvious and prominent e.g. dams, some less so e.g. washlands. Ask students to suggest how these methods can help.

Ideas for plenaries

1 Provide students with a table to compare the hard and soft management methods. In the table have columns for describing the scheme, for evaluating its impact on the environment and for the costs – high, medium or low. They use this to evaluate the choices available.

2 Ask students to discuss their final decisions with a neighbour. Which solutions would be most effective and which would be most sustainable in managing flooding?

3 Students work in pairs to produce a 'flood management' plan.

4 Create an acrostic. Write FLOOD MANAGEMENT down one side of the page. Make each letter the first letter of a word, phrase or sentence about flooding and flood management.

Answers to the Activities

1 Missing words: structures, control, channelisation, dams, with, afforestation, land-use zoning.

2

Hard engineering method	Advantages of using it	Disadvantages of using it
dams	control flow, generate electricity, create lake (fishing, recreation)	flood land upstream so environment and farmland lost; trap sediment so it's not available to downstream areas; very expensive
embankments	protect land beside river	don't look natural; expensive
flood walls	as above	as above
channelisation	speeds the river flow	changes ecosystem; looks unnatural; moves the problem of flooding further downstream
storage areas	helps to prevent floods lower downstream; may create a useful new environment, e.g. attracting water birds	needs a large area of 'spare' land – fairly cheap if it's available!

Students could draw up a similar table for soft engineering methods. This would be useful preparation for working on activity 3.

3 Groups or the class could brainstorm the subject of soft engineering, posing questions as they do so, e.g. Who will plant trees, and where? Who owns the land? Who decides what can and cannot be used for building, or for flooding?

Soft engineering is generally the cheaper option of flood protection, and has the main advantage of working with the environment rather than trying to control it. However, in some places hard engineering is a necessary choice. Student essays should try to weigh up the effectiveness of the various soft engineering measures.

By the end of this unit students should be able to assess the various options, both hard and soft engineering. The teacher might also introduce the idea of the likelihood of risk of future floods: how much money should be spent on measures against an event that may or may not happen (risk assessment)?

Controlling flooding in MEDCs and LEDCs

help at a glance

The unit in brief

This unit looks at how the flood risk has been managed in North Yorkshire and Mozambique – the two case studies included in Units 4.7 and 4.8. In the Activities, students produce their own revision cards for flood prevention on the River Derwent – their MEDC case study and think about why a mixture of hard and soft engineering methods have been used. They also write their own case study notes about flood prevention in Mozambique – their LEDC case study.

Key ideas

◆ In North Yorkshire £7.5 million has been spent on protecting towns like Malton.

◆ A mixture of hard and soft engineering methods have been used in North Yorkshire.

◆ Mozambique is a very poor country, and needs to spend money on things like schools and hospitals rather than flood defences.

◆ The EU has given money to start a flood warning system in Mozambique.

◆ A lot of Mozambique's rivers begin in other countries – like South Africa. What other countries do, affects what happens in Mozambique.

Key vocabulary

hard engineering, soft engineering

Skills practised in the Activities

◆ Geography skills: making revision cards for flood prevention on the River Derwent; making case study notes about flood prevention in Mozambique

◆ Thinking skills: thinking about the advantages and disadvantages of hard and soft engineering

Unit outcomes

By the end of this unit, most students should be able to:

◆ define the terms given in 'Key vocabulary' above;

◆ understand why a mixture of hard and soft engineering techniques have been used in North Yorkshire;

◆ explain why Mozambique has taken a different approach to flood prevention;

◆ describe the flood warning system in Mozambique.

Ideas for a starter

1   Recap: how do these affect the shape of a hydrograph - an urban basin, a wooded basin in winter, a ploughed basin in Autumn, etc. Ask students to draw the hydrograph and describe its shape.

2   Recap: vocabulary and definitions from the water cycle. Use a pairs card game or wordsearch.

3   Show photos of a 'typical' scene in a North Yorkshire town like Stamford Bridge and a 'typical' scene in rural Mozambique. Do students think the approaches to flood management will be the same or different. Why?

Ideas for plenaries

1   Draw a spider diagram of flood management in North Yorkshire and another for flood management in Mozambique. Colour code each method for its effectiveness and sustainability.

2   Ask students if they found anything difficult about the work in this chapter. What? Why? What would help to make it easier to understand/less difficult?

3   Do an alphabet run from A-Z with a word or phrase to do with rivers or flooding for each letter.

Further class and homework activities

Read through your case studies and try to reduce the content to a manageable size so that you can learn it for examinations. Try to apply your examples to actual examination questions.

Answers to the Activities

1   This activity is a continuation of work done in Unit 4.9. It will provide a useful revision case study showing how the various hard and soft engineering methods are applied in a particular river basin. Students should be able to explain in detail the potential effectiveness of each individual prevention measure.

Hard engineering: flood banks; embankments; sluice gates.

Soft engineering: embankments/washlands; restricted building on the floodplain; planting of trees and hedges; reinforced river banks using natural materials; early warning system in place.

2   This activity could be a useful basis for a class discussion on:

♦ how decisions are made about flood prevention;

♦ the issues involved (e.g. cost, local opposition);

♦ who makes the final decision (e.g. local/national government).

a   Hard engineering is expensive. If a 'soft' measure is likely to be effective, that option, which is usually cheaper, is preferred. Soft engineering is also more environmentally friendly and generally more attractive to look at.

b   As well as being expensive, hard engineering is disruptive during building, and can look very noticeable/unattractive when complete. Some measures (sluice gates, for example) need regular maintenance, so the cost is ongoing.

c   Soft engineering is generally cheaper, and more attractive. Such measures are aimed at working with the environment, using

natural local materials (e.g. woven willow to strengthen banks). Some measures can actually attract wildlife, e.g. washlands may bring in wading birds and new plants. New trees and hedges have obvious benefits to the local ecosystem. The Derwent flows through an attractive part of the country (its headwaters are in the North York Moors National Park), so it's another advantage if flood prevention measures can be put in place without damaging or destroying the local environment.

3   Students can be asked to research the topic of floods in Mozambique in more detail (and/or refer back to their work in Unit 4.8). In the case of Mozambique, it's important to explain the reasons for not putting local flood prevention measures in place (too expensive for an LEDC; control of river an international problem; too large-scale even for a single country to deal with). Ask students to suggest how the problem could be tackled (international agreement and co-operation; local contingency plans for evacuation). Again, consider the need for risk assessment: what are the chances of such a flood occurring again in the future? (If the scientists are to be believed, they are high; consider global warming …)

Emphasise the need for good presentation of the students' final piece of work for this chapter – they should check over the work very carefully.

Coastal landscapes

The big picture

These are the key ideas behind this chapter:

◆ The coastline is constantly being shaped and changed by wave action and human activity.

◆ Waves, erode, transport and deposit material along the coastline to create a range of coastal landforms.

◆ Changes in sea level have created landforms such as raised beaches, rias and fjords. Rises in sea levels due to global warming will have a dramatic effect on coastlines.

◆ Coastal management is an expensive, and contentious issue. Some coastlines will continue to be protected, others will not.

Note that the students' version of the big picture is given in the students' chapter opener.

Chapter outline

Use this, and the students' chapter opener, to give students a mental roadmap for the chapter.

5   **Coastal landscapes**   As the students' chapter opener, this unit is an important part of the chapter; see page 11 of this book for notes about using chapter openers

5.1   **All about waves**   What causes waves, and different types of waves

5.2   **Coastal erosion**   How waves erode the coastline, and some of the landforms created by erosion

5.3   **Coastal transport**   How waves transport material along the coast by longshore drift

5.4   **Coastal deposition**   Landforms created by coastal deposition

5.5   **The effects of changes in sea level**   Landforms created by sea level change, and how global warming (and rises in sea level) might affect the coastline around Britain

5.6   **Management of coastlines**   Why and how we try and defend the coast; who decides what happens; the latest ideas – a sustainable strategy

5.7   **Happisburgh hanging on**   A case study of coastal erosion at Happisburgh

5.8   **Chesil Beach flood danger**   The problem of flooding at Chesil Beach – what's being done about it and conflicts caused

5.9   **Protecting Lyme Regis**   A case study of coastal protection at Lyme Regis – an important Dorset tourist destination

Objectives and outcomes for this chapter

Objectives	Unit	Outcomes
Most students will understand:		**Most students will be able to:**
● What causes waves.	5.1	● Explain that waves are caused by the friction of the wind on the surface of the water, and say how its strength, duration and fetch affect them; name two types of waves and say what they do.
● How waves shape the coast through erosion, transport and deposition.	5.2, 5.3, 5.4	● Describe the processes of erosion, transport and deposition by waves.
● That the action of waves leads to characteristic coastal landforms.	5.2, 5.3, 5.4	● Name, describe and identify the coastal landforms covered in the chapter; explain how they are formed.
● The effect of changes in sea level on our coastline.	5.5	● Describe landforms created by sea level changes in the past; say how rising sea levels might affect our coastline in the future.
● Why and how we try to defend the coast.	5.6	● Explain why we try to defend the coast; describe how the coast can be defended; describe the government's sustainable strategy for coastal defence.
● That erosion is causing serious problems at Happisburgh on the Norfolk coast.	5.7	● Explain why the coast is being eroded here as a result of physical processes and human activity; describe what has been done to protect the coast; carry out a cost-benefit analysis.
● Why Chesil Beach needs protection.	5.8	● Describe why the coastline at Chesil Beach suffers from flooding, and what is being done about it; describe the conflicts that coastal protection causes.
● Why some places are being protected from coastal erosion.	5.9	● Explain why and how Lyme Regis is being protected.

These tie in with 'Your goals for this chapter' in the students' chapter opener, and with the opening lines in each unit, which give the purpose of the unit in a student-friendly style.

Using the chapter starter

The photo on page 86 of the *geog.GCSE* students' book shows Durdle Door on the Dorset coast.

Durdle Door is one of the classic examples of a natural arch, the limestone rock having been eroded by the sea. The beach is mixed shingle and sand.

Durdle Door is a tourist honeypot. It's one of the most visited natural tourist attractions in the country – it's estimated that over a million people a year walk along the coast to see it. It's a short walk from Lulworth Cove along the Jurassic Coast, which is a World Heritage Site because of its geology and fossils.

The unit in brief

This unit is about waves – what causes them, what affects their height and strength, and the two types of breaking wave (constructive and destructive). In the Activities, students have to define the terms swash and backwash, consider what affects the height and strength of waves and what else determines the rate of coastal erosion, as well as explaining how constructive and destructive waves work.

Key ideas

◆ Waves are caused by the friction of the wind on the surface of the water.

◆ The height and strength of waves depends on the speed of the wind, how long it blows for, and the fetch (the distance the wind blows over).

◆ There are two types of breaking wave – constructive waves (which build the beach up), and destructive waves (which remove material from the beach).

◆ Waves continually shape the coastline.

Key vocabulary

swash, backwash, fetch, constructive waves, destructive waves

Skills practised in the Activities

◆ Geography skills: defining geographical terms

◆ Thinking skills: thinking and explaining

Unit outcomes

By the end of this unit, most students should be able to:

◆ define the terms given in 'Key vocabulary' above;

◆ describe what causes waves;

◆ understand why some waves are bigger and stronger than others;

◆ explain how constructive and destructive waves work;

◆ understand that waves continually shape the coastline.

Ideas for a starter

1 Ask students to draw a spider diagram to include as many factors as possible that affect the development of the coastline.

2 Why should we study coasts in Geography?

3 Provide photos of coastal features. Ask students to name them and suggest how they are formed.

4 Ask students to open their book on p.86. Now, imagine you are on that beach, all alone. What can you see, and hear? Tell us.

Ideas for plenaries

1 Ask students how they would design fieldwork to classify the waves breaking on a particular stretch of coast? What factors would they try to measure? How would they make the measurements? How would the different types of wave impact on the beach?

2 Provide photos of different types of waves and ask students to classify them.

3 Which type of coastline would you go to for surfing? Name some beaches in the UK where surfing takes place (identify them on a map of the UK if possible). What have they got in common?

4 A quickfire test: call out a student's name and definition (e.g. for swash, backwash, constructive, destructive). The student has 5 seconds to give you the term.

Answers to the Activities

1 a The movement of water up a beach.

  b The movement of water back down a beach.

2 As the beach will be permeable, much of the water will sink down below the surface.

3 The fetch, the strength of the wind and the time over which the wind has been blowing.

4 Constructive – the swash is greater than the backwash, so the net movement of material is up the beach.
Destructive – the backwash is greater than the swash, so the net movement of material is down the beach.

5 The geology of the coastline – harder rocks will be more resistant to erosion. The orientation of the coastline to waves of greatest fetch. Human action on the coastline – for example coastal defence measures.

The unit in brief

This unit explains how waves erode the coastline, and some of the landforms created by erosion. In the Activities, students describe how waves erode the coastline; think about other weathering processes; name other landforms that are eroded by abrasion and solution; find out about a coastal location in the UK which has coastal erosion features and compare them with those in the photograph on p91.

Key ideas

◆ Waves erode the coast by four main processes: abrasion (corrasion); hydraulic action; solution (corrosion); attrition.

◆ The more powerful the waves are, and the softer the rock, the faster the erosion will be.

◆ Weathering processes contribute to coastal erosion.

◆ Cliffs and wave-cut platforms, caves, arches and stacks are some of the main landforms created by coastal erosion.

Key vocabulary

abrasion (corrasion), hydraulic action, solution (corrosion), attrition, cliff, wave-cut platform, wave-cut notch, cave, arch, stack, stump, blow-hole

Skills practised in the Activities

◆ Geography skills: describing how waves erode; naming landforms; describing and explaining landforms and comparing them with a photograph.

◆ Thinking skills: thinking about weathering processes

Unit outcomes

By the end of this unit, most students should be able to:

◆ define or explain the terms given in 'Key vocabulary' above;

◆ describe the different ways in which waves erode the coastline;

◆ identify and explain how coastal erosional landforms are created.

Ideas for a starter

1 Provide photos of named features of coastal erosion. Ask students to locate them on a large map of the UK.

2 Recap: what are the factors that make some waves bigger than others; how are waves classified? Draw diagrams of the different types of wave.

3 Show videos of landforms caused by coastal erosion. Ask students to describe the landforms.

Ideas for plenaries

1 Draw a series of diagrams to show how stacks and stumps develop.

2 How might the formation of a wave-out platform reduce coastal erosion?

3 How might different types of rock be affected by processes of erosion?

4 Do waves erode all the time? When is coastal erosion at its peak?

5 What happens to material eroded from the land?

Further class and homework activities

Investigate the development of Lulworth Cove and its relationship with different rock types. Try to produce a model showing how the coast will have developed over time.

Answers to the Activities

1 By abrasion, hydraulic action, solution and attrition.

2 Where significant parts of the coast are exposed, primarily through cliffs. These can be weakened by groundwater and the action of sun, wind, rain, etc.

3 Numerous examples, many from rivers where several of the processes are similar – so reference to river landforms.

4 This will depend upon the example chosen.

The unit in brief

This unit is about how waves transport material along the coast by the process of longshore drift. Longshore drift can quickly remove beaches, and groynes are commonly used to protect them. In the Activities, students annotate a map of the British Isles to explain the direction of longshore drift; identify the problems it causes, and consider why groynes are not a complete solution. They also draw a diagram to show the process of longshore drift.

Key ideas

◆ Waves transport material along the coastline by the process of longshore drift.

◆ Longshore drift is the link between erosion and deposition along the coast – eroded material is transported and deposited further along the coast.

◆ Beaches can quickly be removed by longshore drift, so large sums of money are spent on sea defences.

◆ Groynes are commonly used to protect beaches, but they can cause erosion further along the coastline.

Key vocabulary

longshore drift, groynes

Skills practised in the Activities

◆ Geography skills: annotating a map to show the direction of longshore drift and explaining the process; drawing a diagram of longshore drift

◆ Thinking skills: identifying problems and thinking of the consequences caused by longshore drift

Unit outcomes

By the end of this unit, most students should be able to:

◆ define the terms given in 'Key vocabulary' above;

◆ understand the process of longshore drift;

◆ know that groynes may help to prevent longshore drift in one place, but can cause increased erosion elsewhere;

◆ draw a diagram to show longshore drift.

Ideas for a starter

1 Recap: the factors that affect the energy of waves.

2 Why are some beaches covered in sand while others are shingle beaches?

3 Show some rounded beach pebbles (and garden stones for comparison), and sand. Ask: Why are the pebbles round? Where did they come from originally? Where did the sand come from? Why are the grains so small?

Ideas for plenaries

1 Explain the process of longshore drift to your neighbour.

2 Design a piece of fieldwork to measure the rate of movement in longshore drift.

3 Why can groynes be dangerous places to play when on the beach?

4 look at the photo on p.93 of the students' book. What would happen if the groynes weren't there? Where would the sand go? Where do you think it would end up?

5 Sum up what you have learned today in less than 40 words.

Answers to the Activities

1 a This will be from west to east.

b Related to maximum fetch, Atlantic Ocean and the south westerly prevailing winds.

c From south to north.

d Also related to fetch and orientation of the coastline.

2 Removal of beach material, beach scouring, coastal erosion, deposition of material further along or off the shore.

3 This will depend upon students' opinions, but focus on the idea that erosion is a natural process which has always taken place. It is only really perceived as a problem when it affects people.

4 They solve the problem in one location, but potentially cause problems such as increased erosion further along a coast. They do not always stop all material from moving along a beach. They may eventually fail.

5 Students' diagrams should look similar to the artwork on page 92.

6 The groyne in photo B isn't on the beach in photo A. Groynes interrupt the downstream movement of material, and retain material on their upstream side. If you were standing on the beach in photo A looking out to sea, the direction of longshore drift would be along the beach from your left to right. If you were standing on the beach in photo B looking out to sea (in the direction the picture was taken), the direction of longshore drift would be along the beach from your right to left. (Students need to think about the process of longshore drift rather than the amount of sand and water they can see in photo B.)

The unit in brief

In this unit students find out about some of the landforms created by coastal deposition. In the Activities, students think about beach formation; explain how longshore drift can lead to the formation of spits and why bars can be temporary features; and use an atlas to locate spits on the coastline of the British Isles.

Key ideas

◆ Beaches are formed when low constructive waves deposit material in a bay between two headlands.

◆ Spits are long narrow ridges of sand or shingle which extend out to sea. They develop as material is added by longshore drift.

◆ Bars are barriers of sand and other material that stretch across river mouths and bays.

◆ Tombolos are ridges of sand and other material that link the mainland to an island a little way offshore.

Key vocabulary

beaches, spits, hooked or recurved end, bars, lagoon, off-shore bars, barrier islands, tombolos, sand dunes

Skills practised in the Activities

◆ Geography skills: using an atlas to find spits and describing their location

◆ Thinking skills: explaining beach formation and how longshore drift leads to the formation of spits; explaining why bars may be temporary

Unit outcomes

By the end of this unit, most students should be able to:

◆ define the terms given in 'Key vocabulary' above;

◆ explain how beaches and spits are created by coastal deposition;

◆ understand that sand dunes are a result of deposition by the wind not the sea;

◆ use an atlas to find spits around the coastline of the British Isles.

Ideas for a starter

1 Provide photos of named features of coastal deposition. Ask students to locate them on a large map of the UK. Compare it with the map showing features of erosion (Starter 1 unit 5.2). What do you notice about the two distributions?

2 Why will material be deposited rather than moved along the coast?

3 Ask students what they knew about the formation of beaches, spits, bars and tombolos so far.

Ideas for plenaries

1 Provide students with OS maps and ask them to find examples of depositional features.

2 Draw a sketch of the photo of Hurst Castle Spit on p.94 of the students' book. Annotate it to show how it formed.

3 What is the difference between bars and tombolos?

4 Explain the formation of a beach to your neighbour.

5 Make a graffiti wall of what students have learned today.

Answers to the Activities

1 These push material up and so help to build the beach.

2 Larger material, such as pebbles, is able to rest and maintain a steep gradient. Smaller material, such as sand, is not.

3 By the movement of material along a beach, until there is a change in the direction of the coast. After this, where there is relatively shallow water and little current, material may be deposited and eventually form a spit.

4 This will depend upon examples chosen by students.

5 They may be broken by the effect of incoming waves or by the river, the mouth of which they have blocked.

The effects of changes in sea level

This unit looks at the landforms created by changes in sea level, and the impact that global warming and consequent rising sea levels will have. In the Activities, students name other countries where raised beaches are found, and consider the differences between fjords and rias. They look at global warming and think about the impact of rising sea levels and whether we should defend the coast or try to stop global warming.

Key ideas

◆ Landforms created by changes in sea level include raised beaches, rias and fjords.

◆ Global warming is causing sea levels to rise – ice sheets and glaciers are melting, water expands as it warms.

◆ Rising sea levels will have an impact both in the UK and around the world.

Key vocabulary

raised beaches, rias, fjords, global warming

Skills practised in the Activities

◆ Geography skills: naming countries

◆ Thinking skills: explaining differences between fjords and rias; thinking of reasons; considering priorities and responsibilities

Unit outcomes

By the end of this unit, most students should be able to:

◆ define the terms given in 'Key vocabulary' above;

◆ understand how raised beaches, rias and fjords have formed;

◆ understand that global warming is causing sea levels to rise;

◆ name areas or places at risk from rising sea levels around the British Isles;

◆ understand the impact of global warming and rising sea levels – both in the British Isles and world-wide;

◆ recognise that we all have a responsibility to try to halt global warming.

Ideas for a starter

1   Ask students: What has global warming got to do with coasts?

2   Ask: Who can tell me what fjords and rias are? Can you give me some examples? Can you describe what they are like? What are they used for?

3   How do we know that sea levels have changed in the past? What evidence do we have?

Ideas for plenaries

1   Use an atlas to find coastlines which are indented with fjords.

2   Brainstorm to find out what students know about measures that have been taken to reduce the effects of sea levels rising in cities such as London.

3   Ask students to find examples of rias on atlas maps – look at Atlantic and Pacific coastlines.

4   Ask students to investigate different methods of managing the coastline. They need to be able to discuss different methods at the beginning of the next lesson.

5   Question time! Think back over the lesson and write down 3 questions related to what you have learned. The teacher will ask a member of the class to try to answer.

6   Write 'coastal landscapes' in the middle of a page. Create a mind map around the phrase. How many ideas can you come up with in 120 seconds?

Answers to the Activities

1   Students should refer to other countries that have been glaciated. These could include other examples from northern Europe, such as Norway and Finland.

2   Larger valleys, more severe glaciation, greater depth and quantity of ice.

3   Due to the extent to which future sea level changes will be natural, or caused by the actions of people – principally global warming.

4   Coasts are often more densely populated than inland parts of a country, and so a rise of 4 metres will affect large numbers of people. Many coasts are low lying and so will be greatly affected – Bangladesh is an ideal example.

5   This will depend upon students' opinions, which should be justified. Defence against sea level rise is possible at a national level, whereas stopping global warming requires global co-operation.

6   This will depend upon students' opinions.

The unit in brief

This unit explains how and why we defend the coastline; who decides and implements the strategy for coastal defence; and the fact that global warming and rising sea levels have led the government to change its ideas about coastal defences. In the Activities, students look at why coastlines are managed; explain the problems caused by coastal management; consider the advantages and disadvantages of 'managed retreat', and whether this should be part of the government's strategy for coastal management.

Key ideas

◆ The coastline is under pressure as an attractive place to live and visit, and from erosion and flooding by the sea.

◆ Coastal erosion can be reduced or stopped using hard engineering methods.

◆ Coastal defences are expensive, and would need strengthening to cope with rising sea levels and increasingly severe storms caused by global warming.

◆ The government wants a sustainable strategy of coastal defence – areas of high population will be protected, in other areas sea defences will be allowed to fail.

Key vocabulary

hard engineering, sea walls, rock armour, rock barriers, groynes, beach replenishment, sustainable strategy

Skills practised in the Activities

◆ Thinking skills: thinking of reasons for managing coastlines; explaining problems caused by this; considering advantages and disadvantages of managed retreat; considering government coastal management strategy

Unit outcomes

By the end of this unit, most students should be able to:

◆ define or explain the terms given in 'Key vocabulary' above;

◆ understand why we try to manage our coastline;

◆ say how coastal erosion can be stopped or reduced using hard engineering methods;

◆ realise that ideas about coastal management have had to change due to global warming and rising sea levels;

◆ understand what is involved in the government's sustainable strategy of coastal defence.

Ideas for a starter

1 Ask students which methods of coastal management they have found out about. Ask them to briefly describe them.

2 What processes are operating on coastlines to make them need managing?

3 How might the management of one part of the coast lead to erosion (or increased erosion) elsewhere?

4 Show a video/news clips which show either the coast being pounded by waves, or land disappearing into the sea.

Ideas for plenaries

1 Activities question **1** could be used as a plenary.

2 With books closed, see if you can name and explain to your neighbour the five hard engineering measures we use to stop coastal erosion.

3 Students work in pairs to create a 'managed retreat' mind map.

4 Choose a student to be in the hot seat. Another student asks him or her a question about coastal management and managed retreat. Then nominate two different students (4-6 pairs in total). There's one golden rule – questions cannot be repeated.

5 Tell me three key things you have learned today.

Further class and homework activities

1 Investigate coastal erosion and coastal management in Christchurch Bay on England's south coast. Write up your findings as a short case study.

Answers to the Activities

1 To prevent erosion, to maintain coasts for the use of people, to preserve valued environments.

2 Protecting one part of a coastline may lead to erosion elsewhere, protection is costly, it is often ugly, and generally it is only successful in the short term.

3 Managed retreat is often more sustainable than hard engineering solutions; it provides a balance between protection and allowing natural process to take place. It does not, however, really solve the problems of people who live in an area, as erosion is generally allowed to take place.

4 This will depend upon students' opinions. Protecting the coastline against erosion at all costs is expensive, and increasingly managed retreat is seen as a possible solution.

The unit in brief

This unit focuses on how erosion is causing problems for Happisburgh on the Norfolk coast. It looks at why the coast is being eroded; what has been done to protect the coastline; the problems Happisburgh faces, and its future. In the Activities, students summarise the causes of erosion; think about whether people's actions are a major factor in coastal erosion; and complete a cost-benefit analysis to decide whether Happisburgh is worth protecting.

Key ideas

◆ The coastline around Happisburgh is being eroded by the North Sea.

◆ Erosion has been made worse by building sea defences elsewhere, and by dredging sand and gravel off the coast of East Anglia.

◆ Happisburgh's sea defences are old and damaged.

◆ DEFRA has decided (using cost-benefit analysis) that the coastline isn't worth protecting.

◆ Happisburgh's future remains uncertain.

Key vocabulary

sea walls, revetments, hard defences

Skills practised in the Activities

◆ Geography skills: completing a cost-benefit analysis

◆ Literacy skills: summarising the causes of erosion

◆ Thinking skills: thinking; giving reasons; justifying decisions

Unit outcomes

By the end of this unit, most students should be able to:

◆ define the terms given in 'Key vocabulary' above;

◆ understand why the coastline at Happisburgh is being eroded;

◆ describe what has been done to protect Happisburgh in the past;

◆ understand how decisions are made about protecting the coast;

◆ complete a simple cost-benefit analysis;

◆ understand that Happisburgh's future is uncertain.

Ideas for a starter

1 Revise the processes of coastal erosion. Write the words abrasion, hydraulic action, solution, and attrition and their definitions on separate large sheets of paper. 8 students hold up the 8 sheets. The rest of the class match them up.

2 Recap: what measures are used to defend coastlines? Try to think of the hard and soft engineering solutions.

3 Find Happisburgh in an atlas. What do you know about this part of the coastline? What's the geology of this area like?

4 Show a photo of a house teetering on the edge of a cliff. Ask students to imagine they live there. How do they feel? Can they hear the sea? When will the next storm come? What will that mean for the cliff and their house?

Ideas for plenaries

1 Provide students with a sketch map of the Happisburgh area (use the multimap site). Ask them to annotate the hard engineering being used on this coastline.

2 Climate change will affect sea levels. The coast is sinking as it readjusts to the last ice age. How sensible or effective can it be to spend money on coastal defences?

3 Draw a spider diagram showing all the interests and people concerned in defending the coastline at Happisburgh.

4 You are a coastal defence expert. Write a letter to the local people advising them on the best value for money in terms of coastal defence.

5 Create an acrostic. Write HAPPISBURGH down one side of a page. Make each letter the first letter of a word, phrase or sentence about coastal management.

6 Ask students to investigate the formation of Chesil Beach on the South coast of UK, and to try to find out about flooding on this part of the coast.

Further class and homework activities

1 Try to find out more about this coast. Search on the internet and try to find suitable sites.

2 Try to download the integrated coastal defense plan for this part of Norfolk. What future has Happisburgh got in this?

Answers to the Activities

1 The main reason is the geology of the coastline – unconsolidated rocks that are easily eroded. The rocks are permeable, and are weakened further by rain water. Offshore dredging reduces the 'buffer' impact against incoming waves, so there is human influence as well.

2 Linked back to the previous answer, the action of dredging in particular contributes to erosion.

3 This will depend upon students' opinions. Benefits of protecting the coastline include preserving jobs, homes and communities. Costs include the financial costs, and the likelihood that the 'sea will win' in the end.

The unit in brief

This unit looks at how flooding is a problem in the area around Chesil Beach – why there is flooding and what has been done about it. In the Activities, students explain why coastal flooding is a problem here; evaluate the effectiveness of existing defences, and think about what should be done; and consider whether it is more important to preserve the natural environment or protect the villages behind the beach.

Key ideas

◆ Chesil Beach is an ancient landform which is neither being formed nor eroded by the sea.

◆ The area floods because Chesil Beach faces south west and is exposed to waves the fetch of which extends across the Atlantic Ocean.

◆ Sea defences include a sea wall at Chiswell, a flood drainage channel and gabions placed along the beach ridge.

◆ There is conflict between local residents who want stronger more effective defences and others who believe nature should take its course.

Key vocabulary

sea wall, drainage channel, gabions

Skills practised in the Activities

◆ Thinking skills: explaining; evaluating; thinking; justifying answer; considering different views

Unit outcomes

By the end of this unit, most students should be able to:

◆ define or explain the terms given in 'Key vocabulary' above;

◆ understand how Chesil Beach was formed;

◆ understand why there is flooding along this part of the coastline;

◆ evaluate how effective the existing defences will be in the long term;

◆ realise that there is conflict between local people who want to be protected, and those who think natural processes should be allowed to work unhindered.

Ideas for a starter

1 Recap: Why does the sea stop transporting material and start depositing it? Draw a diagram on the board to remind students about longshore drift.

2 Ask students to find the Chesil Beach area in an atlas. What sort of feature is it? Ask several students what they found out about how Chesil Beach was formed, and about flooding on this part of the coast.

3 Show photos of coastal flooding. Ask: should we protect the coast, or let nature take its course?

Ideas for plenaries

1 Provide students with a large map of the area and ask them to indicate all the potential conflicts in the area on the map.

2 How can the area be conserved so that everyone wins? The tombolo is a world famous feature and yet the lives and livelihoods of the local people are very important. You have 5 minutes to write a letter to the local newspaper giving your views as an independent expert.

3 Play 'Just a Minute' – the topic is 'Chesil Beach'. Students have the chance to talk for a minute on Chesil Beach without repetition or hesitation. As soon as a student repeats an idea, or hesitates, the next student takes over until the minute is up.

4 Tell me the three main things you have learned today. Now tell me three other things that are interesting but less important.

Further class and homework activities

1 Investigate the local development plan for the Isle of Portland and Chiswell village in particular. Look on the internet and download a copy.

2 Make a study of the coast adjacent to this location. There are a number of sites which can help you. What is the Jurassic coast and why is it important?

Answers to the Activities

1 The coastline is exposed to the maximum fetch of incoming waves. This is worst during the frequent storm conditions.

2 a Most defences such as these will only provide a short term solution to the problem.

b This will depend upon students' opinions. Solutions could include far greater investment in hard engineering defences such as walls, or allowing the natural process to take place and removing people further inland.

3 This will depend upon students' opinions, which should be justified.

4 This will depend upon students' opinions. Reference should be made to the specific context of Chesil Beach, rather than an answer in generalised terms.

Protecting Lyme Regis

The unit in brief

This unit focuses on how coastal protection is impacting tourism and the tourist industry in Lyme Regis, West Dorset, on the south coast of England. The unit looks at why coastal protection is needed at Lyme Regis, the details of the protection scheme, and its impacts. In the Activities, students use an OS map, assess the protection scheme, and evaluate it in terms of cost and sustainability.

Key ideas

◆ Lyme Regis depends on tourism, and is an important tourist centre on the Jurassic Coast, which is a World Heritage Site.

◆ Lyme Regis has a long history of coastal erosion and landslips – it's on a very unstable stretch of coastline.

◆ Houses and businesses have been lost in the past – and if nothing's done, the town and its people will suffer further losses in the future.

◆ The Lyme Regis Coast Protection Scheme is an expensive multi-phase long-term project.

◆ The aim of the scheme is to provide long-term protection for homes and businesses, and to protect the coast and special natural environment that makes Lyme Regis attractive to tourists.

◆ The scheme has some disadvantages for tourism, but overall should bring long-term advantages.

Key vocabulary

sea wall, promenade, foreshore, rock armour, jetties, tourism

Skills practised in the Activities

◆ Geography skills: mapskills

◆ Thinking skills: assessing and evaluating

Unit outcomes

By the end of this unit, most students should be able to:

◆ define or explain the terms given in 'Key vocabulary' above;

◆ explain why the coast at Lyme Regis is being eroded;

◆ say what has happened in the past;

◆ explain that Lyme Regis earns its living as a tourist resort;

◆ understand why there's a need to protect the coastline;

◆ describe the aims and methods of the protection scheme;

◆ explain the possible advantages and disadvantages of the protection scheme to the town and the tourists;

◆ understand that there are cost and sustainability issues that have to be considered.

Ideas for a starter

1 Brainstorm to find out what, if anything, students know already about Lyme Regis. Write all the responses on the board.

2 Ask students why they think people enjoy visiting the coast. Write 'Seaside tourism' [or 'Coastal tourism'] in the middle of the board, and create a spider diagram from the responses.

3 Recap: the processes of coastal erosion.

4 Ask: How could coastal erosion damage a town's tourism industry?

Ideas for plenaries

1 Activities question **4** could be used as a plenary.

2 Activities question **5** could be used as a plenary.

3 Play 'Just a minute' – the topic is 'Protecting Lyme Regis'. Students have the chance to talk for a minute about the Lyme Regis Coast Protection Scheme and its benefits without repetition or hesitation. As soon as a student repeats an idea or fact, or hesitates, the next student talks until the minute is up.

4 Ask a student to give one coastal protection measure at Lyme Regis, and ask another student to describe its purpose or benefit. Write the responses on the board, and continue until you have a suitable/appropriate list.

5 Make a graffiti wall of what students have learned today.

Further class and homework activities

Research: use the internet to find out the latest news about the Lyme Regis Coast Protection Scheme.

Answers to the Activities

1 a *Evidence of coastal processes:* the beach, cliffs, and headlands and bays.

b *Evidence of coastal defences:* The Cobb and harbour wall at the southern end of Lyme Regis, and the groynes on the beach.

c *Evidence of tourism:* attractions labelled on the map are Dinosaurland, aquarium, boat trips; there are also symbols showing a museum and tourist information; there are car park symbols near the sea front; and the South-West Coast Path is shown and labelled.

2 Any three (or similar) from:

◆ extra sand and shingle on the beach will absorb wave energy and protect the foreshore from erosion;

◆ new jetties on the beach will protect the foreshore and beach from wave attack and erosion;

◆ the realignment of the North Wall Rockery will protect the foreshore and beach from wave attack and erosion;

◆ the extension of the rock armour at the end of The Cobb will protect the foreshore and beach from wave attack and erosion;

◆ the new sea wall will protect the foreshore from wave attack and erosion.

3 a Advantages for tourists and the tourism industry:

◆ better beach – people like a good beach;

◆ it will be possible to walk along the whole beach, even at high tide – this makes the beach attractive to people;

◆ a new promenade along the sea front – people like walking along wide and safe promenades, relaxing and looking out at the sea;

◆ calmer conditions in the harbour will make Lyme Regis an even more attractive place for recreational sailors to visit and stay;

◆ behind the sea front, improved roads will improve access to the sea front;

◆ behind the sea front, re-landscaped public gardens with better access will help make the town attractive to a wide range of people;

◆ a more secure future for the town's people and businesses will encourage people to invest in (spend money on) their businesses, which should help create a more attractive tourist environment;

◆ all these improvements could help to extend the tourist season.

All these things should make Lyme Regis an even more enjoyable place to visit, and the town's tourist industry should be more successful.

b Disadvantages for tourists and the tourism industry:

◆in the short-term, there's the disruption caused by the work, and the work spoils the atmosphere and view;

◆in the longer-term, the town might become even more crowded than it already is, particularly at peak times – this could spoil the holiday/visit experience for tourists and make it hard for the tourist industry in the town to cope with the number of visitors.

4 Depends on personal attitude; but without the scheme people could lose their homes and businesses, the town's economy would suffer, and tourists would lose a great place to visit on what is now part of a World Heritage Site – so there are probably strong arguments to say that the scheme will prove value for money.

5 Hard to say – no one really knows how long the improvements will last. They will need to be maintained, and sea level/climate change arising from global warming could have an impact. But the measures on the beach/harbour, and the drainage work on the slopes behind it, mean the scheme is trying to be as sustainable as possible.

Weather and climate

chapter overview

The big picture

These are the key ideas behind this chapter:

◆ Weather and climate are different. Weather is the day-to-day state of the atmosphere, and can change very quickly. Climate is the average weather in a place. It is worked out by taking measurements over a long period (usually 30 years), and calculating the average.

◆ Climate depends on a range of factors – but the main one is the effect of latitude.

◆ Two large scale weather systems control the weather in the UK – depressions and anticyclones.

◆ Droughts can affect MEDCs like the UK and LEDCs like Niger, but the causes and impacts are very different.

◆ Tropical storms are extreme weather events which can have devastating effects.

◆ Weather, climate and climate change affect all of us.

Note that the students' version of the big picture is given in the students' chapter opener.

Chapter outline

Use this, and the students' chapter opener, to give students a mental roadmap for the chapter.

6   **Weather and climate**   As the students' chapter opener, this unit is an important part of the chapter; see page 11 of this book for notes about using chapter openers

6.1   **Global climate explained**   The global distribution of climate and factors affecting climate

6.2   **The climate of the British Isles**   The temperate, maritime climate of the British Isles, and the formation of relief and convectional rainfall

6.3   **Weather and weather systems**   Elements of weather and how they are measured, and the effects of anticyclones

6.4   **The depression**   How depressions form, and the weather they bring

6.5   **Synoptic charts and satellite images**   What synoptic charts and satellite images show, and how to read them

6.6   **Climate and human activity in the UK**   How the weather and climate in the UK affects sources of energy, farming, flooding, tourism and sport and leisure

6.7   **The impact of drought**   Causes and impacts of, and responses to, drought in the UK and Niger

6.8   **Tropical storms**   Causes, effects and prediction

6.9   **The hurricane season of 2005**   The effects of Hurricanes Katrina and Wilma in 2005

6.10   **Climate change**   Causes, possible effects and what's being done about it

Objectives and outcomes for this chapter

Objectives	Unit	Outcomes
Most students will understand:		Most students will be able to:
● The difference between weather and climate.	6.1, 6.3	● Define weather and climate; explain how climate is worked out.
● How climate varies around the world, and that climate is the result of a range of factors.	6.1	● Describe the global distribution of climate; give five factors that affect climate and describe their effect.
● That Britain has a temperate maritime climate, but climate varies across the British Isles.	6.2	● Explain why climate varies across the British Isles.
● That three types of rainfall are responsible for the precipitation in the British Isles.	6.2, 6.4	● Describe the formation of relief, convectional and frontal rainfall.
● That weather consists of elements which can be measured.	6.3	● Identify at least six elements of weather; say what instruments are used to measure them and give the units of measurement.
● That anticyclones are high pressure weather systems and that there are differences between winter and summer anticyclones.	6.3	● Describe the differences in weather associated with winter and summer anticyclones.
● That depressions are low pressure weather systems, how they form, and how they affect our weather.	6.4	● Describe how depressions form and the weather associated with them.
● That synoptic charts and satellite images help us to forecast the weather.	6.5	● Explain what synoptic charts and satellite images are; describe weather conditions using a synoptic chart.
● The causes and effects of droughts in MEDCs and LEDCs.	6.7	● Compare and contrast the causes and effects of droughts in an MEDC and an LEDC.
● What causes tropical storms; the effects of Hurricanes Katrina and Wilma; how prediction can save lives.	6.8, 6.9	● Explain how hurricanes develop; describe and classify the effects of Hurricanes Katrina and Wilma; explain how prediction can help to save lives.
● That weather, climate and climate change affect us all.	6.6, 6.10	● Give five examples of how climate affects our lives; explain what is causing climate change; describe the possible affects of climate change; say what is being done about it.

These tie in with 'Your goals for this chapter' in the students' chapter opener, and with the opening lines in each unit, which give the purpose of the unit in a student-friendly style.

Using the chapter starter

The photo on page 106 of the *geog.GCSE* students' book shows a tornado in Kansas, USA. It narrowly missed the house in the picture, but continued on to wreck a house not far away. A tornado is a spinning column of air, shaped like a funnel. They're usually associated with thunderstorms and are known for being destructive – tornado winds can be over 300 mph. Tornado damage-paths can be up to 1.5 km (1 mile) wide and 75 km (50 miles) long. It's impossible to predict exactly where a tornado will hit.

Tornadoes form in storms all over the world. In the UK a tornado in Birmingham in the summer of 2005 left a thousand buildings damaged. But tornadoes are mostly associated with the American Mid-West. In the USA, in an average year about 1000 tornadoes are reported. Tornadoes cause an average of 80 deaths and 1500 injuries a year in the USA.

In the film *The Wizard of Oz* a Kansas girl and her dog are picked up by a tornado and transported to a fantasy land.

Although tornadoes aren't covered in this chapter, the photo was chosen because it's a stunning weather and climate image that should spark interest in the topic.

Global climate explained

The unit in brief

This unit introduces climate, and is about the global distribution of climate and the main factors affecting temperature (and therefore climate). In the Activities, students use a map of climate zones to describe the global distribution of certain types of climate; draw climate graphs, and compare climates with reasons.

Key ideas

◆ Climate is the average weather of a place taken over a long period of time.

◆ The world can be divided into climate zones.

◆ The main factors affecting temperature are: latitude; distance from the sea; the prevailing wind; altitude; ocean currents.

Key vocabulary

climate, latitude, distance from the sea, maritime climate, continental climate, prevailing wind, altitude, ocean currents

Skills practised in the Activities

◆ Geography skills: describing the global distribution of climate zones; drawing climate graphs; comparing climate zones

◆ Numeracy skills: using statistical data from climate graphs

◆ Thinking skills: suggesting reasons for differences

Unit outcomes

By the end of this unit, most students should be able to:

◆ define or explain the terms given in 'Key vocabulary' above;

◆ understand that climate is the average weather of a place taken over a long period of time;

◆ describe the global distribution of climate zones;

◆ draw climate graphs;

◆ identify the main factors affecting temperature and climate.

Ideas for a starter

1 Ask students: Who can define weather and climate for me?

2 In the UK we have a temperate, maritime climate. What does this tell you?

3 Read out the weather forecast for today. How does this match up with the climate description?

4 Use a globe to introduce ideas about the variation of temperature and precipitation over the planet.

5 Tell me a country that's hotter than the UK? And one that's colder? Can you explain why? Elicit that latitude is the main reason.

Ideas for plenaries

1 Produce a spider diagram showing how different factors affect climate. Annotate the diagram.

2 Can you think of an example where altitude has a bigger effect than latitude on the climate? (On very high mountains. Some high mountains in the tropics have glaciers!)

3 How will climate affect human activity in each of the climates shown?

4 How can people influence climate?

5 What is a microclimate? Resource the school's microclimate.

Further class and homework activities

Investigate some of the weather sites on the internet. Collect data for a station near you. You can use the Met Office site www.meto.gov.uk/ or www.bbc.co.uk/weather/

Answers to the Activities

1 The equatorial climate is generally located in a zone around the equator from 0°-5° in latitude, including regions such as the Amazon rainforest, Central Africa and much of Indonesia.

The savanna climate generally exists between 5°-15° latitude in both the northern and southern hemispheres. Regions experiencing this climate include Kenya and Nigeria in Africa and northern parts of Australia.

The desert climate is located in broad zones around 30° latitude. The largest of the deserts is the Sahara in North Africa, although other famous deserts include Nevada in the western USA and the Arabian desert.

The temperate climate exists in broad zones between 40°-60° latitude. This climate zone applies to most of the United Kingdom and other global regions such as the North West USA and southern Chile.

In all cases, it's important that students identify the global latitude bands where the climate is located and then exemplify it with some named areas.

2 a Models of the climate graphs can be found on page 108 of the students' book. Students should use this as a guide and be encouraged to use graph paper to promote accuracy. They should be reminded that the blue bars represent precipitation (measured in mm) and that the red line represents temperature (measured in °C).

b When comparing climate data students are tempted to write simple descriptive paragraphs for each graph all too easily. This is not a comparison. They should be encouraged to calculate the differences between the temperate climate and the other identified climate types. The table below indicates some of the comparative data that students should use.

Climate type	January temp	July temp	Total precipitation	Monthly maximum	Monthly minimum
Temperate (London, UK)	6 °C	22 °C	600 mm	August 65 mm	March 45 mm
Desert	23 °C 17 °C more than London	32 °C 10 °C more than London	162mm 588 mm less than London	August 75 mm	Dec-Mar 0 mm
Savanna	21 °C 15 °C more than London	17 °C 5 °C less than London	1232 mm 632 mm more than London	December 306 mm	Jul-Aug 0 mm
Equatorial	26 °C 20 °C more than London	25.5 °C 8.5 °C more than London	2800 mm 2200 mm more than London	March 330 mm	September 135 mm

3 The table below provides a summary of the main reasons for the differences in climate described in activity 2. Most of the reasons are provided on page 109, although more-able students should be able to identify additional explanations for further pages in chapter 6.

Climate type	Temperature	Rainfall
Temperate	Due to the curvature of the Earth, there are contrasts between summer and winter. The angle of the sun is higher in summer, pushing up temperatures. A lower angle in the winter means cooler.	The mountains found towards the west of the UK encourage relief rainfall and, as the prevailing wind comes from the Atlantic (south west), rain falls reliably all year.
Desert	With clear skies and a very high angle of the sun in summer, temperatures can get very hot. Less intense sunlight in the winter means temperatures dip by about 10 °C.	The prevailing winds blow across the desert land and remain dry. The continental winds pick up no moisture, preventing cloud and rain formation. Convectional thunderstorms in the summer months provide more rain but only up to 35 mm in one month.
Savanna	Closer to the equator, temperatures remain constant for most of the year. For Zambia, the cooler temperatures are in June and July, when most of the sun's energy is concentrated in the northern hemisphere.	A clear seasonal contrast exists between the summer drought and the winter rains for Zambia. Use page 133 from the ecosystems chapter. Note that the movement of the ITCZ is over Zambia in the summer, providing the rainy season, but drought dominates the winter months.
Equatorial	Constant temperatures around 27 °C, as the intense sun shines all year round with no seasonal contrast. The sunlight is direct so temperatures are high.	High precipitation totals are due to the process of convectional rainfall, page 111. The strong intense sunlight means higher temperatures and rapid convection to produce towering cumulonimbus clouds and torrential rainfall.

help at a glance

The unit in brief

This unit is about the climate of the British Isles, and explains the formation of relief and convectional rainfall. In the Activities, students draw their own sketch map of the British Isles, divide it into climate zones and annotate it. They compare climate areas and using a map provided to describe and suggest reasons for the distribution of rainfall across the British Isles.

Key ideas

◆ The British Isles has a temperate maritime climate.

◆ The British Isles can be divided into four climate areas.

◆ Three types of rainfall are responsible for the precipitation in the British Isles: relief, convectional and frontal.

Key vocabulary

temperate maritime climate, relief rainfall, convectional rainfall, frontal rainfall, rain shadow, convection currents

Skills practised in the Activities

◆ Geography skills: drawing a sketch map of the British Isles, dividing it into climate areas and annotating it; comparing climate areas; describing the distribution of rainfall

◆ Numeracy skills: using climate data to annotate a map of climate areas

◆ Thinking skills: explaining differences; suggesting reasons

Unit outcomes

By the end of this unit, most students should be able to:

◆ define or explain the terms given in 'Key vocabulary' above;

◆ describe that the British Isles has a temperate, maritime climate;

◆ divide the British Isles into four climate areas;

◆ understand that three types of rainfall are responsible for the precipitation in the British Isles;

◆ explain the formation of relief and convectional rainfall.

Ideas for a starter

1 Make a graffiti wall of what students have learned so far about weather and climate (focus particularly on factors affecting climate).

2 Provide temperature and rainfall figures for places in the four different climate areas of the UK. Ask groups of students to draw climate graphs for the different places. What do the different graphs show us about climate in the UK?

3 Find the British Isles in an atlas. What would you expect the climate to be like given its latitude? What is the North Atlantic Drift? How does it affect our weather and climate? How does relief affect our weather and climate?

Ideas for plenaries

1 How could the pattern of climate across the British Isles influence the economic activity? How could it affect farming for example?

2 How does the North Atlantic Drift affect the climate in the summer and the winter?

3 Make up 10-15 statements about the climate of the British Isles based on what students have learned so far, some true, some false. Students hold up True or False cards. Where statements are false ask students to correct them.

4 Ask students to use the Met Office website (www.meto.gov.uk) to look up information on the equipment needed for a weather station. They will need this for the next lesson.

Futher class and homework activities

Collect data on temperature and precipitation for a variety of weather stations over the UK and produce a series of isotherm and isohyet maps to show the temperature and precipitation distribution. Do they look like the maps in the Atlas? Make a wall display of these maps and annotate them to explain the pattern.

Answers to the Activities

1 a Using an outline map of the British Isles, students should design their climate map using the example on page 110 as a model.

b Use the table below to help students to identify the main climate descriptive annotations that are required.

UK region	January temp	July temp	Annual range	Total precipitation	Monthly max	Monthly min
North west	3 °C	14.5 °C	11.5 °C	1979 mm	December 235 mm	December 235 mm
North East	3 °C	16 °C	13 °C	761 mm	July 90 mm	July 90 mm
South West	5 °C	16.5 °C	11.5 °C	1090 mm	December 130 mm	December 130 mm
South East	3 °C	18 °C	15 °C	558 mm	July 60 mm	July 60 mm

2 As with the activity for global climate, students are required to compare the regions and not to write descriptive paragraphs for each separate region. They should be encouraged to calculate the differences for both temperature and precipitation, using the words 'more' or 'less' for the two chosen regions. The statistics given in the above table will make it simpler for these comparisons to be worked out.

To explain the temperature contrasts, students should use information from page 109 - altitude, latitude and ocean currents all help to suggest why the west of the UK is mild in winter, compared with the east, and why the south of the UK is warmer than the north in the summer.

To explain precipitation contrasts, the information given on pages 111 and 114 onwards indicates that the west of Britain is wetter than the east, due to frontal and relief rainfall. Higher rainfall totals for the summer months in the east of the UK can be attributed to convectional rainfall associated with the higher temperatures.

3 The rainfall distribution map for the UK shows that most precipitation falls in the west of the country. Over 2400 mm falls in the north west of Scotland and the Welsh mountains, for example. Towards the east, there is less rainfall. Areas such as Cambridgeshire and London only receive between 6-800 mm each year.

The reasons for this are as for activity 2. There is much more frontal and relief rainfall towards the east of Britain. The east is in a rain shadow so receives less.

Weather and weather systems

The unit in brief

This unit is about weather. It looks at the elements of the weather, and how they can be measured, and at the different types of weather associated with winter and summer anticyclones. In the Activities, students look at the single most important weather element – air pressure – and explain how it controls the other elements of weather; describe the weather associated with a summer anticyclone and suggest reasons for the anticyclone weather.

Key ideas

◆ Weather is the day-to-day condition of the atmosphere.

◆ Weather is made up of different elements which can be measured.

◆ Air pressure is the most important weather element.

◆ Anticyclones and depressions are large-scale weather systems which affect the weather in the British Isles.

◆ There are differences in the weather associated with winter and summer anticyclones.

Key vocabulary

weather, precipitation, temperature, wind (direction and strength/speed), visibility, cloud (type and cover), humidity, air pressure, anticyclone, depression, isobars

Skills practised in the Activities

◆ Geography skills: describing summer anticyclone weather
◆ Thinking skills: explaining air pressure; suggesting reasons for summer anticyclone weather

Unit outcomes

By the end of this unit, most students should be able to:

◆ define or explain the terms given in 'Key vocabulary' above;

◆ understand that weather is the day-to-day condition of the atmosphere;

◆ identify the different weather elements;

◆ explain how air pressure controls other weather elements;

◆ describe that anticyclones and depressions are large-scale weather systems which affect the weather in the British Isles;

◆ explain the weather associated with summer anticyclones.

Ideas for a starter

1 Recap: the definitions of weather and climate.

2 How do we measure weather? If you have thermometers, gauges etc. use these as props to ask: What are they? What are they used to measure?

3 Show photos of typical summer and winter conditions. Ask students to describe the weather conditions.

Ideas for plenaries

1 Provide students with a map of Western Europe showing isobars (you can download one from the Met Office site). Ask students to mark on the areas of highest pressure and the wind directions.

2 Draw a diagram showing how an anticyclone operates. Why does it often produce extreme weather?

3 Anticyclones can be associated with high levels of pollution especially over urban areas. Why is this so? Find out about urban microclimates including smog over Los Angeles.

4 Provide students with satellite images of anticyclones. Ask them to annotate them with information about the weather conditions.

5 Notice how much cloud the satellite images used in plenary 4 show. Do you know why?

6 Prepare an odd-one-out for your partner either on the elements of the weather, or on anticyclones.

Answers to the Activities

1 a Atmospheric pressure is effectively the weight of the air pushing down on the Earth's surface. Pressure is the application of force per unit area, so air pressure is the force of the atmosphere on the ground surface. It is measured in millibars or millimetres of mercury using a barometer. Pressure is generally high if over 1000 mb and low if less than 1000 mb.

b Air pressure indicates whether air is warm and rising, which results in low pressure, or cold and sinking which results in higher pressure. In this way, the air pressure controls many other elements of the weather. Low pressure is associated with clouds and wet, windy weather. As warm air rises, moisture cools and cloud develops giving precipitation; visibility becomes poor. High pressure is associated with clear skies, dry and calm conditions. Cool air sinks and warms as it moves towards the ground. It warms up and evaporates moisture, giving dry conditions with generally very clear visibility, with the exception of fog and pollution.

2 The weather associated with a summer anticyclone includes clear skies and dry conditions. The winds are very calm. Daytime temperatures can be very high in the UK at over 25 °C, although evenings can be much cooler. On occasions, anticyclones can bring heat-waves and convectional thunderstorm activity.

The high summer temperatures are due to the higher angle of the sun in the sky during the summer months. The heating from the sun is more concentrated during the day. Temperatures can cool rapidly at night, though, as the daytime heat escapes into space. This cooling leaves dew on the ground in the morning. Sometimes temperatures become so hot that warm moist air rises locally and builds up towering cumulonimbus clouds that give thunderstorms and periods of torrential rainfall.

Students could extend their understanding of anticyclones by also explaining the winter contrasts.

The depression

The unit in brief

This unit is about depressions – how they form, and how they affect our weather. In the Activities, students produce a weather forecast for Birmingham as a depression passes over the UK, and describe the differences between the weather associated with a depression and that associated with a summer anticyclone.

Key ideas

◆ A depression is a low pressure weather system.

◆ In a depression the warm front has warm air behind it, the cold front has cold air behind it.

◆ There are distinct stages in the development of a depression.

◆ Depressions produce a distinct weather pattern.

Key vocabulary

depression, warm front, warm sector, cold front, cold sector, pressure, temperature, cloud cover, wind speed and direction, precipitation

Skills practised in the Activities

◆ Geography skills: describing the differences between weather associated with depressions and summer anticyclones

◆ Literacy skills: producing a weather forecast

Unit outcomes

By the end of this unit, most students should be able to:

◆ define or explain the terms given in 'Key vocabulary' above;

◆ understand that a depression is a low pressure weather system;

◆ remember that in a depression the warm front has warm air behind it, the cold front has cold air behind it;

◆ understand that there are distinct stages in the development of a depression;

◆ describe the weather associated with a depression.

Ideas for a starter

1 Show a satellite image of a depression from the Met Office website on the whiteboard or give students copies of the satellite image. Ask the students to describe what they can see. What type of weather feature is this? What type of weather might it bring?

2 Have a diary prepared which records changes in weather as a depression passes over. Ask students to read it out.

3 Ask students to look out of the window. Describe the weather. What was it like yesterday? What will it be like tomorrow? What weather feature is giving us this weather?

Ideas for plenaries

1 Provide students with satellite images from a depression passing over the British Isles. Ask students to annotate them to explain what is happening.

2 What do you think the weather conditions along an occluded front will be?

3 Show a video of a weather report from the television. Ask: How effective do you think it is? Can you think of ways to improve it?

4 Describe the weather associated with the passage of a depression to your neighbour.

5 Did you find anything difficult about the work in this unit? What? Why? What would help to make it less difficult?

Further class and homework activities

1 Try to log the progression of an actual depression as it moves across the British Isles. Use the Met Office website to help you.

2 Investigate the sequence of cloud formations as the depression advances and passes overhead.

3 Look up the different ways the weather is presented on different websites.

Answers to the Activities

1 An effective way of answering this question would be to divide up the depression chart into 6-hour periods and to encourage students to describe what is happening in each section, structuring their forecast more carefully. Use the table below to identify the correct information for Birmingham.

Time period	Passage of depression	Weather features
0-6 hours	Ahead of warm front	Air pressure starts to fall rapidly with high-level cirrus clouds developing. Conditions are dry with a south to south east wind direction.
6-12 hours	Passage of warm front	Air pressure continues to fall and there is a noticeable increase in temperature. Stratus cloud is low and thick, giving steady and continuous precipitation. The wind direction changes to south westerly.
12-18 hours	Warm sector	The air pressure remains steady and the temperatures are mild in the warm air mass. Cloud development becomes patchy and rain may stop or there could be light drizzle.
18-24 hours	Cold front to cold sector	During the passage of the cold front the cloud will be thick cumulonimbus with heavy precipitation. The winds will change to come from the colder north west. There is a sudden drop in temperature and the air pressure begins to rise. Following the cold front, squally showers persist in cool conditions, the cloud cover becoming increasingly patchy.

2 Five differences between the weather associated with a depression and a summer anticyclone are shown and explained in the table below:

Weather feature	Depression	Summer anticyclone
Average temperature	Mild due to warm sector air from the tropics. Cloud cover in a depression	Very high temperatures due to clear skies and high angle of the sun, with no cloud to block the
Precipitation	prevents the temperatures from getting very warm in the summer.	penetrating heat.
Cloud cover	Very wet conditions at both the warm and cold fronts, particularly the latter. Frontal rainfall means that warm is rising over cold in the case of the warm front, or being undercut in the case of the cold front. Cooling leads to condensation and cloud development.	Sinking air warms as it moves towards the ground surface. This encourages the evaporation of moisture, limiting the development of clouds. Consequently the skies are clear and there is no precipitation. The exception comes from convectional activity on very hot summer days, which can result in thunderstorms.
Wind speed	See above.	See above.
	Higher wind speed as the isobars will be much closer together, indicating a greater change in air pressure.	Calm wind speed as the isobars will be further apart, indicating a more gradual change in air pressure.
Air pressure	Low as air is rising to form frontal rainfall.	High as air is descending to give clear and dry conditions.

Synoptic charts and satellite images

The unit in brief

This unit introduces students to synoptic charts and satellite images. In the Activities, students study synoptic charts to write a weather forecast, describe weather conditions at specific places, and suggest how the weather will change.

Key ideas

◆ Synoptic charts are maps that show weather conditions.

◆ Satellite images are photos taken from space.

◆ Satellite images show cloud cover and are used for weather forecasting.

◆ Weather symbols are used to show conditions at specific places.

Key vocabulary

synoptic chart, depression, occlusion, anticyclone, high-pressure ridge, precipitation, satellite image, weather symbols

Skills practised in the Activities

◆ Geography skills: using synoptic charts to describe weather conditions

◆ Literacy skills: writing a weather forecast

◆ Thinking skills: analysing synoptic charts; suggesting reasons for changes in weather

Unit outcomes

By the end of this unit, most students should be able to:

◆ define or explain the terms given in 'Key vocabulary' above;

◆ describe weather using a synoptic chart;

◆ know that satellite images are photos taken from space;

◆ understand that satellite images show cloud cover and are used for weather forecasting;

◆ understand that weather symbols are used to show conditions at specific places.

Ideas for a starter

1. Recap: the precipitation process (cooling → condensation → cloud formation → precipitation); relief, convectional and frontal rainfall; weather conditions associated with the passage of a depression.

2. Show a satellite image and synoptic chart for the same time period. What does each show?

3. Brainstorm to find out what students know about synoptic charts and satellite images. What are they? What are they used for?

4. How do weather forecasters find out about the weather? (Satellites provide much of the information. They can show weather systems some distance away from the UK that may be heading our way. This helps forecasters make to predictions.)

Ideas for plenaries

1. Show students flashcards of weather symbols and ask them to say what they are in a quick-fire quiz.

2. What is the really important thing on satellite images that give us clues about the weather? (The clouds. The cloud patterns give meteorologists a great deal of information).

3. Provide students with a synoptic chart and satellite image for the same time period. Ask students to draw the likely cloud formation on the synoptic chart and then check the actual formation against the satellite image.

4. Weather forecasters don't like to predict the weather more than 5 days in advance. Why do you think this is?

5. Make a graffiti wall of a range of jobs that would find the weather forecast useful.

Answers to the Activities

1. The synoptic chart for 11 August indicates a large area of high pressure to the west of the British Isles. This is an anticyclone. The isobars are far apart indicating a gradual change in air pressure so winds would be expected to be light or calm. The winds would be circulating in a clockwise direction an approaching the UK from the North West. For most of the country skies would be clear giving rise to higher temperatures as the intense sun heats the land during the day, although these temperatures may fall quite readily during the evening. In all areas conditions will be dry.

b There is a trick to showing how the weather conditions at place A might change over a 24-hour period. As the depression moves across the UK, the conditions described at place B will be heading towards place A, and will eventually reach the area over the time period indicated. The reason for the change is that the weather system is tracking across the UK from west to east and the winds are circulating in an anti-clockwise direction. This means that after 24 hours, place A will be behind the cold front and the winds will have veered to the west-north west.

2 a The second synoptic chart shows a classic depression over the UK.

Weather feature	Place A	Place B
temperature	4 °C	5 °C
precipitation	dry	rain showers
cloud cover	Overcast, 8 oktas	partial cloud cover, 4 oktas
wind direction	south to south west	westerly
wind strength	28-32 knots	18-22 knots
air pressure	low, declining	increasing

Climate and human activity in the UK

The unit in brief

This unit looks at how weather and climate affects human activity in the UK – ranging from providing sources of energy through to its effect on sport. In the Activities, students look at farming – comparing maps of hours of sunshine and areas of wheat growing and explaining the patterns shown; produce a mind map which shows the links between climate and human activity.

Key ideas

◆ Climate and weather has a direct impact on human activity.

◆ The UK's temperate maritime climate provides two sources of alternative energy – HEP and wind power.

◆ There is a direct link between farming and climate.

◆ The threat from flooding determines land use.

◆ Weather and climate affect tourism and sport.

Key vocabulary

temperate, maritime, hydro-electric power, wind power

Skills practised in the Activities

◆ Geography skills: comparing maps and explaining patterns

◆ Thinking skills: producing a mind map and explaining the links between climate and human activity

Unit outcomes

By the end of this unit, most students should be able to:

◆ define or explain the terms given in 'Key vocabulary' above;

◆ produce a mind map to show that climate and weather has a direct impact on human activity;

◆ understand how the UK's temperate maritime climate provides two sources of alternative energy – HEP and wind power;

◆ explain the link between farming and climate;

◆ realise that the threat from flooding determines land use;

◆ understand that weather and climate affect tourism and sport.

Ideas for a starter

1 Ask: Who can remind me of the climate we have in the British Isles? What type of rainfall and weather systems do we have?

2 Recap: Show a map with the British Isles divided into 4 climate areas. Show students 4 climate graphs (one for each area). Ask them to match the correct graph with the correct area.

3 Ask: How does the climate in the British Isles affect you? Record answers on a spider diagram on the board. Then ask: How does climate affect other people, or other activities in the British Isles? Record answers on the spider diagram in a different colour.

Ideas for plenaries

1 The construction industry uses the services from the Met Office. Can you suggest why?

2 Test your neighbour! Spend 3 minutes testing your neighbour on the key vocabulary and definitions you have covered in this chapter so far.

3 Write 'climate and human activity in the UK' in the middle of a page. Create a mind map around the phrase. How many ideas can you come up with in 2 minutes?

4 Ask students to investigate drought in both the UK and in Niger. They will need to prepare a short presentation for the next lesson

Further class and homework activities

Contact a local farmer and find out what information is required for the effective running of the farm. You may find that the farmer buys in specialist services from the Met Office. Try to find out about what these are and how important the weather forecast is.

Answers to the Activities

1 The maps show a very close relationship between the climate in terms of sunshine hours and the major areas for the growth and ripening of wheat crops. The map for wheat production clearly shows that over 30% of this crop in the UK is grown in eastern counties. This is due to the drier conditions in the summer and the average 4-4.5 hours of daily sunshine needed for the ripening process. Since the west of Britain is much wetter, there is a greater dominance of cloud. This is less ideal for arable wheat farmers and, therefore, only around 10% of production is based in western counties, where sunshine is typically around 3 hours per day or less.

2 Further examples of how the climate of the UK has a direct impact on human activity could include:

◆ Drought and hosepipe bans/lawn sprinklers. A problem for gardeners who want to show their home lawns off to their best.

◆ Retail sales are very strongly influenced by the British climate. Ice cream sales rise dramatically in the summer months. As do the sales of summer clothing and other fashion items such as hats and sun glasses.

◆ Attractions based on landscaped gardens, such as National Trust properties, showcase places with various plants in flower at different times of the year. Snow drops in February, Bluebells in May, etc. The number of visitors in each month is dependent upon the flowers on show, which is ultimately controlled by the climate.

◆ Retirement homes along the south coast have increased in number, due to more elderly members of the population preferring the milder climate found in the south. Examples include settlements such as Bournemouth and Weymouth.

3 Students should be encouraged to design a mind map using climate features as the main branches. For example:

◆ Strong winds

◆ High sunshine hours

◆ Low sunshine hours

◆ Heavy rainfall

◆ Low rainfall

◆ High temperatures

◆ Low temperatures

They can then add human activities that are influenced by each of these climatic features. Students could use the example from activity 1 about wheat growing as a starting example. They can then map out the ideas from the text pages and their own ideas. The more able should be able to spot some interrelationships between human activities. For example, wheat growth and ice cream sales are largely controlled by sunshine and higher temperatures. Sailing and wind power are connected by the need for stronger wind speeds. Flooding and reservoirs for drinking water are related by the requirement for heavy rainfall.

There should be no shortage of ideas for activities 2 and 3!

The impact of drought

The unit in brief

This unit looks at the differing impacts of, and responses to, drought in the UK (an MEDC) and Niger (an LEDC). In the Activities, students look at the differing impacts of drought in the UK and Niger and explain the differences; identify the causes of desertification in the Sahel and find out what could be done to reduce the impact of desertification there.

Key ideas

◆ Drought in the UK results mainly from physical causes, but human factors play a part.

◆ In the UK, drought mainly causes inconvenience, but some impacts are longer-term.

◆ In Niger, drought results when the rain fails.

◆ Drought and land mismanagement cause desertification.

◆ Drought and desertification cause crop failure, livestock deaths, hunger and famine.

Key vocabulary

drought, desertification

Skills practised in the Activities

◆ Geography skills: producing a chart to show the impact of drought in an LEDC and an MEDC and explaining the differences; explaining desertification

◆ Thinking skills: identifying causes of desertification; researching solutions

Unit outcomes

By the end of this unit, most students should be able to:

◆ define the terms given in 'Key vocabulary' above;

◆ understand that drought in the UK results mainly from physical causes, but human factors also play a part;

◆ understand that in Niger drought results when the rain fails;

◆ identify the main causes of desertification;

◆ explain the differences between the impact of drought in an MEDC and an LEDC.

Ideas for a starter

1 Show pictures of the effects of drought, and drought conditions named in LEDCs and MEDCs. Ask the students to try to locate the images in an atlas.

2 Ask: Who can tell me what drought is? Is drought just something that happens in LEDCs?

3 Do we ever have drought conditions in the UK? From your knowledge of precipitation over the UK where do you think drought conditions might be found?

4 Ask several students to present their findings on drought in the UK and Niger.

Ideas for plenaries

1 How can a drought be averted in an MEDC?

2 The UK has too much water in the west and too little water in the east. How could water be brought from the west to the east?

3 What could we do to reduce our demand for water?

4 Provide students with figures or graphs showing the rainfall trends in the Sahel over time. Ask how far do these confirm that the problem of desertification is caused mainly by lack of rainfall rather than human factors such as population increase?

5 Create an acrostic – write DROUGHT down the side of a page. Make each letter the first letter of a word, phrase or sentence about drought.

6 Produce two consequence maps. One for drought in the UK, one for drought in Niger. Start with the causes of drought in the first box

Further class and homework activities

1 Design a poster to try to get the message across to the population.

2 How can desertification be halted? Investigate water schemes in West Africa such as the Niger River Project. Report back to the rest of the class.

3 Investigate drought in the USA. Go to the following website and try to look for specific case studies where drought has been managed successfully:
www.drought.noaa.gov/
Prepare a presentation for the rest of the class.

Answers to the Activities

1 A contrast chart to show the main differences between the impact of drought on an MEDC and an LEDC. Reasons for the contrasts are given in the table below:t chart to show the main differences between the impact of drought on an MEDC and an LEDC. Reasons for the contrasts are given in the table below:

MEDC (UK)	LEDC (Niger)
Lower earnings for commercial crop sales if crops are not successful.	Severe drought can mean complete crop failure and starvation for thousands of people who depend upon a rural livelihood.
High domestic use of water for cleaning, cooking, etc. can lead to water shortages due to the lifestyle demands that society has developed.	The lack of reliable water supply can mean problems of dehydration for many people/animals.
The high wealth of the UK means it can afford to pipe water from the wetter parts of the country to the drier.	The poor wealth of Niger means that water is a scarce resource and cannot be piped. Neither can the country afford to buy water from elsewhere.
Much water is wasted through old leaking pipe works across the country.	The dry state of the land in places has resulted in the spread of deserts - known as desertification.

2 a Desertification refers to the spreading of a desert into areas that were once productive and fertile in terms of vegetation. The outcome of desertification is a dry and barren landscape where plant life finds conditions too difficult to re-establish.

b The main causes of desertification are:
- climate change, resulting in less reliable rainfall;
- overcultivation;
- overgrazing;
- deforestation for fuel wood and land clearance.

Details on each of these can be found on pages 121 and 141 of the students' book. Students must be encouraged to write in their own original words rather than copy from the text material.

3 Approaches that could be used to protect regions like Niger from becoming desertified include:
- reducing human-initiated fires, and using organic fertiliser from animal dung to maintain the nutrient quality of the soil. However, families are under increasing pressure to burn animal dung as a source of fuel.
- restricting the movement of domestic animals, especially herds of goats, to prevent massive overgrazing.
- the construction of stone terraces to protect valuable topsoil from erosion during periods of heavy rain in areas where the vegetation cover has been removed.
- adopting sustainable approaches to harvesting wood as a fuel source; cutting branches rather than the whole tree would encourage natural regeneration.

See page 141 for detail on these ideas.

The unit in brief

This unit introduces tropical storms. It looks at how they develop, their primary effects, and how having the money and technology to predict hurricanes (as in MEDCs) can help to save lives. In the Activities, students draw and label a simple cross-section of a hurricane using a satellite image, and consider whether LEDCs are able to predict hurricanes or whether countries need to work together on hurricane prediction.

Key ideas

◆ Tropical storms are intense, destructive low pressure weather systems.

◆ Tropical storms develop: when sea temperatures are at least 27°C; between latitudes 5° and 15° north and south of the equator; when there is low atmospheric shear.

◆ Primary effects include the destruction of buildings and infrastructure, loss of life, flooding and landslides.

◆ Predicting hurricanes can save lives.

Key vocabulary

tropical storms, eye of the storm, primary effects, prediction, Saffir-Simpson scale

Skills practised in the Activities

◆ Geography skills: draw and label a sketch of a cross-section of a hurricane

◆ Thinking skills: considering the importance of interdependence and hurricane prediction

Unit outcomes

By the end of this unit, most students should be able to:

◆ define or explain the terms given in 'Key vocabulary' above;

◆ understand how tropical storms develop;

◆ draw and label a cross-section of a hurricane;

◆ give examples of the primary effects of a hurricane;

◆ understand that predicting hurricanes can save lives, but that countries may need to work together.

Ideas for a starter

1 Read the start of a news report of the impact of a hurricane. Ask the students to finish or continue the story.

2 Show a series of pictures of a tropical storm. Ask the students what is happening.

3 Recap: convectional rainfall. Ask for diagrams and explanations.

Ideas for plenaries

1 Show students a simulation of the development and progress of a tropical storm/hurricane.

2 Which countries are affected by tropical storms? How can prediction help?

3 Should an international agency be set up to help manage the problems caused by tropical storms? Or should it be the responsibility of the government of each country affected? Remember many of these countries are LEDCs.

4 Make a graffiti wall of what students have learned today.

Further class and homework activities

Investigate the arrangements in place in Bangladesh to provide early warning and to try to protect the people from the cyclones.

Answers to the Activities

1 A simple sketch of a hurricane cross-section based on the information at the top of page 123 of the students' book.

2 a LEDC nations do not possess sufficient wealth to invest in highly technological approaches to hurricane forecasting. The majority of people with a trained eye will know the tell-tale signs of what to look for. However, they rely on rapid information from other countries to help them to respond quickly enough to any present danger. For example, many LEDCs depend upon a successfully sustained tourism industry. The safe evacuation and welfare of the foreign visitors is of paramount importance. Hotel operators and travel companies rely on information about hurricane strength and direction from neighbouring richer MEDCs.

b Interdependency between nations is, therefore, very important in hurricane prediction. The USA has an advanced National Hurricane Centre based in Miami, Florida. The country can afford trained personnel in weather forecasting, plus satellite technology and other prediction techniques, including hurricane hunters who fly into approaching storms to collect valuable data. LEDC nations in the Caribbean and in Mexico are very reliant on the exchange of this information. Therefore, LEDCs are very dependent on the USA. The USA, however, is much more self-sufficient and does not require the assistance of other nations so directly. However, Hurricane Katrina in 2005 could be used to challenge this to some extent.

The hurricane season of 2005

The unit in brief

This unit provides examples of the effects of two major hurricanes – Katrina and Wilma – both of which occurred in 2005. In the Activities, students think about why people live in areas at risk from hurricanes; consider the safety of tourists caught in hurricanes and produce a chart to show the causes, effects and responses to hurricanes.

Key ideas

◆ Hurricane Katrina was one of the most damaging hurricanes ever to hit an MEDC.

◆ Much of the US coast from Louisiana to Alabama was devastated by Katrina.

◆ New Orleans was flooded – much of it lies below sea level, and the levees weren't big or strong enough to hold back the storm surges.

◆ Cancun in Mexico, and southern parts of Florida were hit by Hurricane Wilma.

◆ Some scientists think that global warming may be causing stronger tropical storms.

Key vocabulary

Hurricane Katrina, Hurricane Wilma

Skills practised in the Activities

◆ Geography skills: producing a chart of causes, effects, and responses to hurricanes

◆ Thinking skills: thinking, identifying consequences; sorting by effect and response

Unit outcomes

By the end of this unit, most students should be able to:

◆ describe the effects of Hurricanes Katrina and Wilma;

◆ understand why New Orleans was flooded;

◆ suggest why some scientists think that global warming may be causing stronger tropical storms.

Ideas for a starter

1 Show photos of New Orleans before and after Hurricane Katrina struck in August 2005. Ask students what they remember about the hurricane? What damage was caused? What happened to the people of New Orleans?

2 Show video or news clips of the situation in New Orleans after Katrina had passed through. Elicit comments on how the disaster was managed.

Ideas for plenaries

1 Who was responsible for managing events before and after Hurricane Katrina? And who should pay? The federal government, the state government or the city of New Orleans?

2 Should the priority be investing in early warning systems and ways of evacuating people or should it be about protecting people and property? How should any schemes be modified for LEDCs?

3 Draw up a table of the effects of a Hurricanes Katrina and Wilma dividing them into primary effects and secondary effects.

4 Write down as many words as you can relating to tropical storms/hurricanes.

5 Ask students to investigate the topic of climate change. Prepare a 3 minute presentation (such as a PowerPoint) for the beginning of the next lesson.

Answers to the Activities

1 Hurricane-prone coastlines are popular places to live for many people whose livelihood or lifestyle is closely related to the coastal environment. Most perceive the risk of a direct hurricane strike to be very small and to be outweighed by the benefits to be gained by choosing to live where they do. Specific reasons for locating along hurricane-prone coastlines include:

◆ Employment in the tourist industry – travel, hotels, leisure complexes, restaurants, shops and so forth.

◆ Environmental attractiveness of the coastal environment and the lifestyle opportunities it presents.

◆ Family/friendship connections.

◆ Opportunities to live affluently and develop businesses in places like Florida or Cancun.

◆ Peaceful settlements for retirement or second homes for holiday destinations. Many coastal stretches of the southern USA are dominated by mobile holiday homes or trailer parks.

2 Tourism safety during the approach and duration of a hurricane is essential if domestic and foreign visitors are to return and sustain the industry year on year. This is particularly important in MEDC and LEDC regions where tourism is the dominant industry, because jobs will be at stake. The evacuation of as many tourists as possible before an event needs to be assured to minimise fatalities/injury, compensation claims, media reports and bad press and to ensure the longevity of the industry. Tourists do not forget bad experiences quickly, and the poorer nations in particular cannot afford for this to happen.

3 The 2005 hurricane season was the most active and costliest on record. The cause of both hurricanes Katrina and Wilma are the same and these reasons are expressed on page 122. The key location facts can be found on pages 124 and 125. Students need to be encouraged to express ideas on their information charts clearly and concisely. Some may choose to complete a large spread on A3 paper. The tables below set out the main effects of these hurricanes and the approaches taken to respond to them.

It is very important for students to gain practice in sorting out information and gaining the confidence to categorise information in their answers to examination questions.

Effects

Category of effect	Katrina	Wilma
Economic	• Offshore oil facilities damaged and fuel supplies reduced, resulting in higher fuel prices. • Looting for goods, not all of it for essential survival.	• $1.5 billion damage caused in just one resort. • Damage to homes and power lines. • Storm-damaged shops looted.
Social	• Almost 1200 people died from drowning. • 1 million people made homeless. • 10 000 sought refuge in the city Superdome stadium.	• Thousands of poorly built homes destroyed. • 6 million left without electricity. • Over 10 000 British tourists stranded without access to clean water or electricity. • 30 deaths recorded.
Environmental	• Over two-thirds of the city of New Orleans submerged under water.	• Heavy erosion to prided beaches in the area around Cancun.

Responses

Scale of response	Katrina	Wilma
Individual	• 80% of city residents evacuated to safety, 20% remained to 'hunker down'. • Mainly poorer people without personal transport stayed behind. • Looters	• Stranded tourists had to seek shelter in hotel accommodation. • Looters
Regional	• Setting up the Superdome evacuation centre. • Mayor of New Orleans ordered a mandatory evacuation.	• Military command centre set up to stop looting and assist tourists.
National	• FEMA criticised for slow response. • Government ordered 30 000 National Guard troops to restore order and control looters. • Initial funds released for recovery was $50 billion.	
International	• Army ready meals sent by the UK Government.	• Flights organised to return tourists to their home countries.

The unit in brief

This unit looks at the issue of climate change – what it is, what's causing it, what the effects will be and what we are doing about it. In the Activities, students explain the process of global warming; consider whether there is enough evidence to say that climate is changing; produce a diagram or table to show the impact of global warming; and suggest what individuals can do to reduce the production of greenhouse gases.

Key ideas

◆ The process by which world temperatures are rising is known as global warming.

◆ The enhanced greenhouse effect is causing global warming.

◆ The effects of global warming will be felt around the world.

◆ The Kyoto Protocol is the main international agreement which commits MEDCs to reduce greenhouse gas emissions.

◆ Developing alternative energy sources, using less fuel, cutting down on car use and decreasing the rate of deforestation will all help to slow down the rate of global warming.

Key vocabulary

climate change, global warming, greenhouse effect, Kyoto Protocol

Skills practised in the Activities

◆ Geography skills: producing a table or diagram to show the impacts of global warming

◆ Thinking skills: explaining global warming; considering evidence; suggesting ideas

Unit outcomes

By the end of this unit, most students should be able to:

◆ define or explain the terms given in 'Key vocabulary' above.

◆ explain the process of global warming;

◆ identify the effects of global warming;

◆ name the main international agreement which commits MEDCs to reduce greenhouse gas emissions;

◆ understand that there are many ways to reduce greenhouse gas emissions and slow down the rate of global warming.

Ideas for a starter

1 Ask students: What is the greenhouse effect? Why are plants grown in a greenhouse? How does it work?

2 Ask two or three students to show their presentation on climate change.

3 You live here in the UK but the date is 2106. How has the climate changed? Tell us what the winter is like; what the summer is like. Is it hotter, colder, wetter or drier than now? How does that affect the way you live, and what you do?

Ideas for plenaries

1 Produce a graffiti wall display about the global effects of climate change.

2 Make up a pairs game (key terms and definitions on separate cards) to check students' understanding of the key terms in this chapter, or have a quickfire test – call out a term and ask students to provide the definition.

3 Choose a student to be in the hot seat. Another student asks him or her a question about climate change. Then nominate two different students (4-6 pairs in total). There's one golden rule – questions cannot be repeated.

4 Do an alphabet run from A-Z, with a word or phrase to do with weather and climate for each letter.

Answers to the Activities

1 Global warming is effectively the warming of the planet due to a rise in the average global temperature. It is based on the greenhouse effect, which is an essential process to sustain life on Earth. Incoming radiation from the sun warms the planet and heat escapes back into space. A layer of greenhouse gases, such as carbon dioxide and methane, traps some of the escaping heat - resulting in a warm planet capable of supporting life. Essentially it works like a greenhouse, hence the terminology used. However, the increased burning of fossil fuels and developments in agriculture has increased the atmospheric composition of the greenhouse gases, amplifying the process. Therefore, the planet is steadily warming. This is referred to as global warming and media reports suggest that the planet is 3 °C away from disaster as far as human society is concerned.

Commonly students mention the ozone layer in their responses to global warming and they need to be encouraged away from this confusion.

2 Climate needs to be monitored over sufficiently long periods of time before accurate claims about global warming can be made. The time period for this must be a minimum of 30 years. However, measurements taken on the Greenland ice sheet and Antarctica suggest that ice masses are melting at a faster rate than previously known. Accurate measurements showing an increase in atmospheric carbon dioxide have also been recorded. It would be appropriate for students to state that there is sufficient evidence to promote a cause for concern, only the future and continued careful monitoring will show whether climate is actually changing.

3 The impact of global warming on MEDC and LEDC nations is highlighted in the table below. The skill is enabling students to automatically sort information out into appropriate categories.

Impact on MEDCs	Impact on LEDCs
• Decline in national forests due to heat and drought in places like Canada and Russia. • The location of wheat-farming areas changes in the USA to be further north. • Increased storm activity in places like Florida. • Loss of skiing industry in Alpine resorts in Europe. • Oil pipelines and supply damaged in regions like Alaska, USA. • Disappearance of beaches in tourist hot spots, due to sea level change. • looding in major economic centres, such as London.	• Extensive flooding in low-lying countries such as Bangladesh. The same areas could also be affected by increased storm activity. • Increased desertification in the Sahel. The Sahara desert could also expand further north into the Mediterranean. • Low-lying islands such as the Maldives could disappear. • Water shortages in the Middle East and Africa. • Amazon rainforest damaged by heat and drought conditions.

4 The text provides information about the national and international responses to global warming. However, as global citizens it is important that individual choices and behaviours are recognised to combat the potential threat of the problem of climate change. Possible individual actions include:

◆ Reducing energy consumption by using less electricity in the home and not wasting heat. In the UK, in 2005/06, a campaign started to encourage all home owners to reduce their energy bills by 20%, saving both money and carbon dioxide emissions.

◆ Sharing transport instead of using individual cars for all journeys. Ride sharing is becoming more popular and is encouraged, particularly in the USA, although more to beat urban traffic congestion than to halt climate change.

◆ Choosing to buy energy from renewable supplies.

◆ Using more public rather than private transport.

Ecosystems

 chapter overview

The big picture

These are the key ideas behind this chapter:

◆ An ecosystem is made up of living things and their non-living environment.

◆ Ecosystems vary in size, but the world can be divided into eight big ecosystems or biomes.

◆ Climate is the main factor affecting the global distribution of ecosystems.

◆ The vegetation in different ecosystems has adapted to the climate and soils.

◆ As humans we use different ecosystems in different ways. Our impact has often been negative, and we have caused much damage.

◆ We are learning to use and manage ecosystems in a sustainable way.

Note that the students' version of the big picture is given in the students' chapter opener.

Chapter outline

Use this, and the students' chapter opener, to give students a mental roadmap for the chapter.

7   **Ecosystems**   As the students' chapter opener, this unit is an important part of the chapter; see page 11 of this book for notes about using chapter openers

7.1   **Introducing ecosystems**   What they are, how they work, how humans fit in and what we've done

7.2   **The global distribution of ecosystems**   Distribution of the world's biomes and factors affecting their distribution (temperature and precipitation)

7.3   **Tropical rainforests**   Climate and soils of the rainforest and how the vegetation has adapted

7.4   **Human impact in the tropical rainforest**   How people have cleared the rainforest for mining, logging, cattle ranching and peasant farming, and sustainable management strategies

7.5   **Savanna grasslands**   Climate and soils of the savanna and how the vegetation has adapted

7.6   **Human impact in the savanna grasslands**   How human activity affects the savanna grasslands, and sustainable land management in the Sahel

7.7   **Coniferous forests**   Climate and soils of the coniferous forests and how the vegetation has adapted

7.8   **Human impact on coniferous forests**   How people are using coniferous forests in Scandinavia and sustainable forest management

Objectives and outcomes for this chapter

Objectives	Unit	Outcomes
Most students will understand:		Most students will be able to:
● What an ecosystem is.	7.1	● Define an ecosystem, and give examples.
● How ecosystems work.	7.1	● Explain that all ecosystems work in the same way and have producers, consumers and decomposers; explain what food chains and food webs are.
● That climate is the main factor affecting the global distribution of ecosystems, or biomes.	7.2	● Match climate graphs with ecosystems or biomes; explain why climate is the main factor affecting the global distribution of ecosystems; describe the global distribution of tropical rainforests, savanna grasslands and coniferous forests.
● That vegetation has adapted to the climate and soils in different ecosystems.	7.3, 7.5, 7.7	● Describe the climate and soils of tropical rainforests, savanna grasslands and coniferous forests; give examples of how the vegetation has adapted to the climate in tropical rainforests, savanna grasslands and coniferous forests.
● The impact that people have had on different ecosystems.	7.1, 7.4, 7.6, 7.8	● Give examples of human activity in tropical rainforests, savanna grasslands and coniferous forests, and describe the consequences.
● That it is possible to use and manage ecosystems in a sustainable way.	7.1, 7.4, 7.6, 7.8	● Give examples of sustainable management in tropical rainforests, savanna grasslands and coniferous forests.

These tie in with 'Your goals for this chapter' in the students' chapter opener, and with the opening lines in each unit, which give the purpose of the unit in a student-friendly style.

Using the chapter starter

The photo on page 128 of the *geog.GCSE* students' book shows brown bears fishing for salmon, in Alaska, USA.

Brown bears are famous for their strength and stamina; they are also surprisingly quick and can hit speeds of 35 mph. Males can be over 10 ft tall when standing, and can weigh over 700 kg. Contrary to popular belief they are not particularly carnivorous, getting most of their energy needs from plants – but they do like a nice salmon! They are normally solitary, but gather along rivers during the salmon run in the autumn.

Salmon are born in fresh water, migrate to the oceans, and then return to fresh water to breed and spawn. All species of Pacific salmon die within a few weeks of spawning. Folklore says they return to the exact spot where they were born to spawn – and there seems to be some truth in this as scientific research shows that 90% of salmon spawning in a stream were born there. Thousands swim upstream to their spawning grounds, sometimes hundreds of miles inland. How they navigate back to these streams is a mystery, but smell might play a part.

Watching bears fish is now a holiday attraction offered by a number of operators.

Introducing ecosystems

The unit in brief

This unit introduces ecosystems – what they are, how they work, and how we affect them. In the Activities, students show their understanding of ecosystem terms by writing definitions; complete a paragraph about how ecosystems work; and consider the effect humans have on ecosystems.

Key ideas

◆ Ecosystems are made up of two parts: living things and the non-living environment.

◆ Ecosystems vary in size, e.g. from a pond to a tropical rainforest.

◆ All ecosystems work in the same way, with producers, consumers and decomposers.

◆ Food chains link together to form food webs.

◆ The human impact on ecosystems can be measured in terms of our ecological footprint.

◆ Ecosystems need to be treated in a sustainable way.

Key vocabulary

ecosystem, environment, producers, consumers, decomposers, food chain, food web, ecological footprint, sustainable

Skills practised in the Activities

◆ Geography skills: defining ecosystem terms

◆ Literacy skills: completing a paragraph on ecosystems

◆ Thinking skills: explaining; thinking; justifying answer

Unit outcomes

By the end of this unit, most students should be able to:

◆ define or explain the terms given in 'Key vocabulary' above;

◆ understand that ecosystems are made up of two parts;

◆ understand that ecosystems vary in size;

◆ describe how ecosystems work;

◆ give examples of food chains;

◆ explain how humans affect ecosystems.

Ideas for a starter

1 Show photos of the tropical rainforest, savanna grasslands and the coniferous forests. Ask: Why are they different? What is the vegetation like? What animals live there? How are the vegetation, soils and animals linked in each ecosystem? What would happen if one of these was changed in some way?

2 Draw a concept map for an ecosystem with natural vegetation, soils and animals. Ask students to explain the links, and add anything else to the concept map.

3 Brainstorm to find out what students know about the destruction of ecosystems. Why should we be concerned about their destruction?

Ideas for plenaries

1 Think about what you eat. Draw a food chain with you at the top. Identify the producers, the consumers and the decomposers.

2 Go back to the concept map drawn in starter 2. Delete any links that are incorrect, and add anything else you have learned.

3 Draw out the food chain for a deciduous woodland. Try to identify the plants, animals and soil type of this ecosystem.

4 Test your neighbour on the key vocabulary covered in this unit.

5 Write down the five key things you have learned from today's lesson.

Further class and homework activities

1 Go to one of the ecological footprint sites and try to calculate your own footprint. Now do this for the class, year group and school. Plot these areas on a map. What does this tell you about our use of resources? How sustainable is this?

2 Now can we live in a more sustainable way?

Answers to the Activities

1 Definitions

Students must demonstrate their understanding of the key terms with reference to the following:

Ecosystem: This is an interactive environment where living things depend upon their non-living surroundings. The Earth has some very large ecosystems, where the living organisms depend upon and interact with the climate, vegetation and soils.

Food chain: A sequence of food energy transfers from one living organism or creature to another. The sequence always starts with plants.

Food web: This is similar to the food chain but is much more complex. The web is based on separate food chains from different parts of an ecosystem, such as a forest. A food web may have many interlinks from one part of the ecosystem to another.

Ecological footprint: This term refers to the human impact on ecosystems. Human activities have spread across the globe and it is suggested that, in one lifetime, each human individual 'uses' two hectares of land for food, water, transport, shelter, waste disposal and so forth.

2 Every ecosystem works in the same way. The plants use sunlight, water and nutrients from the soil to produce their own food. They're called producers. The animals feed on the plants or each other. They're called consumers. Fungi and bacteria feed on dead and waste material, and make things break down or rot. They're called decomposers. Without plants all other things would die.

3 Two possible food chains from the diagram are:

Leaf ➝ Caterpillar ➝ Robin ➝ Fox

Bark ➝ Beetle ➝ Spider ➝ Wood Mouse ➝ Owl

4 A good answer to explain why geographers study ecosystems would be to emphasise the interdependence of all living things on their non-living environment, particularly humans. This should help to foster a respect of natural ecosystems because without them nothing would survive. Studying ecosystems gives students a much better insight into what humans and all forms of wildlife survive on and take advantage of (such as water, mineral resources, soil, sunlight, wood from vegetation, energy sources, etc.).

5 The answer to this question requires some justification and not a simple 'yes' response. A good answer would mention greater respect and appreciation for plants and animals, whatever their size, as they are all important and sustain our existence. As with question 4, there could be reference to appreciating the interdependence between the living and non-living environment. For example, fostering respect for earthworms in the soil to protecting the habitats for owls. The best answers would be where a student could independently give an example(s) about how studying ecosystems will affect how they think about the world around them. These examples could be from the local scale, such as the preservation of hedges, to the global scale and helping to save on energy consumption (thereby contributing to help reduce global warming).

6 The response to the notion of humans being the greatest global 'pest' requires a balanced response, even though the conclusion will be the student's own individual opinion. It is important that their view is justified. There are clearly many negative examples of human impact on ecosystems which justify the term 'pest'. Mass deforestation, soil erosion, harnessing energy and global warming plus the exploitation of other natural resources, provide clear examples of the harm human civilisation has caused to the planet. However, on the positive side there are sustainable human activities that actively protect the Earth's ecosystems. Conserving core areas of virgin rainforest, reducing greenhouse gas emissions and preventing soil erosion are good examples of this. The question for the future is whether the negative impacts will continue to outweigh the positive measures that people can do.

The global distribution of ecosystems

help at a glance

The unit in brief

This unit is about the global distribution of the world's ecosystems. In the Activities, students use an atlas to help match climate graphs with ecosystems; describe the climate of ecosystems; show their understanding of various terms by writing definitions; draw a diagram to explain the differences in equatorial and desert climates, and explain the savanna climate.

Key ideas

◆ The world has eight major ecosystems or biomes.

◆ Climate is the main factor affecting the distribution of ecosystems.

◆ Temperature varies according to latitude.

◆ Precipitation is controlled by atmospheric pressure.

Key vocabulary

biomes, temperature, precipitation, atmospheric pressure, convection, Inter-Tropical Convergence Zone (ITCZ)

Skills practised in the Activities

◆ Geography skills: using an atlas to find the location of climate graphs; matching climate graphs and ecosystems; describing climate features using climate graphs; defining geographical terms; drawing a diagram to show air movement

◆ Numeracy skills: reading climate graphs

◆ Thinking skills: explaining savanna climate

Unit outcomes

By the end of this unit, most students should be able to:

◆ define or explain the terms given in 'Key vocabulary' above;

◆ describe the climate features of four major ecosystems;

◆ understand that climate is the main factor affecting the distribution of ecosystems;

◆ draw a diagram to explain why the equator is hot and wet and deserts are warm and dry.

Ideas for a starter

1 Recap: the links within an ecosystem.

2 Write words (ecosystem, biomes, temperature, precipitation, atmospheric pressure) and their meanings on separate sheets of paper. Ask 10 students to hold up the 10 sheets. The rest of the class have to match them.

3 Ask students to describe a journey from the equator to the North Pole. They can use atlases to trace their journey. They should concentrate on the change of natural vegetation as they move northwards.

Ideas for plenaries

1 Take one biome each and investigate the nature of the biome and its characteristics. Describe the features to other members of the class.

2 Make 10-15 statements based on what students have learned so far in this chapter, some true, some false. Students should hold up True or False cards. Where statements are false ask students to correct them.

3 Mid you find anything difficult about the work in this unit? What? Why? What should help to make it less difficult?

4 Write down as many words as you can relating to today's work.

5 Investigate the tropical rainforest – its characteristics, human use, and deforestation. Prepare a short presentation for the next lesson.

Answers to the Activities

1 a Students may need support in locating all the locations for the four climate graphs.

 b See table below

 c See table below

Biome	Location	Climate summary
Tropical rainforest	Iquitos, Peru	Hot all year with average temperatures of 28°C and wet with over 2000 mm of rain falling annually. There are no real seasons as the conditions are similar from one month to the next.
Coniferous forest	Yakutsk, Russia	Warm summers at 29°C and cooler winters around 6°C. Conditions are dry during the winter and wetter during the summer months, with up to 45 mm of rain monthly.
Temperate deciduous forest	London, United Kingdom	Warmer summers, approximately 20°C and cooler but mild winters at around 7°C. Conditions are wet throughout the year, with a typical monthly maximum of 60 mm.
Savanna grassland	Dakar, Senegal	The climate has distinct wet and dry seasons. Summer months are wet with up to 250 mm of rain and temperatures over 30°C. Drought conditions persist in winter, although temperatures remain warm at 25°C.

2 *Precipitation:* All forms of moisture that are released from clouds in the atmosphere (rain, sleet, hail and snow).

Latitude: A reference line for global navigation, either north or south of the equator at 0 degrees. Lines of latitude run around the planet. The tropics of Cancer and Capricorn are two important lines of latitude.

Atmospheric pressure: The effective 'weight' of the air pushing down on the Earth's surface. Warm, less dense, rising air means

lower air pressure. Cool, dense, sinking air means higher air pressure. This concept is a very strong control over the prevailing weather conditions.

Inter-Tropical Convergence Zone: This is a global zone of low atmospheric pressure that can be found close to the equator and the tropics, where the trade winds collide. Thick cumulonimbus clouds and torrential rain are the typical weather conditions associated with the ITCZ.

3 A fully annotated cross-section diagram can be as simple as this text-only diagram:

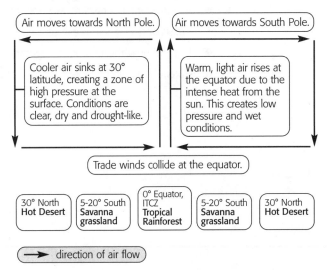

4 Students must show that they understand that the ITCZ moves with the changing latitude position of the overhead sun during the year. In the summer, the strongest sun is in the northern hemisphere and so the ITCZ moves or 'migrates' north, providing the rainy season in the savanna grasslands. During the winter, the sun and the ITCZ migrate into the opposite hemisphere to the south, meaning that the savanna biome in the north is dominated by a high pressure drought.

The unit in brief

This unit introduces tropical rainforests. It investigates the climate and soils of the rainforest and looks at how the vegetation has adapted to the climate. In the Activities, students refer back to the previous unit to explain the equatorial climate; explain how and why the vegetation has adapted to the climate and soils of the rainforest, and compare the tropical rainforest with another ecosystem.

Key ideas

◆ Tropical rainforests are found in the tropics (in places with an equatorial climate).

◆ There are no real seasons in the equatorial climate, but the weather has a daily pattern.

◆ Rainforest ecosystems are very fragile.

◆ Rainforest vegetation is divided into four distinct layers.

◆ Rainforest vegetation has adapted to the climate.

Key vocabulary

laterites, inputs, recycling, outputs, emergent trees, canopy, under-canopy, shrub layer, drip tips, buttress roots, lianas, epiphytes

Skills practised in the Activities

◆ Geography skills: comparing and contrasting the tropical rainforest with another ecosystem

◆ Thinking skills: explaining equatorial climates; explaining connections between vegetation and climate and soils

Unit outcomes

By the end of this unit, most students should be able to:

◆ define or explain the terms given in 'Key vocabulary' above.;

◆ explain where tropical rainforests can be found;

◆ explain why rainforests receive lots of rain, and why temperatures are consistently high;

◆ understand why rainforest ecosystems are very fragile;

◆ describe how the rainforest vegetation is divided into four distinct layers;

◆ explain how rainforest vegetation has adapted to the climate.

Ideas for a starter

1 Ask students: Who can tell me what an ecosystem is? Who can give me some examples of food chains.

2 Ask two or three students to go through their presentation in the tropical rainforest. Why is deforestation a key issue?

3 Mind movie time! You are in a tropical rainforest – all alone. What can you see, hear and smell? Tell us.

Ideas for plenaries

1 Show photos of rainforest animals and insects. How have they adapted to the tropical rainforest?

2 Use the photos of rainforest animals and insects to draw a detailed food chain for the rainforest.

3 Draw a diagram of linked boxes to show how the climate, the natural vegetation and the soils are linked in the tropical rainforest. Explain the links. What would happen if the natural vegetation was removed?

4 Climate as the driving force in an ecosystem. Ask students whether this is true for the rainforest ecosystem and give reasons for their answer. Students could work in pairs or small groups and give feedback to the class.

5 Sum up what you have learnt today in 35 words, or less.

Answers to the Activities

1 Constantly high temperatures in the rainforest are due to the relentless heat from the sun. The energy is focused on a small area of the Earth's surface, making the heat concentrated. Rainfall is heavy on a daily basis in the rainforest, due to the process of convection. The intense heating from the sun causes air to rise as it becomes less dense. As it does so, moisture begins to cool, condense and form very thick cumulonimbus clouds. These produce torrential rain and associated thunderstorms.

2 There are many connections between the climate, vegetation and soils. These are called interrelationships. For a good answer a student would show an understanding of at least three of these links. Expected interrelationships would be:

   ◆ the decomposition of dead vegetation in hot temperatures puts nutrients into the soil (climate to soil)

   ◆ drip tips help the vegetation to shed the excess weight of torrential rainfall (vegetation to climate)

   ◆ buttress roots help to stabilise the tallest trees in thin, shallow soil, and keep them upright (vegetation to soil)

   ◆ branchless trees develop so that growth is directed towards the sunlight for photosynthesis (vegetation to climate)

3 When contrasting natural environments, students should make reference to direct comparisons between two ecosystems, showing any appropriate similarities and differences in climate, vegetation species and adaptations and soils. The best answers will clearly explain any differences identified, particularly when climatic data is used. Weaker responses will simply describe the two natural environments in separate paragraphs, without making any reference to direct comparisons or explanations.

For example:

Throughout the year the rainforest temperatures remain constant, typically at 28°C with little variation. However, the coniferous forests experience a much greater range of temperatures between winter and summer. The winters can be exceptionally severe down to −40°C. This is almost 70°C cooler than the rainforest. Precipitation in the rainforest is 2000 mm, over 1000 mm more than coniferous forests.

The reason for the higher temperatures is related to the position of the overhead sun. Over the equatorial rainforests the angle is directly overhead, meaning concentrated heating on the ground. In turn, this results in the convectional rainfall process where warm moist air rises rapidly, cools and condenses to produce towering cumulonimbus clouds and very heavy precipitation. In the Boreal forests, the angle of the sun is never as high, which means lower temperatures. This is especially true in winter, when most of the sun's energy is directed towards the southern hemisphere.

Additional elements to this question could be based on the way the vegetation adapts to the climate. For example, students could contrast the deciduous and coniferous nature of the vegetation. Broad leaves can be found in the rainforests where the trees are attempting to photosynthesise as much sunlight as possible. In the coniferous forests, the needles help to seal in moisture – reducing transpiration. The laterites (soils) of the rainforest could also be compared to the podzol soils of the boreal latitudes.

The unit in brief

This unit is about the economic exploitation of the tropical rainforest and considers the effects of mining, logging, cattle ranching and peasant farming in the Amazon rainforest. It introduces a variety of sustainable management strategies. In the Activities, students describe the causes of deforestation in the Amazon rainforest; consider which are the most important sustainable management strategies and identify the problems that could be caused by some of these strategies.

Key ideas

◆ Current rates of deforestation mean that the world's rainforests might all disappear by 2030.

◆ The Amazon rainforest is being destroyed by mining, logging, cattle ranching and peasant farming.

◆ Large-scale deforestation breaks the natural nutrient cycle, so rainforests can't regenerate.

◆ There are a range of sustainable management strategies which can be adopted to protect the rainforest ecosystem.

Key vocabulary

deforestation, sustainable management, agro-forestry, tree measuring, education, selective logging, afforestation, forest reserves

Skills practised in the Activities

◆ Geography skills: describing causes of deforestation

◆ Thinking skills: prioritising sustainable management strategies; finding out about slash and burn farming; justifying opinions; identifying problems caused by sustainable management strategies

Unit outcomes

By the end of this unit, most students should be able to:

◆ define or explain the terms given in 'Key vocabulary' above;

◆ recognise that current rates of deforestation mean that the world's rainforests might all disappear by 2030;

◆ describe how the Amazon rainforest is being destroyed;

◆ understand why large scale deforestation means rainforests can't regenerate;

◆ give examples of sustainable management strategies which can be adopted to protect the rainforest ecosystem.

Ideas for a starter

1   Use the diagram of linked boxes (climate, vegetation and soils) which students drew in plenary 3 Unit 7.3. Redraw the diagram with the natural vegetation removed. What are the consequences?

2   Provide students with a quick wordsearch on the key terms to do with tropical rainforests.

3   Produce a spider diagram on the board of the use and abuse of the rainforest.

4   Show a video of deforestation in tropical rainforests. Ask: Why is deforestation happening? How quickly is it happening? What can be done about it?

Ideas for plenaries

1 You are an economic adviser to the Brazilian government. Argue the case for the Brazilians to develop the Amazon region as much as possible.

2 As a conservationist write a letter to the United Nations advising them of the problems caused by the loss of habitat in the tropical rainforest.

3 What influence might the loss of rainforest have on climate change?

4 How could countries in MEDCs help in conserving the rainforest? Consider ethical farming methods and wood from renewable sources.

5 Draw up a table showing different ways of managing the rainforest from national park (no development), agroforestry, logging and replanting, ecotourism, zonation to deforestation (total redevelopment). Include a column for the possible impacts - economic, social and environmental including the global dimension. Use your table to evaluate the ways of managing the rainforest. How should the rainforest be managed so that it is sustainable?

Further class and homework activities

Role play a development meeting in which a variety of interested parties are present and contribute their views – loggers, farmers, indigenous Indians, government officials, miners, conservationists, etc. Prepare speeches in advance and then argue the best way to develop the rainforest.

Answers to the Activities

1 Page 136 describes in some detail the range of human activities that are currently exploiting the natural resources of the rainforest. Students should be able to use these ideas but express them in their own words rather than copying. They may choose to design a mind map or other diagram to represent the information. The extension requires students to think of additional activities they have discovered. Some possibilities include:

- the development of transport links such as the Trans-Amazon Highway

- the development of settlements such as Manaus as a result of prospecting for mineral resources such as gold, the growth of the rubber trade and tourism. The citadel Carajas was specifically planned for the workers who operate the opencast mining operation shown in the photograph on page 136.

- construction of dams for reliable water and power supplies.

2 The best sustainable strategies are always integrated. So expect students to choose three ideas that link together very well. For example, forested reserves, selective logging and afforestation. However, students should also be prepared to justify their choices and explain the links. This part should focus on the need to protect the tree canopy and maintain the natural nutrient cycle to ensure the survival of the ecosystem. Forest reserves allow economic activity which facilitates Brazil's continued need to develop, whilst protecting vast areas of virgin forests at the same time.

This particularly applies to preventing the timber trade by illegal loggers. Selective logging is more sustainable, as only mature trees are carefully lumbered for their economic value without causing damage to 20 or 30 other trees in the process. It is a more controlled operation. Afforestation ensures that the tree roots bind the soil together, preventing erosion. The tree canopy

also feeds the nutrient cycle and prevents soil erosion by torrential rains. Expect agro-forestry to be a popular choice also for similar reasons. Students should emphasise the point that one strategy on its own will not be effective, and that the enforcement of sustainable strategies needs to be vigorously applied if they are to work. This is difficult in a rainforest as vast as the Amazon.

3 Slash and burn farming refers to a type of small-scale farming where trees are burnt to clear land for farming and also to provide ash as a source of nutrients. This means that crops can be grown but only for a limited period of time, as the nutrients soon become exhausted and the farmers then have to move to a new plot of land and repeat the process. Consequently, this form of farming practice is regarded as unsustainable as the nutrient cycle is broken, particularly if the scale of the slash and burn increases over larger areas of land. However, students could also argue that, if over small areas of land, the forest could naturally regenerate more easily and therefore be a sustainable practice. It is the scale of the slash and burn which is important in this case.

4 The problems associated with sustainable forest management could include:

- the difficulty of enforcing the strategies and combating the problems presented by groups of illegal loggers, peasant farmers or cattle ranchers seeking to increase their plots of land.

- the time taken for the sustainable strategies to have a positive impact on preserving the forest. For example, tropical hardwoods such as mahogany will take decades to mature before they can be harvested. Society has a tendency to be too impatient for natural regeneration processes.

- the success of programmes such education and ecotourism can never be guaranteed.

The unit in brief

This unit introduces savanna grasslands. It looks at the climate and soil conditions and investigates how plants have adapted to survive the climate. In the Activities, students describe the environmental problems that the vegetation has adapted to and draw a mind map explaining how the vegetation has adapted to the savanna climate.

Key ideas

◆ Savanna grasslands are found between 5° and 15° north and south of the equator.

◆ The type and density of vegetation changes with latitude.

◆ The savanna climate has alternating wet and dry seasons.

◆ Savanna soils are porous.

◆ Savanna plants are xerophytes and have adapted to the savanna climate.

Key vocabulary

savanna grasslands, porous, xerophyte, elephant grass, acacia tree, transpiration, baobab tree

Skills practised in the Activities

◆ Geography skills: describing the environmental problems that savanna vegetation has adapted to

◆ Thinking skills: drawing a mind map to explain how vegetation adapts to the savanna climate

Unit outcomes

By the end of this unit, most students should be able to:

◆ define or explain the terms given in 'Key vocabulary' above;

◆ describe that savanna grasslands are found between 5° and 15° north and south of the equator;

◆ explain how the type and density of vegetation changes with latitude;

◆ understand that the savanna climate has alternating wet and dry seasons;

◆ understand the problems that porous soil causes for vegetation.

◆ explain how savanna plants have adapted to the climate.

Ideas for a starter

1 What do you know about the savanna grasslands? Tell me five things about the savanna.

2 Show a climate graph for the savanna. Ask questions about temperature and rainfall patterns.

3 Show photos of animals and vegetation of the African savanna. Ask students to describe what they see.

4 What effect have humans had on the savanna?

Ideas for plenaries

1 Describe a journey from the rainforest to the desert and explain the effect of climate on the vegetation.

2 Provide students with photographs of the savanna. Ask them to annotate them to explain what they show.

3 Draw two diagrams showing how the climate changes from season to season in the savanna.

4 Provide students with temperature and rainfall figures and ask them to draw climate graphs of places within the savanna grasslands.

5 Produce a table on the savanna grasslands showing natural vegetation, climate, soils and animals.

6 Tell your neighbour the 3 most important things you learned today.

Answers to the Activities

1 The environmental conditions that savanna vegetation has to adapt to in order to survive this biome include:

◆ winter droughts in the northern hemisphere, with monthly rainfall totals down to 0 mm. The vegetation has to adapt to survive, resulting in many xerophytic or drought resistant features.

◆ high temperatures for most of the year, which encourages high rates of water loss or transpiration through plants. Temperatures are typically around 25°C or higher.

◆ the progress of rainfall is not reliable each year and 'open' savanna areas can suffer from prolonged droughts. The trade winds, especially, can dry savanna areas severely.

◆ the porous soils mean that both water and nutrients can be lost from the ecosystem easily.

2 Students could design a mind map with three main branches to represent the three named vegetation species shown on page 139.

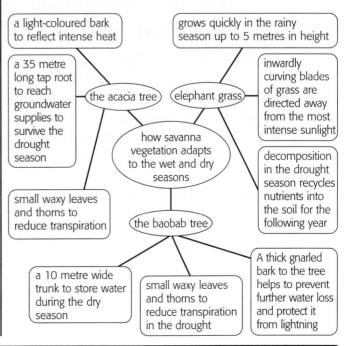

a light-coloured bark to reflect intense heat

grows quickly in the rainy season up to 5 metres in height

a 35 metre long tap root to reach groundwater supplies to survive the drought season

the acacia tree

elephant grass

inwardly curving blades of grass are directed away from the most intense sunlight

how savanna vegetation adapts to the wet and dry seasons

decomposition in the drought season recycles nutrients into the soil for the following year

small waxy leaves and thorns to reduce transpiration

the baobab tree

a 10 metre wide trunk to store water during the dry season

small waxy leaves and thorns to reduce transpiration in the drought

A thick gnarled bark to the tree helps to prevent further water loss and protect it from lightning

The unit in brief

This unit is about the effect people are having on the savanna grasslands in Africa, and about some of the ways in which the savanna can be preserved through sustainable land management. In the Activities, students focus on desertification – looking at where it occurs, the causes and how it can be prevented.

Key ideas

◆ The savanna covers almost half of Africa.

◆ Human activity can have a negative effect on the savanna.

◆ Desertification is a process of land degradation.

◆ Causes of desertification include overcultivation, overgrazing, deforestation, and climate change.

◆ There are examples of sustainable land management in the Sahel that benefit people and the savanna.

Key vocabulary

the Sahel, desertification, overcultivation, overgrazing, deforestation, climate change, sustainable land management

Skills practised in the Activities

◆ Geography skills: defining desertification and stating where it occurs.

◆ Thinking skills: explaining the 'spiral into desertification'; considering the causes of desertification; identifying ways of preventing desertification.

Unit outcomes

By the end of this unit, most students should be able to:

◆ define or explain the terms given in 'Key vocabulary' above;

◆ know that the savanna covers almost half of Africa;

◆ understand that human activity can have a negative effect on the savanna;

◆ understand that desertification is a process of land degradation;

◆ explain the causes of desertification;

◆ give examples of sustainable land management in the Sahel.

Ideas for a starter

1 Draw a diagram on the board to show how climate, natural vegetation and soils are linked in the savanna grasslands. Ask students what happens if the soil is damaged?

2 Ask: Who can tell me what desertification is? Do you know what causes it?

3 Show 'before' and 'after' photos of savanna grasslands – i.e. in its original state, and one of an area suffering desertification. Ask: what has happened? What problems does this cause? What can be done about it?

Ideas for plenaries

1 Draw a spider diagram showing how human activity affects the savanna. How is this human activity damaging the ecosystem?

2 Consider a range of management options – controlled burning of grasses; building stone walls; national parks, afforestation, irrigation, changing farming practice, etc. Develop a table similar to the one for comparing management schemes in the rainforest (See Unit 7.4 plenary 5). Use this to evaluate ways of managing the savanna.

3 Write a letter to the Kenyan government explaining the need to protect and conserve the savanna grasslands.

4 Investigate the coniferous forests – their characteristics, where they are found and what they are used for. Prepare a short presentation for the next lesson.

5 Compare destruction in tropical rainforests with that in the savanna. In what ways has human impact on the tropical rainforest system been similar to our impact on savanna grasslands? In what ways has it been different? Students could draw a Venn diagram for this.

6 Make a graffiti wall of what students have learned today.

Further class and homework activities

1 Investigate how much of the problem of desertification is physical – to do with climate change and how much is human based – to do with population and economic change.

2 Role play the management issues of the area – local tribes, farmers, tourists, national park managers, etc.

Answers to the Activities

1 a Desertification refers to the spreading of a desert into areas that were once productive and fertile in terms of vegetation. The outcome of desertification is a dry and barren landscape where plant life finds conditions too difficult to re-establish.

 b In Africa the issue of desertification is apparent in the Sahel region, south of the Sahara desert. This region includes countries such as Niger, Chad, Ethiopia and Burkina Faso.

2 Students should make reference to the problems of climate change, overgrazing, overcultivation and deforestation to comprehensively explain how the process of desertification can commence and drastically change the characteristics of places in the Sahel. In this context, climate change can be regarded as the natural element, whilst the other reasons are all linked to the pressure of rapidly growing population in LEDC countries. Once the process of desertification becomes established, it is very difficult to stop. As the population of an area increases and people continue to need more food and wood as a fuel source, the cycle of human impact becomes ever more severe. If the rainy season fails, the spiral into desertification becomes ever more severe.

3 Desertification is partly due to natural climate change, although it could be strongly argued that even this is a direct result of global human activity, especially climate change related to global warming. The rapidly increasing population pressure of many African states in the Sahel requires ever more intense use of the land and deforestation for fuel wood. Therefore, it could be considered that the issue of desertification is very much a problem of human creation, both regionally and globally.

4 Approaches that could be used to protect savanna grassland areas from becoming desertified include:

◆ reducing human-initiated fires and using organic fertiliser from animal dung to maintain the nutrient quality of the soil. However, families are under increasing pressure to burn animal dung as a source of fuel.

◆ restrict the movement of cattle, especially herds of goats, to prevent massive overgrazing.

◆ the construction of stone terraces to trap valuable top soil from erosion during periods of heavy rain in areas where the vegetation cover has been removed.

◆ adopting sustainable approaches to harvesting wood as a fuel source. Cutting branches rather that the whole tree would encourage natural regeneration.

The unit in brief

This unit introduces coniferous forests. It investigates the climate and soil conditions that coniferous forests grow in, and looks at how the trees have adapted to the harsh climate. In the Activities, students describe the global distribution of coniferous forests, and annotate their own drawing of a coniferous tree to show how the vegetation has adapted to the climate and soil conditions.

Key ideas

◆ Coniferous forests are found between 50° N and 60° N.

◆ Climate is harsh: long cold winters and short summers; most precipitation falls as snow; strong northerly winds.

◆ Soils are thin. The most common type is the podzol.

◆ Coniferous trees have adapted to the climate.

Key vocabulary

coniferous forests, growing season, podzol, boreal forests, taiga, softwoods

Skills practised in the Activities

◆ Geography skills: describing the global distribution of coniferous forests; annotating a drawing of a coniferous tree to show adaptations to climate and soil

Unit outcomes

By the end of this unit, most students should be able to:

◆ define or explain the terms given in 'Key vocabulary' above;

◆ describe the global distribution of coniferous forests;

◆ describe the climate where coniferous forests are found;

◆ identify the most common type of soil;

◆ draw and annotate a diagram to show how coniferous trees have adapted to the climate and soil conditions.

Ideas for a starter

1 Ask several students to go through their presentation on coniferous forests. What are they used for? What issues arise from their use?

2 Draw a concept map showing how the vegetation, climate and soils of coniferous forests are linked. Explain the links from what you already know. Return to the diagram once you have read through this unit.

3 Show a climate graph for an area of coniferous forest. Ask questions about the temperature and precipitation patterns. What effect will this have on vegetation?

4 show a photo of a 'typical' conifer. Brainstorm. Why is this tree like this? How has it adapted to climate and soil? Where do you find them?

Ideas for plenaries

1 How important are coniferous forests to us? What do we use them for?

2 Describe a journey from the deciduous woodland through the coniferous forests to the tundra. What animals, people, and vegetation would you see? What would the climate/weather be like?

3 Return to the concept map you drew in Starter 2. What else can you add to it now? Do you need to delete anything which is incorrect?

4 Prepare an odd-one-out for your partner on what you have learned today.

5 Sum up what you have learned today in 35 words (or less).

Further class and homework activities

1 Try to find out more about podzols. Try to draw a diagram on which you can annotate to show the processes operating within the soil.

2 How can you manage a podzol so that the area can be developed?

Answers to the Activities

1 The coniferous or boreal forests exist between 50–60° latitude, mainly in the northern hemisphere. Named countries include Russia, Canada and the Scandinavian nations.

2 Students should draw a simple sketch of a coniferous tree and annotate it with key features showing the natural adaptations, with reasons to explain their importance. The explanation aspect of this activity is essential, simple labelling will not maximise achievement.

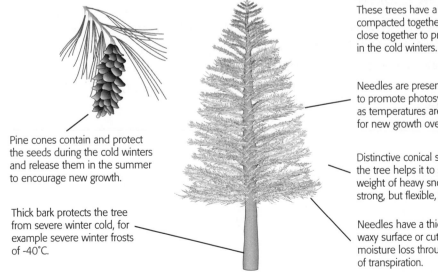

These trees have a high density, compacted together, and grow close together to promote warmth in the cold winters.

Needles are present all year round to promote photosynthesis as soon as temperatures are warm enough for new growth over 6°C.

Pine cones contain and protect the seeds during the cold winters and release them in the summer to encourage new growth.

Distinctive conical shape to the tree helps it to shed the weight of heavy snowfall on strong, but flexible, branches.

Thick bark protects the tree from severe winter cold, for example severe winter frosts of -40°C.

Needles have a thick, hard and waxy surface or cuticle to prevent moisture loss through the process of transpiration.

The unit in brief

This unit focuses on Scandinavia and is about how people use coniferous forests and how they are trying to preserve them through sustainable forest management. In the Activities, students identify the reasons why coniferous forests are important; consider which are the most important methods of sustainable forest management in Norway; and think of additional ways to protect the forest.

Key ideas

◆ Until quite recently there was no real control over deforestation in Scandinavia.

◆ Forests in Norway are used for producing timber, pulp and paper, bio-energy and as areas for leisure and recreation.

◆ Forests absorb carbon dioxide, and so help to stabilise the climate.

◆ Forests help to maintain biodiversity.

◆ Scandinavian countries have now adopted a sustainable approach to forest management.

Key vocabulary

afforestation, bio-energy, biodiversity, sustainable forest status

Skills practised in the Activities

◆ Geography skills: defining 'sustainable forest management'

◆ Thinking skills: identifying reasons; prioritising methods of sustainable forest management; thinking of additional ways to protect forests

Unit outcomes

By the end of this unit, most students should be able to:

◆ define the terms given in 'Key vocabulary' above;

◆ understand that until quite recently there was no real control over deforestation in Scandinavia;

◆ explain how forests in Norway are used;

◆ understand that forests absorb carbon dioxide (and so help to stabilise the climate), and that they help to maintain biodiversity;

◆ give examples of sustainable forest management methods used in Scandinavian countries.

Ideas for a starter

1 Ask students: How are climate, vegetation and soils linked in coniferous forests? Do we need to preserve the forests? Why?

2 Brainstorm what coniferous forests are used for.

3 Ask: Who can tell me what afforestation, deforestation, biodiversity, sustainable mean?

Ideas for plenaries

1 Draw a spider diagram identifying the major human impacts on the coniferous forest. Try to show how these impacts are causing damage to the ecosystem.

2 Consider a range of management options – national parks, afforestation, natural regeneration etc. Develop a table similar to the one for comparing management schemes in the rainforest (See Unit 7.4 plenary 5). Use this to evaluate ways of managing forests.

3 Write a letter to one of the Scandinavian governments explaining the need to protect and conserve the coniferous forests.

4 How can developing better recycling practices help the coniferous forest?

5 Write 'ecosystems' in the middle of the board. Create a mind map covering as much of the work in this chapter as possible.

6 Did you find anything difficult about the work in this chapter? What? Why? What would help to make it easier to understand?

7 Make up 20 statements based on what students have learned about ecosystems, some true, some false. Students hold up **True** of **False** cards. Where statements are false, ask students to correct them.

Further class and homework activities

1 Role play the management issues of the area – local tribes, tourists, national park managers, logging managers, etc.

2 Investigate some of the schemes put in place by the Russian and Canadian authorities to conserve and implement sustainable management practices.

Answers to the Activities

1 Coniferous forests are important to both Norway and globally because:

- they supply the timber industry for softwoods, such as pine, and provide the tree pulp for paper production.
- the trees help to stabilise the global climate by absorbing carbon dioxide and releasing oxygen, thereby limiting the onset of global warming.
- the forests provide a habitat for a wealth of animals, insects and other plants that depend on the forest for their survival. This is called biodiversity.
- the forests could one day become a source of bio-energy for Norway in the future.

2 Sustainable forest management means the careful and controlled planning of felling trees for the timber/paper industry to meet the needs of today, without compromising the longevity of the forests and the ability of future generations to also benefit from the resource. Sustainable management also implies reducing any harm to the natural environment to maintain its beauty.

3 The expected answer to this activity should be similar in approach to the unit on tropical rainforests (7.4). The aim is to help students to consolidate their ideas about what sustainable management of natural environments means, and how it is best achieved. Again, integrated management schemes are often the

more ideal ones and a possible approach that students could present could be:

- afforestation allowing the rapid regeneration of the forests as coniferous species are known to grow quickly.
- adopting a forest reserve approach, whereby some ecologically sensitive environments are offered full legal protection whilst in other locations, controlled economic activity is permissible. Protecting forests in a virgin state also means that the habitats for wildlife are also protected.
- minimising wastage in industry by ensuring that all parts of a felled tree are used (page 145 shows how the bark can be used for bio-fuel, whilst the thicker trunk of the tree can be sawn for timber).

4 Additional approaches that could be adopted to ensure the longevity of the coniferous forests could include:

- the purchase and promotion of sustainable forest products, spreading the message about sustainable development. The pages of the students' book are printed on paper from a sustainable source, and many products have a recognised logo to show where the product has come from.
- tree measuring to ensure the correct height of a tree before it is felled. This is actually part of the requirements for an economically useful forest to be properly certified.
- education and awareness programmes in schools and to forest land owners.

8 Population

The big picture

These are the key ideas behind this chapter:

◆ The world's population hit 6.5 billion in the spring of 2006, and continues to rise.

◆ The world's population is unevenly distributed – some places are densely populated, others are sparsely populated.

◆ Population is rising fastest in LEDCs.

◆ Migration is the movement of people from one place to another. It can be voluntary, forced (creating refugees), permanent or temporary. It affects population sizes and structures, and of course, individuals.

◆ Changes in population can cause problems for countries – rapid population growth and too many young people in LEDCs slows down development, an increasingly elderly population in MEDCs could mean the economy runs short of workers.

◆ Immigration may help to solve the shortage of workers in the UK; population control and family planning - and economic development - can help in LEDCs.

Note that the students' version of the big picture is given in the students' chapter opener.

Chapter outline

Use this, and the students' chapter opener, to give students a mental roadmap for the chapter.

8   **Population** As the students' chapter opener, this unit is an important part of the chapter; see page 11 of this book for notes about using chapter openers

8.1   **Where in the world is everyone?** Why the world's population is unevenly distributed

8.2   **World population increase** How quickly the world's population is rising, but it's not rising at the same rate everywhere

8.3   **The demographic transition model** The model shows the pattern of population increase over time

8.4   **Population contrasts** Population increase varies between MEDCs and LEDCs; how to use population pyramids

8.5   **Migration** What it is; voluntary, forced, permanent and temporary migration; international and internal migration; push and pull factors

8.6   **Migration and the UK** International and internal migration, and how it affects the UK

8.7   **Darfur refugee emergency** A case study of international refugees

8.8   **The problems of population change** Rapid population growth in LEDCs, and ageing populations in MEDCS

8.9   **How the UK is coping** An ageing population means immigration is needed to fill labour and skills shortages

8.10   **How India is coping** India has tried to control population growth. Population control is now seen in the context of improving social and economic conditions

Objectives and outcomes for this chapter

Objectives	Unit	Outcomes
Most students will understand:		Most students will be able to:
• That a range of physical and human factors affect population density, and that some areas are densely populated and others are sparsely populated.	8.1	• Give physical and human factors which affect population density; give four examples of densely populated areas and four examples of sparsely populated areas.
• How quickly the world's population is rising; population increase is not the same everywhere.	8.2, 8.4	• Draw the graph to show world population growth; define birth rate, death rate and natural increase; name the six countries which account for the largest increase in population; name countries where population is declining.
• That many countries have had similar patterns of population increase, as shown by the demographic transition model.	8.3	• Draw the demographic transition model and explain what happens at Stages 1–5; give examples of countries at each stage of the model.
• That population pyramids show the age and structure of a country's population, and that they can be used for planning, and comparing countries.	8.4	• Say what population pyramids show and what they can be used for.
• What migration is; why people migrate; the differences between international and internal migration.	8.5	• Define migration; describe four types of migration; explain the differences between international and internal migration; give four push and four pull factors for migration between countries.
• How migration affects the UK.	8.6	• Describe the pattern of international migration to and from the UK; describe where migrants to the UK come from; explain the effect migration has on the UK's population; describe the pattern of internal migration in the UK.
• That forced migration creates refugees.	8.7	• Give an example of international refugees; explain why they have become refugees; describe what is being done to help them.
• That rapid population growth in LEDCs is slowing down their development, and that countries such as India have tried to control their population growth.	8.8, 8.9	• Explain why death rates have fallen, but birth rates remain high in LEDCs; describe the problems LEDCs with growing populations face; describe how India tried to control population growth in the past, and the policies and targets in place today.
• That ageing populations in MEDCs could lead to labour shortages, and that in countries such as the UK immigrants could help to fill the shortages.	8.8, 8.9	• Explain why populations in MEDCs are ageing and why this is a problem; explain how immigration can help to fill the labour and skills shortage in the UK; describe the problems migrants face.

These tie in with 'Your goals for this chapter' in the students' chapter opener, and with the opening lines in each unit, which give the purpose of the unit in a student-friendly style.

Using the chapter starter

The photo on page 146 of the *geog.GCSE* students' book shows newborn babies in a hospital nursery. It's not the UK where nurseries like this are no longer used; they're tightly-swaddled, which suggests it could be Eastern Europe. Generally, we could suggest the babies are likely to live more comfortable and more varied lives than previous generations. They're likely to produce fewer children than previous generations. They're likely to live longer than previous generations – there's even a view we could live to a 1000! Life expectancy is going up in most countries – the exceptions are those countries being devastated by HIV/AIDS. In the UK, life expectancy is 78 years; in Botswana it's 30.

The unit in brief

In this unit students learn why the world's population is unevenly distributed. In the Activities students use the map of population density to describe the distribution of the most densely populated parts of the world. They explain why population density is low in certain parts of the world and why it varies so much within the UK. They also consider a statement about population density and physical and human factors.

Key ideas

◆ The population density of an area or place is the average number of people per square kilometre.

◆ The world's population isn't evenly distributed. Some places are densely populated, some are sparsely populated.

◆ Population density is affected by a range of physical and human factors.

◆ There can be variations in population density within a country.

Key vocabulary

population density, densely populated, sparsely populated, physical factors, human factors

Skills practised in the Activities

◆ Geography skills: describing the distribution of densely populated areas

◆ Thinking skills: explaining low population density; explaining variations in population density in the UK; identifying and explaining sparsely populated environments likely to remain so; stating how far they agree with a statement

Unit outcomes

By the end of this unit, most students should be able to:

◆ define or explain the terms given in 'Key vocabulary' above;

◆ understand that the population density of an area or place is the average number of people per square kilometre;

◆ understand that the world's population isn't evenly distributed;

◆ describe the distribution of the most and least densely populated parts of the world;

◆ explain how population density is affected by a range of physical and human factors;

◆ explain why there can be variations in population density within a country.

Ideas for a starter

1 Ask students to stand up, and move around the room, to a spot where they feel comfortable. Explain that they are showing population distribution. Which parts of the room are densely populated? Which are sparsely populated? Ask why they chose those places – perhaps near a window or radiator (light, sunshine, heat, fuel) etc. Ask whether people might settle in different parts of the world for similar reasons.

2 What factors will encourage people to live there? Which factors will discourage people from living there? Use the responses to develop a model of population distribution.

3 Why is Western Europe densely populated?

4 Why do we study population distribution in Geography?

Ideas for plenaries

1 Apply the population distribution model developed in starter 2 to the UK. Use your atlas to draw a sketch map of the UK showing the distribution of population. Annotate it giving likely reasons for the distribution.

2 What's the difference between **population distribution** and **population density**?

3 Question time! Think back over the lesson and write down 3 questions related to what you have learned today. The teacher will ask a member of the class to try to answer.

Further class and homework activities

Go to this news page:

news.bbc.co.uk/1/hi/special_report/1999/06/99/world_population/top

print off the report. It's part of a special report on world population. Read the report carefully and have answers to the following questions:

- Why should the birth of babies be a cause for worry?
- Why have births continued to rise?
- What is the projected stabilized population for 2050?
- Why is it important to meet this figure?
- Why will the economy suffer?
- In what ways is Kenya a success story?
- Why has family planning not been as successful as hoped?
- What other key areas have got to be addressed?
- Why is a high population increase damaging the environment?
- Why is population a political issue?

Answers to the Activities

1 a Much of Asia, notably India, SE Asia, NE China and Japan. Western Europe and NE USA.

b This will depend upon the locations chosen, but will generally refer to the nature of the physical environment, e.g. extreme heat in the Sahara, extreme cold in Greenland.

2 Australia and Canada – size of the country and inhospitable nature of some environments. Others relate to the nature of the environment.

3 Although a temperate climate overall, the north and west of the British Isles have a harsher climate. These areas also have the most mountainous conditions, and least fertile soils. In combination, this leads to a relatively low population density. Conversely, in the milder, undulating and fertile south and east, population densities are much higher.

4 This depends upon students' opinions and is difficult to predict, but it is probable that Antarctica will remain an area unpopulated for the foreseeable future.

5 The physical environment is the basis for variations in population density, although the situation is made increasingly more complicated by human factors such as accessibility and relative wealth.

The unit in brief

This unit is all about the increase in the world's population. In the Activities, students use the table showing world population increase to see when the world's population was increasing fastest both in percentage terms and in actual numbers. They identify when the world's population explosion began and think about its causes, particularly in relation to LEDCs. They also have to think about the situation in various named countries.

Key ideas

◆ The world's population is growing by just over 70 million people a year.

◆ You can measure a country's birth rate, death rate and natural increase.

◆ The world's population explosion began around the beginning of the nineteenth century.

◆ There are big differences in population increase from country to country.

◆ A few countries have a falling population.

◆ Overall the rate of world population growth is slowing down slightly.

Key vocabulary

birth rate, death rate, natural increase

Skills practised in the Activities

◆ Numeracy skills: analysing tables of population data; identifying the beginning of the population explosion from a graph and tables;

◆ Thinking skills: thinking about the causes of the population explosion; stating whether a statement is correct

Unit outcomes

By the end of this unit, most students should be able to:

◆ define the terms given in 'Key vocabulary' above;

◆ describe the growth in the world's population from 1800;

◆ describe some of the differences in population increase between countries;

◆ be aware that a few countries have a falling population;

◆ understand that overall the rate of world population growth is slowing down slightly.

Ideas for a starter

1 If the population of the world was like the water in a bath, then the taps letting water in would be like the birth rate, and water emptying out of the plug hole would be like the death rate.

  ◆ If the birth rate increased and the death rate stayed the same what would happen to the size of the population?

  ◆ If the birth rate stayed the same and the death rate decreased what would happen to the size of the population?

2 Ask: About how many people are on the earth right now? How many will there be in a minute from now? About how many more by this time tomorrow?

3 Who can define the terms **birth rate** and **death rate**?

4 What does the natural increase of the population depend on?

Ideas for plenaries

1 World population obviously has to be estimated for the future. What changes may take place to speed up or slow down population increase?

2 What will happen to the natural increase in these situations:

  ◆ The age of first marriage goes up

  ◆ Contraception is readily available

  ◆ People eat a much better diet

  ◆ Better health care is provided

  ◆ Better water supplies are installed in most houses.

3 What problems might there be if the population keeps on rising? What will we need more of? What will the effect be on the world's ecosystems? Students could work in pairs and draw a spider map.

4 Do you think the world's population could fall? What might cause that?

Further class and homework activities

Look up data about population change on the internet and try to find the population change figures by continent. Draw a suitable graph to show the relative sizes of the population in the continents and try to show how they have been changing over time.

Answers to the Activities

1 You should expect something like this:

Birth rate is the number of births in a country in a year, per 1000 people. Death rate is the number of deaths in a country in a year, per 1000 people. Natural increase is the birth rate minus the death rate, often given as a percentage. The world's population is currently increasing by over 70 million people a year. Overall, the rate of increase is slowing down a bit.

2 a The twentieth century.

  b The second half of the twentieth century.

3 About 1950.

4 a Both Afghanistan and Angola have a high rate of natural increase because they have very high birth rates / their birth rates are

much higher that than their death rates.

  b Both Germany and Bulgaria have a negative rate of natural increase – so the population of both countries is falling.

  c Both Brazil and China have more young people in their population, so they have fewer deaths per 1000 / both the UK and Germany have an ageing population.

5 The rapid growth was more due to declining death rates, particularly in many LEDCs.

6 It is true to say that population growth has been most rapid in LEDCs – the USA being a notable exception of an MEDC undergoing continuous population growth.

The unit in brief

This unit is about why the world's population is increasing, and looks at the demographic transition model. In the Activities, students analyse the five stages, predict whether there might be a stage 6 of the model in the future and suggest what it might look like. They also explain why some LEDCs might not follow the stages of the model.

Key ideas

◆ Many countries have had a similar pattern of population increase over time. The demographic transition model shows and explains this pattern.

◆ The demographic transition model is divided into five stages:
  - Stage 1 High stationary = high death rate, high birth rate, low natural increase in population.
  - Stage 2 Early expanding = death rate starting to fall, birth rate still high, high natural increase.
  - Stage 3 Late expanding = death rate still falling, birth rate starting to fall, some natural increase but lower than before.
  - Stage 4 Low stationary = death rate remains low, birth rate is low, little or no natural increase.
  - Stage 5 Declining = death rate could go up (greater proportion of population is elderly), birth rate remains low and could get lower, if more people die than are being born population falls.

◆ The demographic transition model fits what happened in the UK, the rest of Europe and other MEDCs, but LEDCs might not follow the same pattern.

Key vocabulary

demographic transition model, high stationary, early expanding, late expanding, low stationary, declining

Skills practised in the Activities

◆ Thinking skills: predicting a stage 6 for the demographic transition model; explaining why some LEDCs might not follow the model

Unit outcomes

By the end of this unit, most students should be able to:

◆ define or explain the terms given in 'Key vocabulary' above;

◆ explain what happens in the five stages of the demographic transition model;

◆ explain why some LEDCS might not follow the stages of the demographic transition model.

Ideas for a starter

1 Ask: Who can remind me what factors affect natural increase?

2 How has the population of the UK changed over time? Has it increased? Are families smaller or larger than families of 80 years ago? Do people live longer nowadays? What else can you tell me about the population of the UK?

3 Have other countries' populations changed in the same way as the UK? Who can tell me 2 countries that have changed in the same way, and 2 that are different.

Ideas for plenaries

1 Read the following statements and try to fit them in the various stages of the DTM:

◆ The church no longer wants a team of full time grave diggers.

◆ A family planning clinic has just opened up in the area.

◆ Jill has just set herself up as a silver wedding arranger.

◆ Families are now very big and children have to share rooms.

◆ The family are very sad as they are burying their fifth out of 12 children.

◆ The area is growing very quickly as more houses are being built..

◆ The town can be very proud of its new sewerage system.

◆ The planners were very surprised as many big houses only had a couple living in them.

◆ Very few children know their grandparents.

◆ The pension age is probably going to go up and people will have to work longer.

2 In some countries population is falling. Is this a good thing? What benefits or problems could it cause?

3 a Quick fire test: call out a student's name and ask them to tell you what is happening in Stage 1 of the demographic transition model. Then move on to another student for Stage 2 and so on.

Further class and homework activities

Look up the birth rates and death rates of a range of countries – say 10 in all – and try to position them on the Demographic Transition Model (DTM). Now look up their rate of population increase. Has the model accurately predicted the growth rate? If not try to explain why this country does not fit the model.

Answers to the Activities

1 a Stage 1 has a high birth rate and a high death rate.

b MEDCs are in Stages 4 and 5.

c LEDCs are in Stages 2 and 3.

d Population will increase in stages 2 and 3 – because the birth rate is higher than the death rate.

2 In theory there could be many more stages - a stage 6 could see the gap between death rate and birth rate grow, leading to a continued decline in world population. There are, of course, numerous other possibilities.

3 Some countries, such as Brazil, have rapidly industrialised - it is possible that such countries could miss out one or more of the stages.

The unit in brief

In this unit students learn how population increase varies between MEDCs and LEDCs, and about population pyramids. In the Activities, students explain the causes of population increase in LEDCs and think about the reasons for high birth rates. They explain why many MEDCs have an ageing population; compare population pyramids for India and the UK; make the connection between population pyramids and the demographic transition model, and draw an outline population pyramid.

Key ideas

◆ Population increase isn't happening everywhere at the same rate. Over 90% of the world's increase is in the LEDCs, in many MEDCs population increase is slowing down (in some European countries population is declining).

◆ In the last 50 years the world's population has increased from 2.5 to 6.5 billion.

◆ Population pyramids show the age structure of a country's population.

◆ Population pyramids tell us how the population might develop which can be used for planning for the future. They also enable us to compare populations of countries.

◆ The stages of the demographic transition model produce different shaped pyramids.

Key vocabulary

population pyramid

Skills practised in the Activities

◆ Geography skills: comparing and contrasting population pyramids; drawing outline population pyramid

◆ Thinking skills: explaining causes of population increase; thinking about reasons for high birth rates; explaining ageing populations in MEDCs; making connection between population pyramids and demographic transition model

Unit outcomes

By the end of this unit, most students should be able to:

◆ define the term given in 'Key vocabulary' above;

◆ explain where population is increasing the most and what is happening to population in many MEDCs;

◆ describe what population pyramids show and what they can be used for;

◆ understand that the stages of the demographic transition model produce different shaped pyramids.

Ideas for a starter

1 Remind the class how the demographic transition model works. Ask them to identify countries at different stages of the model.

2 Ask students to work in pairs. How does population increase vary between MEDCs and LEDCs? Allow pairs to discuss before opening up to the class.

3 Ask: Does anybody know what a population pyramid is? What does it show?

Ideas for plenaries

1 Work in pairs. Take 30 seconds to look at the world map of population change on p.154. Close your book and describe the patterns on the map to your neighbour.

2 Look at the population pyramids for Stages 1-4 of the demographic transition model on p.155. Close your book and draw the pyramids from memory.

3 You are going to look at migration in the next unit. How many types of migration can you think of? Can you classify them into different groups?

4 Tell your neighbour the three key things you have learned today. Then tell them another three things which are less important.

Further class and homework activities

1 Go to www.census.gov/ipc/www/idbpyr.html and find the following countries which represent stages in the DTM – Burkino Faso (Stage1), India (Stage 2), Brazil (Stage 3), UK (Stage 4) and Sweden (Stage 5). Draw the pyramids for 2005 and copy them to a Word document. Project them on to 2050 and compare the pyramids. Describe the changes in each pyramid and make suggestions about the planning and resource issues in these countries over the time e.g provision of hospitals and schools.

2 What do you think are the problems faced by countries in the 5th stage? You may like to look up a number of web references, for example:

♦ news.bbc.co.uk/1/hi/uk/2287650.stm

♦ news.bbc.co.uk/1/hi/uk/2288275.stm

♦ news.bbc.co.uk/1/hi/world/asia-pacific/1083097.stm

Read the articles and write a short commentary on the issues raised.

Answers to the Activities

1 Continued high birth rates, for reasons such as lower use of contraception, desire to have larger families, etc. together with decline in death rates, due to factors such as improved medical facilities and better diet.

2 Tradition to have large families linked to culture and / or religion. Slow take up / realisation of effects of declining death rates. Continued dominance of subsistence agriculture in some countries leading to the wish to have children to work in the family.

3 Low birth rates, improving medical facilities, diet, care, etc, leading to people living for longer.

4 UK = stage 4, with low birth and death rates, high life expectancy. India = Stage 2, with high birth rate, falling death rate, increasing life expectancy but still lower than UK.

5 The DTM links the changes in birth and death rates in each country to the shape of the pyramids. In the UK, the 'stable' nature of the pyramid is due to both birth and death rates being low. In India,

the shape of the pyramid is explained by reference to the changing nature of the birth and death rates, with the former being high and the latter declining.

6

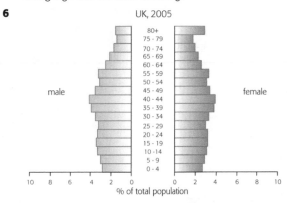

UK, 2005

male   female

% of total population

The unit in brief

In this unit students learn what migration is, what causes it and about population change due to migration. In the Activities, students look at the effects which economic migration is likely to have on the migrants' home countries and identify different push and pull factors for different types of migration. They also consider a statement about push and pull factors and migration.

Key ideas

◆ Migration is the movement of people from one place to another.

◆ There are four types of migration: voluntary, forced, permanent and temporary.

◆ Migration between countries is international migration. It can affect the population size and structure of the countries involved.

◆ Migration inside a country is internal migration. It affects the distribution of the country's population.

◆ International and internal migration take place because of push and pull factors.

  - Push factors encourage people to leave their own country or area.

  - Pull factors attract people to a new country or area.

Key vocabulary

migration (voluntary, forced, permanent, temporary), economic migrants, refugees, environmental refugee, international migration, push and pull factors, net migration, population growth rate, internal migration, rural-urban migration

Skills practised in the Activities

◆ Thinking skills: suggesting the effects of economic migration on migrants' home countries; identifying different push and pull factors; stating how far they agree with a statement

Unit outcomes

By the end of this unit, most students should be able to:

◆ define or explain the terms given in 'Key vocabulary' above;

◆ give examples of voluntary, forced, permanent and temporary migration;

◆ explain how international migration can affect the population size and structure of the countries involved;

◆ describe the push and pull factors causing internal migration in LEDCs.

Ideas for a starter

1 Ask: Why do people migrate? What might encourage them to leave their own country (push factors) and attract them to a new country (pull factors)? What obstacles are there to migration?

2 Brainstorm to identify as many types of migration as possible. Ask students to devise a way of classifying the types of migration.

3 Show a video/news clip which shows people on the move fleeing war, environmental disasters etc.

Ideas for plenaries

1 Draw a spider diagram showing the impact migrants have on the country they migrate to. Use different colours to show the positive and negative effects on the host country.

2 Test each other. Work with your neighbour (close your books) and ask them to identify as many push factors as possible. Your neighbour then asks you to identify as many pull factors as possible.

3 Quick fire test: call out a student's name and a definition (of one type of migration). The student has 5 seconds to tell you which type of migration it is. Then move on to another student and another definition.

4 What's the difference between international and internal migration? What is net migration? What is the population growth rate?

Further class and homework activities

1 Migration is highly political. Try to collect as many newspaper cuttings as possible that feature aspects of migration. Make a wall display of your findings.

2 Many families may have recently migrated. Conduct a survey of people in your year group to find the percentages of people who have moved within the last two or three generations. Find out where people have come from and if possible the reason for moving. Remember you may find out about people who have migrated short distances as well as international migration.

Answers to the Activities

1 It will have a negative effect, because the migrants leaving the country are economically active and, therefore, could contribute most to their own country.

2 Much internal migration in LEDCs is determined by rural push – people leaving poor conditions in the countryside, often knowing that conditions will be far from ideal in the cities. In MEDCs and with international migration, push and pull factors will be important and there will often be more choice over locations.

3 This depends upon students' opinions, and should follow on from the previous question. Ensure that students justify their answers. It is possible to argue in line with the statement, or against. Migrants from the new EU countries, for example, may be 'pulled' by the attractions of higher wages and better living conditions in western Europe. On the other hand, internal migrants in LEDCs move to urban areas generally with an understanding of what life will be like in the cities – they are pushed from conditions in the countryside, rather than pulled to the city.

Migration and the UK

The unit in brief

This unit is all about how migration is affecting the UK. It looks at international and internal migration. In the Activities, students describe changes in international migration patterns and the pattern of internal migration within the UK. They look at the effect of international migration on the total UK population and the expansion of the EU in terms of migration to the UK. They consider the consequences of large-scale migration from other countries, and why London is a special case in migration terms.

Key ideas

◆ Immigration now accounts for about 80% of the UK's population growth.

◆ 50% of immigrants settle in South-East England (mostly London).

◆ People coming to the UK are mainly economic migrants.

◆ A new trend has been the arrival of workers from the EU's new eastern countries.

◆ Internal migration in the UK has two clear trends:

  - A movement of people from the north to the south.

  - A movement of people out of cities.

◆ We need to know about internal migration so that we can see how the distribution of the population is changing.

Key vocabulary

economic migrants, counter-urbanisation

Skills practised in the Activities

◆ Geography skills: describing change in international migration patterns; describing and explaining pattern of internal migration

◆ Thinking skills: identifying consequences of migration and expansion of EU on migration; thinking; suggesting reasons; justifying answer

Unit outcomes

By the end of this unit, most students should be able to:

◆ define the terms given in 'Key vocabulary' above;

◆ explain the effect immigration has on the UK's population;

◆ describe how international migration patterns to and from the UK have changed since the early 1970s;

◆ explain the effect that expansion of the EU has had on migration to the UK;

◆ describe and explain the pattern of internal migration in the UK;

◆ explain why it is important to know about internal migration.

Ideas for a starter

1 Students conducted a survey into migration in Unit 8.5. Ask a few to report back on their findings.

2 Recap: the factors that bring about migration (push and pull factors, and other factors).

3 Brainstorm to find out what students know about migration in the UK. Where do international migrants come from? How many come? What about internal migration? Where do people move from and to?

Ideas for plenaries

1 What benefits do migrants bring to an area? Make a list and include a wide range of socio-economic-cultural factors.

2 Provide census figures for the class so students can see where the migrants come from, and how many there are. Ask them to map where they live. Is there an obvious pattern?

3 Ask students to investigate the refugee situation in Darfur, Sudan. Two of them will be asked to present a short talk (maximum 3 minutes) at the beginning of the next lesson.

4 What are economic migrants? What is the new trend in migration to the UK?

5 Make a graffiti wall of what students have learned today.

Further class and homework activities

Read the article at this web address and summarise the contents.
news.bbc.co.uk/1/hi/world/685332.stm

Answers to the Activities

1 From 1973 to 1982 430 000 net migration out of the UK. From 1983 to 1992, a smaller number net inward migration – 240 000. Since then, much higher inward flow – 1 million.

2 Over the last decade, half of the UK's population growth has been due to migration – it now accounts for 80% of the country's growth in population.

3 It has increased the number of people migrating to the UK, as well as the range of countries from which people migrate.

4 Increased population, greater diversity of population, increased need for services, e.g. languages and schooling, to assist migrants, possible tensions over new migrants, loss to the donor countries of often the economically active people.

5 Illegal immigrants by definition have arrived secretly, so records are not kept of their arrival and estimates have to be based on the numbers being caught.

6 Growth continues to be in the south of the UK, greatest in the south west. Population continues to decline in the north. The exception to this in Northern Ireland, where population is growing.

7 The largest city in Europe, and where a disproportionate number of people head.

8 This will depend upon students' opinions, which need to be justified. The case for building more homes refers to the increase in demand in certain areas of the country where there are shortages, notably the south east (particularly affordable housing). There are also more single occupancy dwellings, and people are living longer.

Darfur refugee emergency

The unit in brief

This unit provides an example of international refugees – those from Darfur fleeing the fighting in Sudan. In the Activities, students describe the background to the conflict in Darfur; explain why the UNHCR moved the refugees who fled to Chad, and why the government of Chad had to rely on the UNHCR. They think about the effects on Chad of having such a large number of refugees, and find about about another example of international refugees to compare with the situation in Darfur and Chad.

Key ideas

◆ By early 2006 there had been three years of civil war in Sudan's western region of Darfur.

◆ Black African Darfuris say that Sudan's government favours the ruling Arab elite in the north of the country. There has been tension in Darfur for many years over land and grazing rights.

◆ Refugees fled to Chad. In 2004 the UNHCR moved most of them to camps a safe distance from the border.

◆ Aid workers have warned that many thousands are at risk of starvation and disease in the camps, with 1 million children threatened by malnutrition.

◆ No one knows if, or when, the refugees will be able to go home.

Key vocabulary

There is no key vocabulary in this unit.

Skills practised in the Activities

◆ Geography skills: describing the background to a conflict; finding out about another example of international refugees and comparing and contrasting it with the situation in Darfur and Chad

◆ Thinking skills: thinking; explaining; identifying the effects of large numbers of refugees on Chad

Unit outcomes

By the end of this unit, most students should be able to:

◆ describe the background to the conflict in Darfur;

◆ explain why the UNHCR moved most of refugees to camps a safe distance from the border;

◆ understand why the government of Chad had to rely on the UNHCR for emergency relief and aid;

◆ describe the problems the refugees face in the camps.

Ideas for a starter

1 Ask two students to give their talks on the refugee situation in Darfur.

2 Refer back to the classification of migration (starter 2, Unit 8.5). Did you include refugees? What are the push/pull factors involved in refugee migration? What is the difference between political refugee and economic migrant?

3 Ask students to find Sudan and Chad in an atlas. Ask them to identify the Darfur Region of Sudan.

Ideas for plenaries

1 You are a news reporter travelling in Darfur reporting the refugee emergency to the world. Prepare a 2 minute report on the refugee crisis.

2 Close your books. Tell your neighbour why there is fighting in Darfur; how many people have been killed; where the refugees are going and what the situation is like for the refugees.

Answers to the Activities

1 People living in Darfur say that the government favours the ruling classes in the north of Sudan. Tension over land and grazing rights escalated as Darfur rebels started attacking government targets in 2003. The government struck back, directly and through the support of other groups against Darfur.

2 Entrenched attitudes and beliefs of both sides. War crimes committed cause reprisals and make the conflict worse. The difficulty of external mediators to intervene in the situation.

3 They were originally within easy reach of the militia groups, so they were still not safe. They were also in an area where there was little water.

4 Better resources – Chad was not well placed to deal with the refugee situation using its own limited resources.

5 Putting enormous strain on the resources of the country.

6 This will depend upon the example chosen.

The problems of population change

The unit in brief

This unit is about the different problems caused by population change in LEDCs and MEDCs. In the Activities, students explain why birth rates have remained high in LEDCs and suggest solutions to reduce them. They draw scattergraphs and describe and explain the patterns shown. They look at the problems of ageing populations and suggest how some of these could be solved, and the consequences if they're not.

Key ideas

- ◆ Over 90% of the world's population increase is in LEDCs.
- ◆ LEDCs have falling death rates and high birth rates.
- ◆ Rapid population growth is slowing down the development of LEDCs and putting pressure on resources.
- ◆ Population growth in most MEDCs is slow – in some MEDCs population is falling.
- ◆ MEDCs have low birth rates and low death rates, with an increasing life expectancy.
- ◆ MEDCs have ageing populations with increasing numbers of elderly dependents, and a possible shortage of labour in future.

Key vocabulary

family planning, fertility rate, infant mortality, life expectancy, ageing population, elderly dependents

Skills practised in the Activities

- ◆ Geography skills: describing and explaining patterns shown on scattergraphs
- ◆ Numeracy skills: drawing scattergraphs; comparing graphs
- ◆ Thinking skills: explaining; suggesting solutions; explaining answer

Unit outcomes

By the end of this unit, most students should be able to:

- ◆ define or explain the terms given in 'Key vocabulary' above;
- ◆ understand that over 90% of the world's population increase is in LEDCs;
- ◆ explain why birth rates are still high in LEDCs;
- ◆ describe how rapid population growth is slowing down the development of LEDCs;
- ◆ explain why population growth in most MEDCs is slow;
- ◆ explain the problems that an ageing population can cause, and suggest ways in which some of these problems could be solved.

Ideas for a starter

1 Recap: the demographic transition model – the stages and countries at different levels of development at each stage.

2 Ask different students to draw sketch of stylised population pyramids for stages 1-4 of the demographic transition model on the board. Ask the class for comments on the likely birth rate (the base), the death rate (the slope) and the life expectancy (the height) of pyramids at different stages of the model.

3 Show images to convey the idea of large numbers of children/young people in LEDCs and few children but large numbers of elderly people in MEDCS.

Ideas for plenaries

1. Work in a small group to prepare a short report on the problems of either population growth in LEDCs or population change in MEDCs. Divide up the work between you. Use the format:
   - the basic problem
   - a series of solutions
   - an analysis of each of the solution – maybe use a table for this section
   - a conclusion and recommendation

2. Why are people living longer in MEDCs? Why is population still growing rapidly in LEDCs?

3. Choose a student to be in the hot seat. Another student asks him or her a question about population change in LEDCs and MEDCs. Then nominate two different students (4-6 pairs in total). There's one golden rule – questions cannot be repeated.

4. Write down as many words as you can relating to today's work.

Answers to the Activities

1. Family, cultural and religious traditions. Lag time between fall in death rates and acceptance that change is taking place. Subsistence farmers still wanting large families to work on the farm.

2. Improvement in education, particularly for women. Increased economic prosperity and stability.

3 a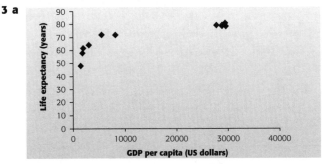

b Per person.

c There is a positive correlation between life expectancy and GDP.

d It is a good indicator in that it gives an overall measure of wealth in a country. It is, however, a crude measure as it does not take in to account actual standards of living, or other social indictors that will influence quality of life (cf. the HDI)

4 a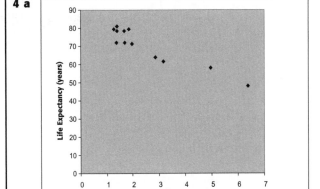

b there is a negative correlation – generally, as fertility rates increase, life expectancy decreases.

5. Both show that there is a connection between the two indicators, one positive and one negative – high GDP is an indicator of relatively high life expectancy, and high fertility rates of relatively low life expectancy.

6. Social and other facilities, such as pensions, are insufficient to cope with the growing number of dependent people. As the number of older people grows, there is a declining number of people of working age to support them, and the economy of the country.

7. By providing better services for older people. By overhauling pensions systems. By encouraging migration of working age people from other countries. Without this, a growing pensions and economic crisis.

How the UK is coping

The unit in brief

This unit looks at how the UK is coping with population change and how individuals are coping. In the Activities, students explain why life expectancy in the UK is increasing and identify the problems this might cause. They look at why the UK is relying more on foreign workers and consider comments made (some by immigrants) about living and working in the UK. They draw graphs of population data and explain the trends shown.

Key ideas

◆ The UK's population is getting older. There will be an increasing number of elderly dependents and a possible shortage of workers.

◆ We may have to work longer, save more towards our pensions, and pay higher taxes.

◆ The labour and skills shortages are being filled by immigrants.

◆ New migrants to the UK can face a whole host of problems.

Key vocabulary

elderly dependents

Skills practised in the Activities

◆ Numeracy skills: drawing graphs and explaining the trends shown

◆ Thinking skills: explaining increasing life expectancy; identifying problems; explaining why the UK is relying on foreign workers; justifying opinions

Unit outcomes

By the end of this unit, most students should be able to:

◆ define the term given in 'Key vocabulary' above;

◆ describe the problems that the UK's ageing population may cause;

◆ explain why the UK will have to rely on immigrants to fill our jobs;

◆ identify the problems migrants to the UK might face.

Ideas for a starter

1 Draw a mind map to show what is happening to population in the UK.

2 Brainstorm the issues created by an ageing population?

3 Visit the census website to check on the current state of the UK population. Put the statistics you find on the board and ask students: What do these figures tell us?

Ideas for plenaries

1 If you used starter 1, ask students to return to their mind map at the end of the unit and make any additions/deletions.

2 One of the UK's advantages according to many people is its multicultural nature. What is your view?

3 What problems do immigrants face in the UK?

4 Sum up what you have learned today in 35 words.

5 Investigate population growth in India. Prepare a short presentation focussing on how the government has tried to control population.

Further class and homework activities

Download the following article on International migration and summarise the major points. Discuss these with your neighbour and then put them to the rest of the class.

news.bbc.co.uk/1/hi/world/europe/1003324.stm

Answers to the Activities

1 a Better health care, education, diet, life styles.

 b fewer people of working age to support the economy, increased demand for services from older people, problems of managing pensions for a growing elderly population.

2 To help fill the gap of a declining number of people of working age.

3 This will depend upon students' opinions – ensure that they are justified.

4 One graph type students could draw would be a cumulative graph, as shown here.

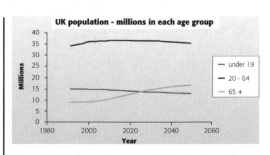

The principal changes are – a decline in the under 19 population, together with an increase in the over 65 population.

How India is coping

The unit in brief

This unit looks at how India has tried to use family planning to tackle population growth. In the Activities, students think about and explain whether India's new policies are likely to be more successful than the old ones in controlling population growth; consider the effect of population policies in India and China, and explain what is happening in Kerala – a state with a fertility rate as low as some European countries.

Key ideas

◆ Some LEDCs are relying on economic development to bring higher living standards, many see population control as more important.

◆ In the early 1950s, India's population was growing very quickly. In 1952 the government started offering contraception advice and sterilisation.

◆ By the 1970s, the population was still growing too quickly – forced sterilisations began (first on men, then changed to women), a policy to encourage only two children per family led to abortions and the killing of children.

◆ The population still trebled between 1952 and 2006.

◆ Better health and welfare (including education) is now seen as a key part of controlling population growth.

◆ There are big variations in fertility rates and rates of population increase across India.

Key vocabulary

population control, family planning

Skills practised in the Activities

◆ Thinking skills: explaining the partial success of early attempts at population control, and whether new policies will be more successful; thinking about the effect of population policies in China and India; explaining the low fertility rate in Kerala

Unit outcomes

By the end of this unit, most students should be able to:

◆ explain the terms given in 'Key vocabulary' above;

◆ explain why India has tried to control population growth since the 1950s;

◆ describe the policies India has used to try to control population growth;

◆ suggest why the new policies are likely to be more successful than the old ones;

◆ list some of the targets set for 2010 (at least 4).

Ideas for a starter

1 Quick fire key terms check – call out a student's name and a definition (or lay term) or any key terms covered in this chapter. The student has 5 seconds to give you the term.

2 If you have not recapped the demographic transition model, then do so here. Recap the stages and countries at different levels of development at each stage.

Ask a few students to show their presentation on population growth in India. What have they discovered about how the government has tried to control population?

Ideas for plenaries

1 What type of population policies are likely to be most successful in terms of slowing population growth?

2 What targets has India set for 2010?

3 Question time! Think back over the lesson and write down 3 questions related to what you have learned. The teacher will ask a member of the class to try to answer.

4 Think about all the work you have done in this chapter. *Why do we study population?*

5 Create an acrostic. Write POPULATION down the side of a page. Make each letter the first letter of a word, phrase or sentence about Population.

Further class and homework activities

Other countries of South East Asia have tried to implement population policies to slow down the growth of population. China is a well known example but there are others. Download and read the following articles and see if there are any lessons for India:

◆ www.cpirc.org.cn/en/eindex.htm

◆ news.bbc.co.uk/1/hi/world/asia-pacific/906114.stm

◆ news.bbc.co.uk/1/hi/world/asia-pacific/1011799.stm

Answers to the Activities

1 Rigidly set targets, that were attempted to be enforced through sterilisation and contraception. Did not have sufficient parallel economic growth and development.

2 As these countries are the largest in the world, they will increasingly dominate the world economy and the global environment.

3 Population is stable, birth rates have fallen to European levels, with relative economic prosperity.

4 This will depend upon students' opinions, which need to be justified. More recent policies are likely to be more successful as they are based on a broader based approach – and include the importance of factors such as education, the role of women, and building economic prosperity.

9 Settlement

chapter overview

The big picture

These are the key ideas behind this chapter:

◆ A settlement's site is the land it is built on. A range of factors were important for the original sites of settlements.

◆ All settlements have at least one function, most have several.

◆ A settlement hierarchy is a ranking of settlements with the largest at the top.

◆ Urbanisation is increasing in both MEDCs and LEDCs.

◆ Land use changes across cities, and there are different models of land use for MEDC and LEDC cities.

◆ The cost of land and accessibility create different urban zones.

◆ Cities in MEDCs and LEDCs suffer from problems of deprivation but these problems can be tackled.

◆ Other urban problems include traffic and urban sprawl.

Note that the students' version of the big picture is given in the students' chapter opener.

Chapter outline

Use this, and the students' chapter opener, to give students a mental roadmap for the chapter.

9   **Settlement**   As the students' chapter opener, this unit is an important part of the chapter; see page 11 of this book for notes about using chapter openers

9.1   **Site**   Factors important in choosing a site for a settlement

9.2   **Settlement functions**   The main activities that happen in settlements, and Oxford's functions

9.3   **Settlement hierarchies**   How settlements are ranked in order of size and importance, and sphere of influence

9.4   **Urbanisation**   Increasing numbers of people are living in urban areas in MEDCs and LEDCs

9.5   **You are entering the twilight zone**   How land use changes across a city, and the Burgess urban model

9.6   **Urban zoning: why does it happen?**   Urban zones develop due to cost of land and accessibility

9.7   **Urban problems in MEDCs**   Inner cities can have high levels of deprivation; redevelopment can bring a higher quality of life back to inner cities

9.8   **Urban problems in LEDCs**   Shanty towns develop in less favourable parts of cities, but governments can try to improve conditions

9.9   **Urban models in LEDCs**   Land use in LEDC cities; an urban model for LEDC cities; comparing the model with land use in Rio de Janeiro

9.10   **Traffic – everybody's problem**   Traffic problems in Bangkok and Moscow and ways to keep the traffic moving

9.11   **Urban sprawl**   Counter-urbanisation; problems of building at the rural-urban fringe; green belts

Objectives and outcomes for this chapter

Objectives	Unit	Outcomes
Most students will understand:		Most students will be able to:
• That there are different factors which were important in choosing the original site of a settlement.	9.1	• Give at least six factors that would have influenced a choice of site.
• What settlement functions are; that most settlements have several functions.	9.2	• Define settlement function; describe the functions settlements of different sizes might have.
• That settlements are ranked in order of size and importance, and that settlements have a sphere of influence.	9.3	• Describe a settlement hierarchy; explain how settlements are ranked; define sphere of influence.
• That urbanisation is happening later and faster in LEDCs than in MEDCs.	9.4	• Describe how urbanisation happened in the nineteenth century in MEDCs; explain the differences in urbanisation in LEDCs; describe the location of the world's fastest growing cities.
• That land use changes across cities in both MEDCs and LEDCs; that there are different models of land use for MEDC and LEDC cities.	9.5, 9.9	• Describe the patterns of land use in MEDC and LEDC cities; draw the Burgess urban model (for MEDC cities) and the urban model for LEDC cities.
• That the cost of land and accessibility create different urban zones.	9.6	• Explain how the cost of land and accessibility create different urban zones.
• That cities in MEDCs and LEDCs suffer from deprivation, but that these problems can be tackled.	9.7, 9.8	• Describe the deprivation in inner cites in the UK; identify the reasons for deprivation in the inner cities ;describe how the inner cities can be improved; describe the problems in Rocinha in Rio de Janeiro; describe the Favela Bairro project (to upgrade the favelas).
• How increasing numbers of cars create traffic problems worldwide.	9.10	• Describe the problems traffic causes in Bangkok and Moscow; explain the reasons for the traffic problems; describe what could be done to reduce traffic problems.
• That counter-urbanisation creates problems and puts pressure on green belts.	9.11	• Define rural-urban fringe and counter-urbanisation; give reasons why people are moving out of cities; give reasons why some people don't want more building at the rural-urban fringe; give an alternative to building at the rural-urban fringe.

These tie in with 'Your goals for this chapter' in the students' chapter opener, and with the opening lines in each unit, which give the purpose of the unit in a student-friendly style.

Using the chapter starter

The photo on page 168 of the *geog.GCSE* students' book shows a view of Haines (population 2800), in the Alaskan panhandle. The area was a route centre for native tribes. A mission and school were built in 1881. But Haines really got its start soon after as a gold mining and fishing town. The army built a fort in 1904. Logging became important.

The fort closed in 1946. The last fish cannery closed in 1972 due to declining fish stocks. Logging declined. Tourism is now the town's most important source of income. Wildlife and outdoor activities attract thousands of visitors. Many come in the autumn, when 4000 bald eagles gather to feast on spawning salmon. Haines is surrounded by mountains and is close to 20 million acres of protected wilderness.

Haines was named by 'Outside Magazine' as one the top twenty places to live. There's little crime, little unemployment, few social problems, and living standards are quite high. But Haines is quite remote, mosquitoes can be a nuisance in summer, and winters are long and cold.

The unit in brief

This unit is about the things people looked for when choosing a place to settle. In the Activities, students use the knowledge gained from the unit to describe the site of their own school. They decide which site factors apply to a range of different settlements shown in the photos in this unit; and, using the maps of London at different periods, think about why London's site was first chosen, and how London changed and adapted to become a site with many advantages.

Key ideas

◆ A settlement's site is the land it is built on.

◆ Sites were chosen for different reasons.

◆ The sites where people chose to locate their settlement changed over time.

◆ Now settlements can develop almost anywhere, if there's a strong enough economic reason.

Key vocabulary

site, resources, wet point, dry point, defence, shelter, aspect, gaps, trade, route centre, economic

Skills practised in the Activities

◆ Geography skills: describing the site of the school

◆ Thinking skills: deciding about site factors for different settlements; thinking about sites, change and adaptation

Unit outcomes

By the end of this unit, most students should be able to:

◆ define the terms given in 'Key vocabulary' above;

◆ understand that a settlement's site is the land it is built on;

◆ give six different location factors for choosing different sites;

◆ explain why the sites people chose to locate their settlement on might change over time;

◆ understand that now settlements can develop almost anywhere if there's a strong enough economic reason.

Ideas for a starter

1 Brainstorm: What do we mean by the terms settlement and site? Why have settlements developed in different places?

2 Ask students: Think about our own settlement (or nearest large town/city). What things do we use there (e.g. shops, leisure facilities, etc.)?

3 Show a photograph of a city in the UK. Ask the students about their perception of urban areas. What are the three words that they think of when they see the photograph? Are these positive or negative views of the urban area?

Ideas for plenaries

1 Use an atlas and choose four towns and cities across the UK. Why did they develop in these places? What factors were important?

2 Provide students with an OS map of the local area. Ask them to choose four settlements (but not their own). What factors led to the development of these places? Why were these sites chosen? What evidence can you find on the map?

3 Use the OS map of your local area. Draw an annotated sketch map to show the advantages of the site of your own settlement.

4 You have 30 seconds. Tell your neighbour as many location factors (wet point, dry point, etc.) as you can for the site of a settlement.

5 Investigate one major city and try to find out which factors were important in its development. Why was this site chosen?

Answers to the Activities

2 A is Ely – a dry point site in the middle of the fens, with good farmland created from the drained marshes.

B is Durham, a wet point site located within a river meander, so that the town is almost entirely surrounded by water; it's an excellent defensive site, since it's also on a steep hill. It's also a bridging point for trade, and the river provides water for households and small industries.

C is a coastal hilltop defensive site, with good all-round observation. It is also located on the Riviera, which attracts thousands of tourists each year.

D is a Dogon settlement in Senegal. The houses are sheltered under a cliff overhang from the sun, and are high up, again for defence.

E is a typical alpine valley, with an adret, or sunny side, usually south-facing.

F is another defensive site, located next to a road for trade at the end of a pass between hills.

3 a Its on a major river - good for water transport, which was much faster than roads at the time. It provided an easy route to the coast, and inland for trade; and a safe harbour. The Thames also supplied water, as did the streams to the west and centre of the site. It was also a defensive site, with one side protected by the river.

b By Tudor times, London was the lowest bridging point (the one closest to the sea). Routes ran to the bridge, and London became a route centre. Victorian London was obviously much bigger, with seven bridges over the river. It also had railways radiating out from the centre.

The unit in brief

This unit is about settlement functions – the things that happen in settlements and the role that settlements play in our lives. In the Activities, students use the OS map extract of Oxford included in this unit to identify the city's main function and to find evidence of other functions. They describe the main function of the place where they live and of any nearby settlements.

Key ideas

◆ The term 'function' describes the main activities of a settlement.

◆ All settlements have one or more functions. Most have several.

◆ Land use in urban areas reflects the primary functions of the settlement.

Key vocabulary

function, route centre, hamlet, village, market town, primary function

Skills practised in the Activities

◆ Geography skills: explaining the term 'urban function'; using an OS map to provide evidence of functions; describing the functions of own settlement and nearby settlements

Unit outcomes

By the end of this unit, most students should be able to:

◆ define the terms given in 'Key vocabulary' above;

◆ explain what an urban function is;

◆ identify Oxford's functions using map evidence;

◆ understand that land use in urban areas reflects the primary functions of the settlement.

Ideas for a starter

1 Recap: definition of site, and location factors for settlements from unit 9.1.

2 Ask several students to report back on the city they investigated in unit 9.1.

3 Brainstorm to find out what students know about settlements of different sizes. You are looking for terms such as hamlet, village, etc. Develop to ask what they know about 'functions'. Ask for examples of functions and draw a spider diagram on the board.

Ideas for plenaries

1 Provide students with a variety of OS maps. Ask them to look at a range of towns/cities and try to decide on the range of functions of these places. They should provide evidence of these functions and grid references.

2 Use an OS map of your local area. What is the current function of your settlement? Has it changed over time? What was its main function when it originally developed? What was it 100 years ago? 50 years ago?

3 Quick-fire test. Ask different students to give examples of functions; types of settlements; typical functions in settlements of different sizes; definition of function etc.

Further class and homework activities

Urban areas change their functions over time. Investigate the London docklands and find out how functions have changed here over the last 100 years. Try to produce a 'before' and 'after' picture/wall display of the docklands. There are a number of websites that could help you.

Answers to the Activities

1 a A job or a process which happens in a town or city.

 b Education. The university, shown as coll or colleges on the map. The university accounts for almost 15 000 of Oxford's 115 000 population.

 c Encourage students to use headings:
 Shopping, including a daily or weekly market (retail)
 Business (commerce)
 Religion
 Entertainment and leisure
 Industry
 Residential
 Route centre

2 The colleges in the city centre. [Students could give a number of appropriate grid references.]

3 For cultural centre – museums, overall size of city; for industrial centre – motor works; for historic town – the colleges, various antiquities, e.g. Godstow Abbey or castle remains; for recreational centre – golf courses, country park, the river, museums; for route centre – major roads converging on ring road, railway; for tourist town – the colleges, riverside pubs; for residential settlement – areas of housing. [Students could give a number of appropriate grid references.]

The unit in brief

This unit is about settlement hierarchies – how settlements are ranked in order of size and importance. In the Activities, students explain the terms hierarchy and sphere of influence and give examples of settlements of different sizes in the UK. They make and explain the connection between the size of towns and the urban percentage of a country's population. They analyse an extract from an atlas map in terms of settlement hierachy and sphere of influence.

Key ideas

◆ A settlement hierarchy is a ranking of settlements.

◆ Different countries define different settlement types in different ways.

◆ Settlement hierarchies are pyramid-shaped. The larger the settlement, the fewer there are.

◆ Settlements are ranked by population size, number and variety of functions, the distance between a settlement and the nearest one of similar size, and the sphere of influence.

◆ The sphere of influence is the area served by a particular settlement.

Key vocabulary

settlement hierarchy, ranking, sphere of influence, village, town, city

Skills practised in the Activities

◆ Geography skills: explaining the terms 'hierarchy' and 'sphere of influence'; naming UK settlements of different sizes; analysing an atlas style map

◆ Thinking skills: giving reasons; making and explaining connections between population sizes of towns and urban populations as a percentage of a country's total population

Unit outcomes

By the end of this unit, most students should be able to:

◆ define the terms given in 'Key vocabulary' above;

◆ understand that a settlement hierarchy is a ranking of settlements;

◆ recognise that different countries define different settlement types in different ways;

◆ explain why settlement hierarchies are pyramid-shaped;

◆ describe how settlements are ranked.

Ideas for a starter

1 Ask: Who can remind me about settlement functions? Who can give me five functions of a settlement?

2 Ask: What does the term hierarchy mean? Try to draw out the organisational framework of your school starting at the top with your headteacher and students at the bottom. Establish that this ranking is called a hierarchy and you can rank settlements in the same way based on size and function.

3 Ask: What's a village? What's a city? What size would they be? (Note that different countries have different ideas about this.) What functions will you find in places of different sizes?

Ideas for plenaries

1 Conduct a survey amongst your classmates to find out where people go for certain goods when out shopping. Draw a map showing the most popular settlements for shopping. This should help you see a local shopping hierarchy.

2 Where do people in your class live? Plot where they live on a map of your local area. This is the catchment area of the school – another way of showing a sphere of influence!

3 What other organisations have hierarchies? Think of three examples and draw the hierarchy with the most important person/thing at the top.

4 Use the local OS map to produce a settlement hierarchy for your area. Count settlements of different sizes. (The font size used for names is a clue to settlement size.) Then sketch a hierarchy triangle and write in the numbers of settlements of different sizes. Is there a pattern?

5 Make a graffiti wall of what students have learned today.

Further class and homework activities

Take a number of local settlements of a variety of sizes by population and use the Yellow Pages to look up how many services they offer. Choose a variety of services from small convenience goods services to large comparison goods services. Add up the totals and plot against the population sizes. Is there a pattern?

Answers to the Activities

1 A hierarchy is a ranking, usually with the biggest, the most important, or the best at the top, and the smallest, least important, or worst, at the bottom – like the football premiership, or Wimbledon seeding.

2 The pyramid is a good way of showing a settlement hierarchy because:

(i) the width of each step in the hierarchy represents the number of settlements in each category; there is usually one primate city at the top, but thousands and thousands of isolated buildings/farmsteads;

(ii) it gives a good picture of how each level feeds into the layer above.

3 UK conurbations include Greater Manchester, the West Midlands, Tyneside, and Teesside.

4 Students might think that the more urbanised a country is, the bigger a settlement has to be to be called a town, city, and so on. If the students rank the two columns, it is clear that the rankings don't fit. Japan takes 30 000 people to be a town, but has the second to last percentage urban population. Stress that population size is not the only way to rank a settlement; the number of urban functions might also be significant.

And there are oddities: Woodstock, Oxon, has a population of 2100 and is a town, but Kidlington, also Oxon, has a population of 17 500 and is a village. It doesn't want to upgrade its title because it's in the Guinness Book of Records as Britain's largest village.

5 The sphere of influence is the area surrounding a settlement where people who live within that sphere of influence depend on the settlement for education, employment, retailing, and finance. Many people in the sphere of influence work in the central place, so we can say that they 'serve' the settlement.

6 top level London;
then Bristol;
then Swindon and Reading;
then Chippenham, Newbury;
then Marshfield, Calne, Avebury, Marlborough, Hungerford, Thatcham

7 London. (It's our primate / capital city.)

8 a Bristol
b Oxford
c Swindon (probably – although it looks a smaller town, it serves a wider area)
d Salisbury (there are no other large towns near it)

The unit in brief

This unit is about urbanisation – the increase in the percentage of people living in urban areas. It looks at urbanisation in MEDCs and LEDCs. In the Activities, students draw a cumulative line graph of urban population as a percentage of the total population. They identify and explain which types of countries urbanised first and make the connection between industrialisation and urbanisation. They also identify trends in the changing locations of the world's megacities, and assess whether this trend will continue into the future.

Key ideas

◆ Urbanisation means a rise in the percentage of people living in urban areas.

◆ European and North American MEDCs urbanised during the late eighteenth and nineteenth centuries.

◆ The pattern of urbanisation in LEDCs has some similarities with what happened in MEDCs, but there are some big differences.

◆ Urbanisation is happening a lot later in LEDCs (only since the 1950s). It is also happening a lot faster.

Key vocabulary

urbanisation

Skills practised in the Activities

◆ Geography skills: explaining the term 'urbanisation'; drawing a cumulative line graph from data in a table; marking megacities on a world map and describing the changes shown

◆ Thinking skills: identifying and explaining which types of countries urbanised first; making the connection between industrialisation and urbanisation; explaining the causes of urbanisation; explaining reasons for future trends in urbanisation

Unit outcomes

By the end of this unit, most students should be able to:

◆ define the term given in 'Key vocabulary' above;

◆ explain why European and North American MEDCs urbanised in the late eighteenth and nineteenth centuries;

◆ describe the similarities and differences in urbanisation between LEDCs and MEDC;

◆ give evidence for the speed of urbanisation in LEDCs.

Ideas for a starter

1 Recap: the concept of hierarchy; urban hierarchies (related to the size of the sphere of influence).

2 Ask: What do you know about urbanisation? Who can tell me when people began moving to cities in the UK in large numbers, and why?

3 Ask: What are the factors that would make a family move from the countryside into the town? What are the factors that might prevent this movement? Draw a table on the board of factors.

4 Imagine this. It is 1806. You are 10 years old and you live in the country, but you're about to move to a mill town. Tell us why, what you think it will be like, and what you will do there.

Ideas for plenaries

1 Conduct a quick survey amongst the students in your class. Ask: Who has moved? Where have they moved from/to? What are the reasons for movement?

2 What percentage of the world's population lived in urban areas in 2000? How will that figure change by 2030?

3 What are the similarities in urbanisation between LEDCs and MEDCs? What are the differences? Tell your neighbour.

4 Investigate one of the mega-cities from the list on page 177. What are the main reasons for the growth of the city?

5 Sum up what you have learned today in 30 words.

Answers to the Activities

1 Urbanisation is a rise in the percentage of people living in urban areas (in comparison with rural areas). It's not the same as urban growth. If urban areas grow by 10%, but rural areas grow by the same percentage – or greater – then urbanisation hasn't happened.

2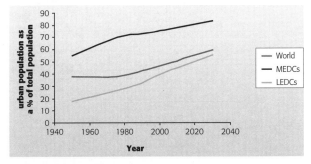

3 MEDCs urbanised first because they industrialised first.

4 Factories pulled people into jobs, these workers brought their families, and other workers moved to the city for jobs in services – like education or shops – to serve the industrial workers.

5 It's not easy to say that one of these events caused the other. If each agricultural worker produces more food, then rural workers are freed up and can move to the industrial towns. But the farmers' production is increased because of new industrial technology, like seed drills. And the surplus workers, wouldn't have any jobs to go to if there had been no industrialisation. The two factors had to come together.

6 c In 1975, there were five mega-cities: two in MEDCs (40%) and three in LEDCs. By 2000, there were nineteen mega-cities, but only four in MEDCs (21%). So the number of mega-cities has risen, but the percentage of MEDC mega-cities has fallen.

d Yes. Most MEDCs depend less on industry; more and more, goods are made in LEDCs. China, for example, is running out of workers, even though thousands of Chinese have moved to factory jobs in cities, so factory managers are recruiting workers from really distant areas, like Tibet. On top of this, services, like electricity or piped water, are poor in LEDCs, so the cities have a bigger 'pull'. You could look ahead to counter-urbanisation, on page 190 of the students' book.

The unit in brief

This unit is about land use, and how it changes across a city. In the Activities, students draw a sketch of a photo of Cardiff and label the land use zones. They have to match sentences describing activities with land use zones, and write some of their own. They write an account of a journey from a town or city centre that they know to the rural-urban fringe and suggest how twilight zones could be improved.

Key ideas

◆ Land use is what the land is used for.

◆ Many cities have a similar pattern of land use: CBD; the inner city (twilight zone); the inner suburbs; the outer suburbs; the rural-urban fringe.

◆ An urban model is a simplified diagram of the way land is used. The Burgess model is the easiest to understand and apply.

◆ Looking at transects helps us to understand how and why a city changes from the centre to the edge.

Key vocabulary

land use, Central Business District (CBD), inner city (twilight zone), inner suburbs, outer suburbs, rural-urban fringe, urban model, transect

Skills practised in the Activities

◆ Geography skills: drawing and labelling a sketch of a photo of Cardiff to show the land use zones

◆ Literacy skills: writing sentences to match land use zones; writing an account of a journey from a town or city centre to the rural-urban fringe

◆ Thinking skills: matching sentences (describing activities) with land use zones and explaining answers; suggesting how the twilight zone could be improved

Unit outcomes

By the end of this unit, most students should be able to:

◆ define the terms given in 'Key vocabulary' above;

◆ understand that land use is what the land is used for;

◆ explain the pattern of land use from the CBD to the rural-urban fringe;

◆ explain what an urban model is;

◆ describe a transect for a city or town that they know from the centre to the rural-urban fringe.

Ideas for a starter

1 Ask a few students to give a short report on their investigation into one of the mega-cities.

2 Show photographs of different parts of the urban area. Ask students to make suggestions as to where they would be found in the town/city. Ask for reasons why they would be found there.

3 Use Activities question 3 as a starter.

Ideas for plenaries

1 What do you think about the various zones of a town or city? What advantages and drawbacks do they have?

2 Prepare interviews (and responses) for people living in different zones of a town or city. What advantages and drawbacks would they point to?

3 Provide students with an OS map of the local area. Ask them to draw a sketch map showing land use in their settlement (or in the nearest town if their settlement is too small). Mark in the main roads, rivers, railway, etc. Shade in the different land use zones.

4 If you did not use Activities question 3 as a starter, it could be used as a plenary.

5 Prepare an odd-one-out for your partner on what you have learned today.

Further class and homework activities

1 Visit the UK census website and collect information about different parts of Cardiff, or another city/town of your choice. You will need to have some postcodes available. Analyse the information and try to draw some conclusions about the variation across the city/town.

2 Collect information from local estate agents about houses on the market and make a wall display showing the property and the locations. Draw concentric circles on the map and try to calculate the average price in each of the circles. What happens to the price of property as you move from the town centre? What happens to the size of the plots (maybe measured in garden size and/or number of bedrooms)?

the Answers to the Activities

1 Students should be able to produce a sketch showing the CBD and identifying the inner city, inner suburbs, outer suburbs, and rural-urban fringe.

2 a A outer suburbs   B CBD   C inner city   D inner suburbs
E rural-urban fringe

b Answers should focus on: house size, street width and shape, provision of green space, and distance from CBD.

4 Refer to the inner city photo on page 178, which mentions gentrification – people 'doing up' old houses. The savings they make on commuting time and cost mean that they can afford to do up an old terraced house. Some middle class Britons would never buy a brand new house. Then there are big redevelopment projects, like docklands in London, Liverpool, Gateshead, Glasgow, and Cardiff Bay. Urban regeneration is a key part of London's 2012 Olympic Games bid.

The unit in brief

In this unit students learn why urban zones develop, and what's happened in the CBD. In the Activities, students use a graph showing rent against distance from the CBD to explain the effect of accessibility on the cost of land. They explain why different activities locate in different parts of the city, and identify and explain the anomaly in land prices shown on the graph. They draw a sketch of a photo of the centre of Bristol to identify land issues.

Key ideas

◆ Urban zones develop due to the cost of land and accessibility.

◆ Different activities/businesses can afford to pay different amounts and therefore locate in different zones.

◆ Urban zones develop as settlements grow.

◆ The CBD is now less accessible than it used to be.

◆ Out-of-town locations may cost almost as much as those in the CBD, but they are more accessible.

Key vocabulary

zones, accessibility

Skills practised in the Activities

◆ Geography skills: explaining the terms 'urban zone', 'accessibility'; drawing a labelled sketch of land uses

◆ Numeracy skills: analysing a line graph

◆ Thinking skills: explaining the effect of accessibility; explaining why different activities locate in different parts of a city; identifying and explaining anomalies

Unit outcomes

By the end of this unit, most students should be able to:

◆ define the terms given in 'Key vocabulary' above;

◆ understand that urban zones develop due to the cost of land and accessibility;

◆ explain why different activities/businesses locate in different zones;

◆ understand that urban zones develop as settlements grow;

◆ explain why the CBD is now less accessible than it used to be and why shops locate in out-of-town locations.

Ideas for a starter

1 Ask students to draw out the Burgess model from memory and label it.

2 Ask students to think about three locations – crossroads, T junction, and between junctions. If you were a shop-owner which location would you want to develop? Which would be the most accessible? How many routes feed into the location? Now apply this to the urban area. Which will be the most sought-after location? The town centre will be the dominant crossroads in town.

3 Show photos showing a range of land uses – large retail store with car park; small specialist shop; coffee shop; small office, e.g. accountants, solicitors; small factory; terraced housing; large detached house etc. Draw the Burgess model on the board and ask students which zones each type of land use would locate in (and why – you are looking to elicit accessibility and cost of land).

Ideas for plenaries

1 Provide students with information about towns which have encouraged development, such as Reading through the Oracle Centre. How have these shopping centres changed the town centre?

2 Provide students with information on out-of-town shopping centres such as Meadowhall, Sheffield (see: www.meadowhall.co.uk/). Ask them to compare these with examples such as Reading.

3 Show photos of the CBD and ask the students to judge the scenes for attractiveness, litter, signage, other management – pedestrian-only roads, street furniture, etc. Then show photos of out-of-town shopping centres, and ask them to compare them.

4 Use your own town or nearest large settlement. What shops/businesses are still in the town centre/CBD? What shops are found on out-of-town retail parks?

5 If starter 3 was not used, it could be used as a plenary.

6 Make 10-15 statements about what students have learned so far, some true, some false. Students hold up *True* or *False* cards. Where statements are false, ask students to correct them.

Further class and homework activities

Do some fieldwork in the CBD and survey the types of shops there. Are there more comparison goods shops? Measure the number of shoppers going into a variety of shops in a number of locations. Are the busiest shops at the major junctions in the CBD? This information could be presented as a wall display.

Answers to the Activities

1 a An urban zone is a distinct area of a town or city – refer students to page 178.

b Accessibility means being able to get somewhere.

2 a Make sure that the students use the costs and distances shown on the graph. Rents fall from £130/m^2 at the CBD to £40/m^2 2000 metres from the CBD. After that, they rise, to £120/m^2 5000 metres from the CBD, but then fall dramatically to £40/m^2 6000 metres from the city centre.

b Land is expensive in the city centre because this is where bus, tram and rail routes meet. (It's also expensive here because there isn't much of it.) Peripheral, out-of-town sites are usually located near ring roads, giving easy access for motorists.

c HMV is happy to pay high city centre rents because this zone has large numbers of pedestrians, out shopping. (They will also want to locate in the CBD because competitors locate there, too.)

3 a Coffee shops get custom from shoppers and workers in the city centre, so they can pay high rents. Solicitors don't get as many walk-in customers, and they can't afford their own car parks. Factory owners used to want to be near the centre, but these days they're more interested in cheaper land and better access; free parking. Land is cheaper in the suburbs, so richer people can buy bigger houses.

b It's all about bid-rent; who can pay high prices, and who needs to be near the CBD. Most chain stores don't want a location more than about 250 metres from the areas of peak pedestrian flow. Marks and Spencers stores are usually located at the point of peak pedestrian flow. Others 'trade off' inner locations for cheaper land.

4 a The anomaly in the graph is the high cost of land at the periphery.

b This is explained by the availability of land, and access to ring roads.

c The CBD is expensive and congested. Businesses often want to provide car parks for their workers and their customers – but city-centre car parking is very expensive. Traffic congestion causes air pollution (see page 188), and the crowds of people drop chewing gum and other kinds of litter. At night, CBDs are often full of young people going to pubs and clubs – refer your students to page 190 – 'My town's under attack'.

5 Sketch should show the CBD in centre-right, an industrial zone along the river in the foreground, residential zones across the top and bottom right of the pic/sketch, with the park at centre-left identified as a recreational zone – the sharp-eyed and thoughtful might/should identify the marina and tall ship at bottom left as another recreational zone.

Urban problems in MEDCs

The unit in brief

This unit is about deprivation in inner cities, and about how the inner city can be improved. In the Activities, students suggest reasons why the inner city declined; list the problems of the inner city for industry and people, and suggest where new industry would locate. They also get to redevelop an inner city area of their own, using a plan of an inner city area included in the unit. Finally they prepare a presentation about their planned redevelopment.

Key ideas

◆ The inner city has high levels of deprivation and is the poorest zone of most MEDC cities.

◆ In the second half of the twentieth century, many of the original inner city factories closed and unemployment rose.

◆ Unemployment, poverty and lack of opportunities can result in high crime rates.

◆ There has been a lot of redevelopment in the UK's inner cities. Brindley Place in Birmingham is one example of large-scale redevelopment.

◆ Redevelopment is one way of bringing a higher quality of life back to inner city areas.

Key vocabulary

inner city, deprivation, redevelopment, social housing, renewal

Skills practised in the Activities

◆ Geography skills: copying a plan of an inner city area and annotating it to show how it could be redeveloped

◆ Literacy skills: preparing a presentation of the redevelopment plan – if presented using PowerPoint would become an ICT skill

◆ Thinking skills: identifying and explaining the most deprived areas of cities; giving reasons for the decline in inner cities; listing the problems of inner cities; suggesting where industry has moved to

Unit outcomes

By the end of this unit, most students should be able to:

◆ define the terms given in 'Key vocabulary' above;

◆ explain why the inner city is the poorest zone of most MEDC cities;

◆ recognise that unemployment, poverty and lack of opportunities can result in high crime rates;

◆ explain how redevelopment can bring a higher quality of life back to inner city areas, and describe one example of redevelopment.

Ideas for a starter

1 Recap: developments in the CBD and out-of-town shopping centres.

2 Ask students: What is meant by the term deprivation? Ask them to suggest variables that could go together to make an index of deprivation in inner cities.

3 Show photographs of deprived urban areas in MEDCs. Ask students to comment on the deprivation they observe.

Ideas for plenaries

1 Work in pairs to write interviews and responses for people who might be affected by redevelopment or renewal of their area. Try to think of a range of people – old people, students, first-time buyers, etc.

2 Provide students with OS maps. Look at locations within the town and try to identify which zone the area belongs to. Use the patterns of buildings and streets as clues.

3 Add to the variables listed in starter 2. Classify them under these headings: Economic stress, Social stress, Housing stress, Environmental stress.

4 Think of an inner city area you know which needs redevelopment. Prepare a two-minute sound-bite for a local radio show. Describe the area, explain why it should be redeveloped, how it should be redeveloped, and who will benefit.

5 Tell me the three most important things you have learned today. Now tell me another three things which are interesting, but less important.

Further class and homework activities

1 Identify and investigate a particular inner city scheme.

2 Collect information from the census at ward level for your (or any other) town to draw population pyramids. Try to annotate the pyramids, pointing out the main characteristics of the population. Locate them on a map of the town. This could be made into a wall display.

Answers to the Activities

1 Deprivation – not having good housing, jobs, or schooling – is high in the inner city because houses are old, and not well built.

2 a Areas with high population density suffer from:

- congestion;
- pollution (litter, noise, many people renting so they don't improve the houses);
- and crime (lots of houses close together, especially student areas, filled with laptops and i-pods) so better-off people move out, and low-paid or unemployed workers move in.
- many of the industries in this zone have closed down because of foreign competition.

b Industry relocated from the inner city because it's dirty, run-down, and crowded.

c

- Congestion – it's difficult to manoeuvre lorries in narrow streets.
- Cost – land is still relatively expensive.
- Access – there is little space for parking.

d To the periphery.

3 Lack of living space; Adele lives in a shared house
High crime levels
Drug dealers and users
Lack of open space
Poor schools
Low-skilled, low-paid jobs

5 Presentations might include:

- providing a mix of more expensive and social housing;
- 'greening' some of the area: trees, parks, solar fuel, recycling points;
- retaining and refurbishing important old buildings;
- that redeveloping inner cities increases the number of better-off people living there, and they pay more local taxes.
- that Inner city redevelopment creates jobs for people living elsewhere in the city. It also gives people a sense of pride in their city.

Urban problems in LEDCs

The unit in brief

This unit is about deprivation in LEDC cities and about what governments can do to help. It includes a case study of Rocinha in Brazil. In the Activities, students read the story of the teenage boy included in the unit and write some questions to ask him for a radio interview. They also write the answers they think he would give. They use the case study of Rocinha to identify the problems of living there; identify what the Brazilian government has done to improve conditions in the Favela Bairro project, and think of some more ideas of their own.

Key ideas

- ◆ Rocinha is the biggest shanty town (favela) in Rio de Janeiro in Brazil.
- ◆ Shanty towns usually grow up in less favourable parts of a city.
- ◆ Homes are built from anything that's available; people are squatters; shanty towns have lots of disease and poverty; education levels are low; most children are sent out to work.
- ◆ In the 1990s the Brazilian government decided to try to upgrade the favelas, rather than remove them.
- ◆ The government's program focused on improving the physical characteristics of the favelas.
- ◆ The program has had mixed results.

Key vocabulary

shanty towns, favela

Skills practised in the Activities

- ◆ Geography skills: explaining the terms 'shanty town', 'squatter'; finding Rio de Janeiro in an atlas and describing its location
- ◆ Literacy skills: writing questions to ask the teenage boy featured in this unit, and his likely responses
- ◆ Thinking skills: explaining where migrants to Rio come from and where you find shanty towns; identifying problems and what's been done to improve shanty town life; thinking of further ways to improve life; thinking of reasons

Unit outcomes

By the end of this unit, most students should be able to:

- ◆ define the terms given in 'Key vocabulary' above;
- ◆ describe the location of Rio de Janeiro and Rocinha;
- ◆ explain where shanty towns are found;
- ◆ describe what life is like in a shanty town;
- ◆ identify what has been done to try to improve shanty town life in the Favela Bairro project;
- ◆ explain why the Favela Bairro project has had mixed results.

Ideas for a starter

1 Ask students to remind you how they defined deprivation in unit 9.7.

2 Show photos or a video of a shanty town in an LEDC. Ask students: Does their definition of deprivation need changing?

3 Ask students to find Rio de Janeiro in an atlas, and describe its location (Activities question 4a).

Ideas for plenaries

1 What should the priority be in developing the favelas? Choose from the following and discuss with a partner to decide on your order of priorities:

- new basic dwellings
- water supply
- basic electricity and sewer system
- access to medical facilities
- access to education
- opportunities for employment in the formal sector
- transport services

- police force encouraged to work in the favelas
- clear temporary houses from the site and build new roads
- developing the areas the people have moved from
- You may decide to combine some of these alternatives.

2 Developments in urban areas should be sustainable. How can governments in LEDCs ensure this happens in future developments?

3 Mind movie time. You are Esat – the boy on page 185. Your favela has been upgraded. Tell us what it is like now and how your life has changed.

4 Play 'Just a minute' – the topic is 'Urban problems in MEDCs and LEDCs'. Students have the chance to talk for a minute on the topic without repetition or hesitation. As soon as a student repeats an idea or hesitates, the next student takes over.

Further class and homework activities

Try to find other examples of development in shanty towns. Many of the Indian cities have schemes which are worth studying.

Answers to the Activities

1 a A shanty town is a squatter community that springs up in an area that used to have no houses – it is usually unplanned, made up of makeshift houses, and located in a less favourable part of the city.

b A squatter is someone who settles on land without the legal right to stay there.

2 A favela.

3 a Questions that might be asked of Esat in a radio interview:

- How long have you been doing this job?
- How far from the market do you live?
- When / what do you eat?
- Have you ever been to school?
- How old are your brothers and sisters?
- What do your brothers and sisters do?
- Do any of your brothers and sisters go to school?
- What do your parents do?
- What do you do for fun?

b Answers will vary according to the student's understanding of shanty life and opportunities and, perhaps, imagination.

4 a Rio de Janeiro is located at 22° South and 43° West; it is just north of the Tropic of Capricorn; it's on the coast of South-East Brazil; it's east of Sao Paulo, another large city in Brazil; the South-East is the most densely populated part of Brazil.

b The rural areas of Brazil.

5 a Shanty towns tend to be found in the less favourable parts of LEDC cities – such as steep and often unstable hillsides or swampy areas.

b Shanty towns develop in these places because they were empty – other people didn't want to live there, or use the land.

6 Six problems of life in Rocinha could include: lack of clean water, lack of running water, lack of toilets / sanitation, lack of sewage system, lack of health care, poor health / high rates of sickness and disease, diarrhoea – especially in young children, high death rates, poor quality housing, overcrowding, street crime, drugs, violence – Rocinha is a dangerous place to live.

7 a The five things done to improve shanty life through the Favela Bairro project: paving roads, installing proper sewage systems, providing better quality low-cost housing, improving law and order, giving people legitimate property rights.

b Four further ideas to improve life could include: i better training in basic literacy and numeracy – this would help people to get better jobs; ii more schools / better schooling for children – this would improve their chances of getting better jobs later on and would help take them off the street; iii improved health care – this would reduce death rates; iv improved community facilities and activities, such as a local radio station or community centre – this would help develop beneficial community spirit; v improved water supply – this would help to improve health; vi improved electricity supply – this would improve living conditions and health (through better cooking facilities and so on); vii help for shanty dwellers to set up banks and businesses – this would help economic development and so make the shanty more prosperous.

8 Having the legal right to stay put helps shanty residents because it gives them a permanent place to live: it gives them a future, a degree of security and confidence; they can work to improve their homes and the whole shanty, knowing that they won't be moved on or their work destroyed; they can invest time and money in improving the physical and social infrastructure of the shanty town (roads, water, electricity, health care, schools, community facilities, businesses).

The unit in brief

In this unit students learn about an urban model for LEDC cities and compare it with actual land use in Rio de Janeiro. They compare the LEDC urban model with the Burgess model which they looked at in Unit 9.5. They also analyse a cartoon map of Rio, looking at what it does and doesn't show.

Key ideas

◆ LEDC cities have land use zones – just like MEDC cities – but the pattern of land use is different:

- The CBD is at the centre.

- The best housing starts near the CBD, often running along a 'spine'.

- Medium quality housing is next to the high-class area.

- Shanty towns develop on unpleasant sites, and can be close to the high-class areas.

- Areas of social housing are found on the periphery.

- Industries are found along the main roads.

Key vocabulary

spine

Skills practised in the Activities

◆ Geography skills: comparing a land use map of Rio de Janeiro with the LEDC urban model; comparing the LEDC urban model with the Burgess model

◆ Thinking skills: analysing a cartoon map of Rio de Janeiro

Unit outcomes

By the end of this unit, most students should be able to:

◆ explain the term given in 'Key vocabulary' above;

◆ understand that LEDC cities have land use zones – just like MEDC cities – but that the pattern of land use is different;

◆ describe the pattern of land use for a 'typical' LEDC city, as shown by the LEDC urban model;

◆ describe how the pattern of land use in Rio de Janeiro is similar to, and different from, the LEDC urban land use model.

Ideas for a starter

1   Recap: What is an urban model? Draw the Burgess model for MEDC cities on the board and label the land use in each urban zone.

2   Ask students: Do you think the patterns of land use will be the same or different in LEDC cities as in MEDC cities?

3   Show photographs of CBDs from cities in LEDCs and ask for comments from the students. What does the quality of life look like?

Ideas for plenaries

1   If employment in LEDCs is largely in the CBD and in the industrial sector, how does this affect poor people's employment opportunities? What problems do they face?

2   Draw a map for tourists visiting Rio de Janeiro (it needs to be more accurate than the cartoon map). What advice would you give tourists visiting the city?

3   Many high quality residential areas in LEDC cities are gated communities. What does this tell you about the income levels in many LEDCs?

4   Compare the problems and development issues in cities in LEDCs with those in MEDCs. Use a Venn diagram.

5   Look at the urban model for LEDC cities on page 186. Now close your book and draw it from memory. You must label it too.

Answers to the Activities

1
- Rio has a CBD.
- Rio also has elite residential areas.
- The favelas are close to the better housing.

2
- Rio has no concentric zones.
- It's not circular.
- The map doesn't show colonial areas, poor-quality permanent housing, housing improvement schemes.

3   Both models have a central CBD, and both have concentric zones, but only for poor-quality housing and shanty towns.

The LEDC city model:
- has sectors, like the industry along the main roads, as well as concentric zones;
- gives much more detail about housing quality than Burgess does;
- has no rural-urban fringe.

4   The cartoon shows the tourist attractions: the concrete Christ, the Sugar Loaf mountain, the National Park, and Ipanema and Copacabana beaches. The marina inland of Ipanema isn't shown on the map. One small favela area is shown, but it doesn't look anything like Rocinha.

5   The cartoon is designed to make Rio look like a very attractive tourist destination. It's not concerned with the downside of Rio.

The unit in brief

This unit is about traffic and the problems it causes. It includes case studies from Bangkok and Moscow. In the Activities, students describe and explain the change in car ownership in Russia using a line graph. They also suggest how traffic problems in Moscow could be improved and rank their suggested improvements by cost and environmental impact.

Key ideas

◆ Traffic problems are often caused by the sheer volume of traffic.

◆ The numbers of cars on the roads are increasing all the time.

◆ Traffic causes air and noise pollution.

◆ Insufficient public transport can increase traffic volumes.

◆ There are different ways to solve traffic problems e.g. congestion charging in London, improving road crossings for pedestrians and making bays at bus stops in Tokyo.

Key vocabulary

There is no key vocabulary in this unit.

Skills practised in the Activities

◆ Geography skills: describing and explaining the change in car ownership in Russia using line graph;

◆ Numeracy skills: ranking improvements

◆ Thinking skills: suggesting ways to improve traffic problems; explaining rankings

Unit outcomes

By the end of this unit, most students should be able to:

◆ understand why traffic problems are often caused by the sheer volume of traffic;

◆ describe and explain the increase in car ownership in Russia;

◆ describe the problems that heavy traffic causes;

◆ describe different ways of solving traffic problems.

Ideas for a starter

1 Use this website to download an article about traffic:
   news.bbc.co.uk/1/hi/uk/2223060.stm
   Or record the local traffic news from the radio and play it to students. Use as a basis for a discussion on 'Increasing traffic in the UK'.

2 Brainstorm to find out why students think traffic is such a problem – not just here, but everywhere.

3 Show a photo of gridlocked traffic. Create a spider diagram on the board of the problems caused by traffic.

Ideas for plenaries

1 Work in small groups. What other ways are there of reducing traffic congestion and managing traffic? Here are a few ideas: multiple-occupancy lanes on roads, free public transport, pollution monitoring, restrictions on private transport entering the city, tramways etc. Complete a table of their advantages and disadvantages.

2 Obtain information from the local planning office on the flow of traffic in the local area and provide it for students. Ask them to show the information diagrammatically, and suggest how the traffic flows could be managed.

3 Write a diary of your own and your family's personal transport over the course of the last week. Is your family dependent on the car for transport? Could this dependency be reduced? How? If your family is dependent on the car, how would family life be different if you had to rely on public transport?

4 Describe a recent scheme in your area to manage traffic. How successful has it been?

5 Create an acrostic. Write TRAFFIC down one side of the page. Make each letter the first letter of a word, phrase, or sentence about traffic.

Further class and homework activities

Carry out some fieldwork measuring the volume of traffic around your town. Try to sample the traffic – you can't count it all – and try to have different people counting different types of vehicle. Represent this information by drawing flow diagrams. Make suggestions on how the flow of traffic could be managed.

Answers to the Activities

1 a Students should use the data on the axes; something like: 'car ownership rose steadily from 100 in 1995 to 160 in 2002'.

 b (Some) people have got richer in Moscow, and car sales are expected to rise by 0.4 million between 2005 and 2008. More cars mean more traffic jams.

2 Moscow could:

◆ build an overhead sky train;

◆ build pedestrian flyovers;

◆ restrict crossing points, by putting barriers along the streets so the traffic won't be slowed down;

◆ build bus bays so that traffic doesn't build up at bus stops;

◆ build more roads;

◆ try to cut down on accidents: better traffic lights, speed cameras, improving accident black spots, fine illegal parking heavily.

3

Rating by cost	Rating by environmental impact
1. Skytrain	1. New roads – more traffic capacity means more air pollution. Habitats are destroyed as land disappears under the tarmac.

Rating by cost	Rating by environmental impact
2. New road	2. Curing accident black spots, restricting crossings, pedestrian flyovers and bus bays will also increase traffic flows, and thus pollution.
3. Pedestrian flyover	3. Pedestrian flyovers will also increase traffic flows, and thus pollution.
4. Restricted crossings, bus bays, improvements to accident black spots	4. Skytrain is much less polluting than thousands of cars, so emissions are lower, but a lot of people live in the shadow of the line.
5. Clamping illegally parked cars – the fines should pay for the wardens.	5. Clamping might reduce the number of people driving into the city, so it would reduce the emission of carbon dioxide, carbon monoxide, and oxides of nitrogen.

4 Because methods which speed up traffic flow or increase road capacity will increase air pollution.

The unit in brief

This unit is about how some of our towns and cities are expanding, and the problems this causes at the rural-urban fringe. In the Activities, students look at why people are leaving cities, and the attractions of a lifestyle at the rural-urban fringe. They name land uses that develop at the rural-urban fringe and explain why this area is attractive to them.

Key ideas

◆ Settlements are growing at the rural-urban fringe. This is called urban sprawl.

◆ In most MEDC cities, people are moving out to smaller towns and villages – the process of counter-urbanisation.

◆ Some people want to build at the rural-urban fringe, others are against it.

◆ The government has tried to protect the countryside by creating green belts.

◆ Developing brownfield sites is one alternative to building at the rural-urban fringe.

Key vocabulary

rural-urban fringe, counter-urbanisation, green belt

Skills practised in the Activities

◆ Geography skills: defining the terms 'counter-urbanisation ' and 'rural-urban fringe'

◆ Thinking skills: giving reasons why people are leaving cities; giving the attractions of the rural-urban fringe lifestyle; naming land uses at the rural-urban fringe and explaining why this area is attractive to them

Unit outcomes

By the end of this unit, most students should be able to:

◆ define the terms given in 'Key vocabulary' above;

◆ explain why people are moving out of cities;

◆ explain why some people want to build at the rural-urban fringe, and why others are against it;

◆ understand how the government has tried to protect the countryside;

◆ name one example of an alternative to building at the rural-urban fringe.

Ideas for a starter

1 Ask: Who can tell me: What does urban sprawl mean? What is the rural-urban fringe and counter-urbanisation? What are green belts?

2 Show photos of activities/developments at the rural-urban fringe, e.g. retail developments, golf courses, garden centres, housing estates, farms. Ask: What do these things have in common? Why do some of them lead to conflict?

Ideas for plenaries

1 You have been to a meeting at the planning office to discuss new developments in the rural-urban fringe. At the meeting there was: a developer wishing to build new houses; a family living in the twilight zone hoping for affordable housing in the suburbs; a farmer with land in the rural-urban fringe; a conservationist; an industrial developer wanting to build there; the local planning office. You are a journalist and now have to write a newspaper article based on the discussions at the meeting. You have a ten-minute deadline. Off you go!

2 What plans are there for development at the rural-urban fringe in your town? What do you and other local people think about the plans?

3 Did you find anything difficult about the work in this chapter? What? Why? What would help to make it less difficult?

4 Question time! Think back over the chapter and write down three questions related to what you have learned. The teacher will ask a member of the class to try to answer.

5 Prepare a crossword for students including the key terms from this chapter.

Further class and homework activities

1 Investigate the pattern of 'green belts' in the UK. Try to find out details about the green belt around one major town.

2 The building of 'new towns' in the UK was one of the ways planners attempted to halt urban sprawl. Find out about the Abercrombie Plan and the Greater London Development Plan. Investigate the development of new towns around large urban areas such as London.

Answers to the Activities

1 a Counter-urbanisation is the fall in the percentage of the population living in towns – contrast this with urbanisation.

b The rural-urban fringe is the area at the edge of town where the city meets the country, so it's half rural and half urban.

2 People are moving out of cities because:
◆ inner cities are often dirty, crowded and can feel dangerous;
◆ the countryside is cleaner and quieter;
◆ trains and fast roads make it easy to commute long distances; many people commute daily from Oxford to London, for example;
◆ businesses and industries are moving out-of-town.

3 Attractions of the rural-urban fringe include:
◆ cheaper land: for car parks and new houses;
◆ space for bigger retail outlets and leisure facilities;
◆ farmers are developing new leisure activities, like golf courses;
◆ business and science parks are much nicer than old industrial sites.

4 Uses include:
multiplex cinemas, sports stadiums, hypermarkets and golf courses. In all cases, stress the cheaper land, the much greater area of the periphery as opposed to the CBD, so there's more land available, good access to ring roads and motorways, and new, modern developments: business parks, science parks, affordable housing.

10 Agriculture

The big picture

These are the key ideas behind this chapter:

◆ Farming is a system, with inputs, processes and outputs. Systems can be applied to any farm, anywhere in the world.

◆ Physical and human factors affect a farmer's choice about what type of farming to do. For most types of farming climate is the most important factor.

◆ Farmers, whether in the UK, the rest of the EU, or in LEDCs, face problems and challenges.

◆ Farming needs to be made more sustainable.

Note that the students' version of the big picture is given in the students' chapter opener.

Chapter outline

Use this, and the students' chapter opener, to give students a mental roadmap for the chapter.

10   **Agriculture** As the students' chapter opener, this unit is an important part of the chapter; see page 11 of this book for notes about using chapter openers

10.1 **Farming – what's it all about?** Introduction to farming and farming as a system

10.2 **Farming – what happens where?** Classifying farms, and different types of farming in the UK

10.3 **Farming – on the flat…and on the edge** Case studies of an arable farm (Lynford House Farm), and a hill farm (Herdship Farm), both in the UK

10.4 **Is farming in crisis?** A look at some of the problems facing the UK's farmers

10.5 **All change for farming** Changes to CAP, animal welfare, agribusiness and mechanisation

10.6 **Making farming sustainable** Some ways of making farming in the UK more sustainable – traditional methods, agri-environment schemes, organic farming and diversification

10.7 **Farming in the EU** A case study of market gardening in the Netherlands, and farming in Eastern Europe

10.8 **Farming in LEDCs** Case studies of subsistence rice farming in the Philippines and commercial flower growing in Kenya

10.9 **LEDCs – challenges and solutions** A look at the challenges facing LEDC farmers and solutions to some of their problems

Objectives and outcomes for this chapter

Objectives	Unit	Outcomes
Most students will understand:		Most students will be able to:
• That farming is a system.	10.1, 10.3, 10.7, 10.8	• Describe a farming system and give examples of inputs, processes and outputs.
• How farms are classified.	10.2	• Explain how farms are classified, and give examples of different types of farms.
• That climate is the most important factor affecting the distribution of farming.	10.2	• Explain the distribution of different farming types in the UK.
• The differences in farming in the UK.	10.3	• Draw a systems diagram for a UK hill farm and explain the differences between this and the arable farm systems diagram.
• That farmers in the UK face a range of problems.	10.4	• Describe the problems facing farmers in the UK today.
• That there are changes which affect farming in the UK.	10.3, 10.5	• Give examples of some of the changes affecting farming, and say how they affect farmers.
• How farming in the UK can become more sustainable.	10.6	• Give examples of traditional farming, agri-environment schemes and diversification; explain what organic means.
• The challenges faced by market gardeners in the Netherlands and farmers in Eastern Europe.	10.7	• Describe the methods used in market gardening and farming in Eastern Europe; describe the problems in both types of farming; explain how farmers in Eastern Europe could survive.
• The nature of subsistence rice farming in the Philippines and commercial flower growing in Kenya.	10.8	• Describe the nature of subsistence rice farming and commercial flower growing; list the problems they face; describe what is being done to make flower growing sustainable.
• That farmers in LEDCs face problems and that some of the solutions to the problems are sustainable and others aren't.	10.9	• List the problems faced by farmers in LEDCs; give six possible solutions to farmers problems and explain why some are sustainable, and others aren't.

These tie in with 'Your goals for this chapter' in the students' chapter opener, and with the opening lines in each unit, which give the purpose of the unit in a student-friendly style.

Using the chapter starter

The photo on page 192 of the *geog.GCSE* students' book shows a dairy cow. Milk is nutritious, and kind to teeth! And from milk we get cheese, butter, ice cream, milk powders, cream, and yoghurt.

There are more than 2 million dairy cows in Britain – that's one for every thirty people. Since the mid-1980s numbers have declined, but yields have increased, so milk production has remained stable. Each cow is milked on average 300 days a year, two or three times a day. A cow can produce 20 litres of milk a day. In an average lifetime, we'll each drink over 6000 litres of milk.

The UK is largely self-sufficient in milk. We're the third-largest milk producer in Europe, the seventh-largest in the world. Our milk production is limited by EU quotas – the quota for 2005 was 14.2 billion litres.

In November 2005 about two thousand British farmers went on strike for three days in protest at the low prices paid by retailers for food and milk. Over 700 dairy farmers went out of business between 2001 and 2005. Many of them blamed the low prices they were getting from the supermarkets. As of February 2006, dairy farmers were getting 18p a litre for their milk, but they said it cost 19p a litre to produce; in the shops, milk was selling for 50p a litre.

The unit in brief

This unit introduces farming, and provides a range of ideas for students to think about from 'How important is farming?' to 'How far does our food travel?'. It looks at farming as a system with inputs, processes and outputs. In the Activities, students look at the issue of battery farming, consider the role of farmers and look at the importance of physical factors in farming.

Key ideas

◆ Farmers produce food, but also look after the countryside.

◆ Farming is a system.

◆ The farming system has inputs, processes and outputs.

◆ Systems can be applied to any farm, anywhere in the world.

Key vocabulary

agriculture, system, inputs (physical, human and economic), processes, outputs, feedback, factors

Skills practised in the Activities

◆ Thinking skills: thinking about the importance of battery farming; considering whether people are influenced by others' opinions; thinking about the role of farmers; explaining the importance of physical factors in farming

Unit outcomes

By the end of this unit, most students should be able to:

◆ define the terms given in 'Key vocabulary' above;

◆ understand that farming is a system;

◆ know that the farming system has inputs, processes and outputs;

◆ explain why physical factors are important in farming.

Ideas for a starter

1 Brainstorm to find out what students know about farming, and what farmers do. Write all the ideas on the board, then try to group them together.

2 Use the photos of Rick Stein and battery hens on page 194 to promote a discussion of different methods of farming and issues to do with farming in the UK.

3 Use the spider diagram on page 194 to introduce the topic. Draw it on the board and ask students for answers to each of the questions.

Ideas for plenaries

1 Provide students with a blank systems diagram. Students can work in pairs to complete a diagram for different types of farming.

2 If you did not use starter 3, divide the class into groups. Give each group one 'bubble' question for the spider diagram on page 194 and ask for responses from each member of the group.

3 Are physical or human factors likely to be most important in farming?

4 Which of the physical factors is most important in farming?

5 Can students think of a type of farming where climate isn't important?

6 Ask your neighbour to name three physical inputs and three human and economic inputs into the farming system. Ask for examples of two processes and two outputs.

Answers to the Activities

1 Increased pressure due to the demand for cheap food. Increased demand overall. This type of farming is the most cost effective, enabling farmers to produce high levels of output.

2 This will depend in part on students' opinions. It is not likely that Rick Stein will have a great influence over farmers. The same could be argued for the general public. There is the counter argument that, as a celebrity chef with forthright views, he will be able to influence a significant minority of consumers.

3 This is only partially true. It is correct to state that, obviously, much of our food is grown in the UK. It is important to note, however, that a large minority of food in the UK is imported. There is also the point that, increasingly, the farmland of this country is used for purposes other than the cultivation of food.

4 The answer will depend upon the factors chosen. Any answer should relate to the importance that physical factors have upon farming.

The unit in brief

This unit looks at how farms are classified, and the pattern of farming types in the UK. In the Activities, students look at farm classification; identify the factors needed for wheat growing; think about why climate is often the most important physical factor influencing farming; and also consider the role of technology for today's farmers.

Key ideas

◆ Farms can be classified in three ways – by processes, input and output.

◆ There's a pattern to the distribution of farming types in the UK.

◆ For most types of farming, physical factors are more important than human factors.

◆ Climate is the most important physical factor.

◆ There are five main types of farming in the UK.

Key vocabulary

processes, arable farms, pastoral farms, mixed farms, market gardening, inputs, intensive, extensive, outputs, commercial, subsistence, pattern, factors, climate, hill sheep farming, dairy farming

Skills practised in the Activities

◆ Thinking skills: explaining; identifying physical and human factors; thinking

Unit outcomes

By the end of this unit, most students should be able to:

◆ define or explain the terms given in 'Key vocabulary' above;

◆ understand that farms can be classified by processes, inputs and outputs;

◆ recognise the pattern of distribution of farming types in the UK;

◆ understand that for most types of farming physical factors are more important than human factors;

◆ explain why climate is the most important physical factor;

◆ identify the five main types of farming in the UK.

Ideas for a starter

1 Show, or give, students maps of annual rainfall in the UK, January and July temperatures, and relief of the UK. Ask for suggestions about where sheep farming, cereal farming, dairying and beef-rearing might be found.

2 Ask students where market gardening might be found. What is the difference between this and other types of farming in terms of physical and human factors? (It is not dependent on climate.)

3 Show photos of rural areas and ask students to identify types of farming. Are there any obvious physical factors influencing farming?

Ideas for plenaries

1 On a blank map of the UK, draw a map showing the distribution of farming types in the UK. Add annotations to explain the distribution.

2 What do the following terms mean:
   ◆ arable
   ◆ pastoral
   ◆ mixed
   ◆ market gardening
   ◆ intensive
   ◆ extensive
   ◆ commercial
   ◆ subsistence

3 How can the words in plenary 2 classify different types of farming systems?

4 What is pastoral farming? Why are most pastoral farms in the UK found in the north and west?

5 Where do you find arable farms in the UK? And why?

6 Make a graffiti wall of what students have learned today.

Answers to the Activities

1 Farming in the UK is usually classified as commercial because the outputs – crops and animals – are mostly sold to make a profit; farming in the UK is geared to selling produce for profit. This contrasts with subsistence farming, where farmers produce food for themselves and their family, with nothing left to sell for a profit.

2 a Physical factors to grow wheat: warm sunny summers, a dry harvest time, flat land suitable for large machines, fertile soils. Human factors to grow wheat: money to buy large machines, good transport links.

 b Wheat isn't grown in the Lake District because the climate is too cold and wet for the wheat to grow well, the soils tend to be poor and thin, and the land is too steep and hilly for large machines.

3 Climate is often the most important physical factor influencing farming because it determines what plants and crops will / won't grow – climate largely determines growth conditions. Other physical factors, such as soils, are more easily modified.

4 The answer here will depend upon students' opinions. To some extent it is in the northern parts of the UK that physical factors play an important role, whereas in the south and east there is greater influence of human factors.

4 Technology helps the modern farmer in the UK to overcome or moderate many physical factors, even climate (think about greenhouses, heaters, irrigation, fertilisers, new strains of crops, fast transport links to markets) – but overall, climate continues to play an important determining role: until a strain of wheat is developed that will grow in cold, wet, windy conditions wheat will never be grown in areas with this type of climate.

The unit in brief

This unit consists of two case studies – Lynford House Farm in East Anglia (an example of a commercial arable farm) and Herdship Farm in Teesdale (an example of an extensive hill sheep farm). In the Activities, students look at the issue of subsidies; think about how farmers could make more money, draw a systems diagram for Herdship Farm and compare it with that for Lynford House Farm.

Key ideas

◆ All farms can be described as systems.

◆ The inputs, processes and outputs differ for different types of farming.

◆ Farms and farmers have to change if they are to survive.

◆ Farmers consider themselves as land managers – not just farmers.

Key vocabulary

arable farming, hill farming

Skills practised in the Activities

◆ Geography skills: drawing a farming systems diagram and comparing it with another

◆ Thinking skills: explaining and thinking about subsidies; suggesting ways for farmers to make money

Unit outcomes

By the end of this unit, most students should be able to:

◆ explain the terms given in 'Key vocabulary' above;

◆ understand that inputs, processes and outputs differ for different types of farming;

◆ realise that farmers have to change if they are to survive;

◆ understand why farmers consider themselves as land managers, not just farmers.

Ideas for a starter

1 Recap: the classification of different types of farm.

2 Show headlines from newspaper articles relating to arable farming and hill farming to generate discussion that farming is not an easy life – and the farms and farmers are changing.

3 Draw two blank systems diagrams on the board. Ask for suggestions for inputs, processes, and outputs for an arable farm and a hill farm.

Ideas for plenaries

1 Activities question 4 could be used as a plenary.

2 Using the systems diagrams for Lynford House Farm, show what decisions the farmer might have to make if the price of the main crop was reduced, or the price of fertiliser increased. Give a number of different scenarios to the students so that they can use their diagrams to raise a number of different decisions the farmers may be forced to make.

3 Should farmers be considered to be 'managers' of the countryside?

4 Make 10-15 statements about farming in the UK based on what students have learned so far, some true, some false. Students hold up True and False cards. Where statements are false, ask students to correct them.

Further class and homework activities

1 Investigate other types of farms and try to draw systems diagrams like those used in the students' book. Compare your models with those given in the students' book. You may wish to use the following website to help you: www.face-online.org.uk/

2 Investigate the current system of farm support in the UK. Look at the DEFRA website.

Answers to the Activities

1 A payment made to support farmers, usually to make something profitable.

2 Many products will otherwise result in a loss to farmers. Subsidies therefore help to keep farmers in business, and farming the land.

3 The farm could diversify into other food products. It could diversify into an increasingly wide range of non-food activities, from activity trails to corporate hospitality events.

4 Inputs would include:

◆ 229 hectares of land, which comprises 22 hectares of flowering hay meadow and the rest is mostly rough pasture

◆ 580 mm of rain a year

◆ 12 cows

◆ sheep: 268 Swaledales and 180 North Country Cheviots

Processes would include:

◆ sheep-dipping

◆ sheep-shearing

◆ lambing

Outputs would include

◆ silage

◆ hay

◆ lambs

Herdship farm will have fewer inputs, processes and outputs.

The unit in brief

This unit is about some of the problems facing the UK's farmers – from those caused by the supermarkets, to things like soil erosion and the use of chemicals. In the Activities, students carry out a small survey to discover where their food comes from; consider why farmers have difficulty competing with those abroad evaluate the factors causing problems for farmers; and look at two past (but fairly recent) problems – BSE and foot and mouth disease.

Key ideas

◆ People want to buy different food, and more cheaply, than in the past.

◆ Supermarkets are very powerful. They choose their suppliers and decide how much to pay farmers.

◆ The food market is global – farmers in the UK compete with those abroad.

◆ Soil erosion, use of chemicals and the number of farmers leaving the industry are further problems.

Key vocabulary

global, soil erosion, overproduction, pesticides, fertiliser

Skills practised in the Activities

◆ Geography skills: carrying out a survey and describing the results; researching past farming problems

◆ Thinking skills: thinking of reasons; assessing how far various factors have caused problems for farmers

Unit outcomes

By the end of this unit, most students should be able to:

◆ define the terms given in 'Key vocabulary' above;

◆ understand the connection between supermarkets and farmers;

◆ understand why the food market has become global;

◆ explain other farming problems such as soil erosion, use of chemicals and numbers of farmers leaving the industry.

Ideas for a starter

1 Go to:

news.bbc.co.uk/1/hi/special_report/1999/09/99/farming_in_crisis/442787.stm

Summarise the main points for students: Do they agree that farming is in crisis?

2 Use a variation on Activities question 1 as a starter. Ask students what they ate at home last night for dinner. List the fresh items with their (likely) source. What does that tell us? How much of the food produced abroad is also grown in the UK? How much of it was not in season?

3 Brainstorm to find out what students know about problems facing farmers in the UK. Some have already been touched on in previous units, but see how many others they can come up with. Some will be dealt with in unit 10.5.

Ideas for plenaries

1 If you used starter 2, students can continue to work on the idea of food miles. For each item work out how far their food has travelled to reach their shop or supermarket. They can use an atlas to measure the distance the food has travelled.

2 Ask students to produce a world map showing where the food listed in starter 2 came from.

3 Would we be prepared to pay more for our food to support local farmers? The countryside is managed by the farmers. If we value the countryside should we be prepared to pay more for our food?

4 Write an email from Robin Spence to his local supermarket. He wants to know why he is paid so little for his milk, compared to the price it is sold for. Now write a reply from the supermarket.

5 Take two minutes with a partner to think up one interesting question about some of the problems facing the UK's farmers that we have not covered today.

Answers to the Activities

1 The answer to this will depend upon the results of students' research.

2 Much production abroad has significantly lower input costs, for example cheap labour. Conditions may be more favourable for certain products, and there could be significant government support.

3 This will depend upon students' opinions. Look for some evaluation of the different factors.

4 Answers will vary according to the example chosen. BSE led to the mass slaughter of cows, the banning of certain cuts of meat, an export ban on British beef; foot and mouth resulted, as well as destruction of livestock, in the 'closure' of much of the countryside to the public during the outbreak.

The unit in brief

This unit is about changes in farming in the UK. It looks at changes to the Common Agricultural Policy (CAP) and other changes such as concern about animal welfare, agribusiness and increased mechanisation (with the subsequent loss of jobs). In the Activities, students look at the differences between the CAP subsidies and the new Single Payment System (SPS) and consider whether farmers will benefit from the SPS; think about the set-aside policy; consider the advantages and disadvantages of agribusiness, and look at the benefits of increased mechanisation for larger farms.

Key ideas

◆ CAP reform means that farmers no longer get several different subsidies – they now get one single payment a year.

◆ There is increased concern about animal welfare in farming.

◆ Some farms are getting bigger as they become agribusinesses.

◆ People working on farms continue to be replaced by machinery, and the numbers employed full-time continue to fall.

Key vocabulary

Common Agricultural Policy, subsidies, Single Payment System, quota, set-aside, animal welfare, agribusiness, mechanisation

Skills practised in the Activities

◆ Thinking skills: explaining food mountains and lakes; explaining differences; thinking of reasons; stating whether they agree with a policy; considering benefits and disadvantages of agribusiness; explaining benefits of increased mechanisation

Unit outcomes

By the end of this unit, most students should be able to:

◆ define or explain the terms given in 'Key vocabulary' above;

◆ understand the differences between CAP subsidies and the SPS;

◆ recognise that there is concern about animal welfare in farming;

◆ describe the advantages and disadvantages of agribusiness;

◆ understand why full-time jobs continue to be lost in farming.

Ideas for a starter

1 How could the following change farming:
    ◆ a guaranteed price for the produce
    ◆ greater consideration for animal welfare
    ◆ amalgamation of farms to create bigger farms
    ◆ increased mechanisation
    ◆ greater diversification – country walks, golf courses and camp-sites instead of farmland.
    Invite discussion of each scenario, and decide how they would change farming.

2 Show a photo of set-aside land (like the one at the bottom of page 202). Ask: Is this farming?

Ideas for plenaries

1 Draw a spider diagram showing changes in farming in the UK. What are the advantages and disadvantages of the changes?

2 Consider this: 'Farming needs to change to stay profitable. Are there any changes which are not acceptable?' Discuss this with a neighbour and be ready to participate in a whole-class discussion on this issue.

3 Show a photograph of traditional hedge and field farmland. Ask students: How would this area change with greater mechanisation and increased farm sizes? Draw a sketch showing how the area could be changed, and annotate it to show the changes.

4 What is the CAP? What are subsidies? What is the SPS?

5 What are quotas and set-aside?

6 Did you find anything difficult about the work in this unit? What? Why? What would help to make it less difficult?

Answers to the Activities

1 As farmers were guaranteed a minimum price for their produce – no matter how much of it there was – there was no market incentive to cap their production.

2 The SPS is a single annual payment that doesn't rely on huge production to ensure significant payment. It breaks the link between production and payment, and is linked more closely to market needs.

3 This will depend in part upon students' opinions. It is likely that larger farms will benefit more.

4 To encourage them not to over produce on their land. To maintain some of their land in a semi-natural state.

5 Agribusiness benefits from economies of scale, and so can meet the ever increasing demand of the British public for cheap food. It can, however, strangle competition and stifle choice. Agribusiness landscapes can be monotonous and unattractive, and lead to a lack of bio-diversity.

6 Economies of scale mean that large farms are likely to benefit most. Benefits are likely to be least in hill farming regions in the north of Britain.

The unit in brief

This unit looks at some of the ways in which farming in the UK can be made more sustainable. It covers a variety of approaches ranging from using traditional methods and agri-environment schemes through to diversification and producing potato chips. In the Activities, students consider the importance of making farming sustainable; think about the attractions and disadvantages of agri-environment schemes; find out how farmers diversify; and think about whether farmers should be paid to look after the countryside.

Key ideas

◆ Farming needs to become more sustainable to overcome some of the problems and challenges facing farmers today.

◆ There are a number of ways in which farming can become more sustainable: using traditional methods; agri-environment schemes; changing to organic farming; diversification.

Key vocabulary

sustainable, agri-environment, Tir Gofal, Environmental Stewardship, organic, diversify

Skills practised in the Activities

◆ Thinking skills: considering the importance of making farming sustainable; explaining; thinking of disadvantages; finding out; justifying opinions

Unit outcomes

By the end of this unit, most students should be able to:

◆ define or explain the terms given in 'Key vocabulary' above;

◆ understand what 'making farming sustainable' means;

◆ understand that there are a number of ways in which farming can become more sustainable;

◆ give some examples of how farmers can diversify.

Ideas for a starter

1 Recap: What challenges has farming faced in the UK in recent years?

2 Ask: What does sustainable mean in a geographical context? Can you think of some examples you have already studied which have included sustainable options?

3 Draw a farming system (inputs/processes/outputs) on the board. Ask for suggestions on how a farm could become more sustainable.

4 Show photos of a variety of ways farming can become more sustainable, e.g. using traditional farming methods, traditional meadows, and examples of diversification. Ask: What do these have in common?

Ideas for plenaries

1 Making farming more sustainable might bring some unwanted problems with it. Food may become more expensive and local farmers may lose if we can buy food produced more cheaply abroad. We might only be able to buy food when it's in season rather than all year round. Can you think of any other problems? Do you think farming should become more sustainable?

2 Draw a poster advertising locally grown organic vegetables in preference to the vegetables from the supermarket.

3 Write a letter to the local newspaper advising local people to demand local products on sale in the supermarkets in the interest of sustainability.

4 Do you value the countryside? Is it worth spending our money collected in taxes to maintain it or should more be spent in the towns? Work out your argument with your neighbour before putting it to the rest of the class. Have a vote and see what the result is.

5 Write 'Making farming sustainable' in the middle of your page. Create a mind map around the phrase. How many ideas can you come up with in two minutes?

6 Investigate market gardening in the Netherlands, and farming in Poland. Some students will be asked to give a short presentation to the class in the next lesson summarising their findings.

Further class and homework activities

1 Visit this website and gather information on the relationship between farming and wildlife: www.rspb.org.uk/countryside/farming/hopefarm/index.asp

Try to write up a small case study of Hope Farm remembering to include location, enterprises, and the plans for the future.

2 Look up sustainability on the website of Friends of the Earth, Greenpeace, and the UK government department DEFRA. Collect examples of sustainable systems and compare the various definitions.

Answers to the Activities

1 To preserve the countryside for future generations. To maintain biodiversity.

2 a To help maintain the environment and preserve biodiversity. There may be economic benefits through grants and subsidies.

b Inability to compete against large producers. Labour intensive work. May not be sustainable in the long term.

3 This will depend upon students' research. Examples may include adventure trails, childrens' playgrounds, corporate hospitality, etc.

4 This will depend upon students' opinions. Ensure that opinions are justified.

The unit in brief

This unit includes a case study of market gardening in the Netherlands (an example of intensive farming) and introduces farming in Eastern Europe. In the Activities, students explain why physical factors aren't important in market gardening; draw a systems diagram for a typical farm in Poland, and compare it with the one they drew for Herdship Farm (the hill sheep farm case study); and consider whether agro-tourism would work
in the UK.

Key ideas

◆ Market gardening is the growing of fruit, vegetables and flowers intensively.

◆ Natural physical factors are not important for market gardening.

◆ Market gardening faces challenges.

◆ Farmers in Eastern Europe face difficulties competing with those in the richer EU countries.

◆ Farmers in Eastern Europe could save their livelihoods by going organic or becoming involved in agro-tourist projects.

Key vocabulary

market gardening, intensive, labour, capital, high-tech, agro-tourism

Skills practised in the Activities

◆ Geography skills: drawing a farming systems diagram and comparing it with another

◆ Thinking skills: explaining why physical factors are not important for market gardening; thinking; explaining

Unit outcomes

By the end of this unit, most students should be able to:

◆ define or explain the terms given in 'Key vocabulary' above;

◆ understand what market gardening is;

◆ explain why natural physical factors are not important for market gardening;

◆ realise that market gardening in the Netherlands faces challenges;

◆ understand why farmers in Eastern Europe face difficulties, and what they can do about them.

Ideas for a starter

1 Ask a few students to give their presentations on the Netherlands and Poland.

2 Ask students to find the odd-one-out, and explain why it is the odd-one-out:
- intensive / extensive / input
- output / labour intensive / mechanised
- CAP / subsidy / quota
- soil erosion / overgrazing / diversification

3 Mental map time! Ask: Where are the Netherlands and Poland? With all books closed and no clues on the walls, ask students to mark them on a blank outline map of Europe.

Ideas for plenaries

1 Activities question 3 could be used as a plenary.

2 List the inputs, processes, and outputs for market gardening.

3 Test your partner on market gardening. Ask (with books closed): What is market gardening? Is it intensive or extensive? What % of the world's commercially grown flowers does the Netherlands produce? What challenges does the Netherlands face?

4 Design an advertisement for an agro-tourist project in Poland. What sort of advantages would you be stressing?

5 Make a graffiti wall of what students have learned today.

Further class and homework activities

Investigate the trade patterns of the two EU countries. How important to the wealth of the country is agriculture? What types of agriculture if any feature in the pattern of trade? How much of this trade is with the UK?

Answers to the Activities

1 There is a high level of technology used. There is relatively little variation in physical inputs, for example relief and soils.

2 There is a huge market for flowers there. They may then be transported throughout Europe.

3 a Taking Szczepan and Helena Master's farm as a typical example, inputs would include:
- 5 hectares of land
- horses (rather than tractors)
- human labour

Processes would include:
- animal-rearing
- crop-growing

Outputs would include:
- a couple of cows
- 4 pigs
- 11 piglets
- 2 horses
- crops

b The scale of the inputs and outputs is a major difference; Herdship Farm is clearly a much bigger operation.

The Polish farm will be more dominated by physical factors.

4 This will depend upon students' opinions. Agro-tourism is more likely to be successful in parts of the UK where tourism is already an industry, for example the Lake District.

Farming in LEDCs

The unit in brief

This unit includes two LEDC case studies – one of subsistence rice growing in the Philippines, the other of commercial flower growing in Kenya. In the Activities, students draw a diagram to show a year in the life of the Philippines farm; consider the advantages of flower growers in Kenya; and identify the problems that intensive flower growing causes in Kenya.

Key ideas

◆ Rice farming in the Philippines is an example of subsistence farming.

◆ Subsistence means farmers produce enough food for themselves and their family – there is usually nothing left to sell.

◆ Flower growing in Kenya is an example of commercial farming.

◆ Flower growing is capital-intensive.

◆ Flower growers have a range of problems, but people are working to make the industry more sustainable.

Key vocabulary

subsistence farming, capital-intensive, sustainable

Skills practised in the Activities

◆ Geography skills: drawing a diagram to show a year in the life of a farm

◆ Thinking skills: thinking; considering the advantages of flower growers in Kenya; identifying problems caused by flower growing in Kenya

Unit outcomes

By the end of this unit, most students should be able to:

◆ define or explain the terms given in 'Key vocabulary' above;

◆ give examples of subsistence farming and commercial farming in LEDCs;

◆ understand what subsistence means;

◆ understand that flower growing in Kenya is capital-intensive;

◆ identify the problems caused by flower growing in Kenya and know how people are working to make the industry more sustainable.

Ideas for a starter

1 Brainstorm to find out what students know about farming in LEDCs. Ask: How important is agriculture in LEDCs? What percentage of people work in agriculture in the poorest countries? How does this compare with MEDCs?

2 Ask: How is subsistence agriculture and population growth rate linked together?

3 Draw the cycle of poverty on the board and ask for suggestions on how this could be broken.

4 Show students a bunch of roses grown in Kenya. Ask: Where do you think these were grown? Why were they grown there? How did they get here? What problems might growing flowers in Kenya cause?

Ideas for plenaries

1 Should LEDCs grow cash crops for MEDCs or should they grow their own food and become more self-sufficient? Have a whole-class discussion. What is your conclusion? Which is the more sustainable?

2 What sort of assistance could be given by MEDCs to help the situation in the LEDCs?

3 Ask students to compare flower growing in Kenya with market gardening in the Netherlands. What are the similarities and differences?

4 Play 'Just a minute' – the topic is 'Farming in LEDCs'. Students have the chance to talk for a minute on farming in LEDCs without repetition or hesitation. As soon as a student repeats an idea, or hesitates, the next student takes over until the minute is up.

5 Write down as many words as you can relating to today's work.

Further class and homework activities

1 Investigate the Green Revolution and its effectiveness today. You might like to start with these websites: www.indiaonestop.com/Greenrevolution.htm ; www.irri.org/

2 Investigate farming in other LEDCs in South-East Asia. How many still have a lot of subsistence farming?

Answers to the Activities

1 a Students diagrams will vary.

   b Inputs will include:
   - soils – rich, clay
   - labour
   - fertiliser
   - pesticide
   - herbicide
   - seeds
   - animals
   - machinery

   Processes will include:
   - cultivating
   - harvesting

Outputs will include
   - rice
   - maize
   - hens
   - turkeys

2 Poor farming communities. Large rural populations. Lack of machinery, investment. Small farms.

3 Warm climate, plenty of water for irrigation, almost uniformly fertile soils.

4 Lowering of water table as a result of water used for irrigation. Increased levels of pollution due to inputs of pesticides and fertilisers. Low pay for workers.

The unit in brief

In this unit students learn about some of the challenges and problems facing farmers in LEDCs, and some of the solutions to their problems. In the Activities, students classify the problems facing LEDC farmers; identify the benefits of land reform in LEDCs; consider whether the use of technology in LEDCs is always appropriate; and find out more about the Green Revolution.

Key ideas

◆ Lots of people in LEDCs don't have enough food – millions of children die from hunger every year, hundreds of millions of people are malnourished.

◆ Farmers face problems of climate change, soil erosion and providing food for an increasing population.

◆ Some of the solutions to farmers' problems work and are sustainable, others can make things worse.

Key vocabulary

malnutrition, climate change, soil erosion, overgrazing, fuelwood, diguettes, water harvesting, soil conservation, seed cross-breeding, hybrids, inappropriate technology, irrigation, waterlog, salinisation, land reform, high yield varieties, Green Revolution, appropriate technology

Skills practised in the Activities

◆ Thinking skills: classifying problems; drawing conclusions; identifying benefits and disadvantages; thinking; explaining; researching

Unit outcomes

By the end of this unit, most students should be able to:

◆ define or explain the terms given in 'Key vocabulary' above;

◆ be aware that millions of people in LEDCs don't have enough food;

◆ classify the problems farmers face according to whether they are to do with the physical environment or are caused by people;

◆ understand that some of the solutions to farmers problems work and are sustainable, others can make things worse.

Ideas for a starter

1   Ask: Who can remind me of the problems farmers in MEDCs like the UK face? Do farmers in LEDCs have similar problems?

2   Produce a spider diagram on the board of problems faced by farmers in LEDCs.

3   Recap: different types of farming. Draw a systems diagram for at least one type of farming.

4   Prepare a wordsearch for students to review all key terms in this chapter.

Ideas for plenaries

1   What are major problems facing farmers in the LEDCs? Are they physical, human, or environmental? Could some of the developments in the MEDCs help (things like technology, seed development, etc.)?

2   If students investigated the Green Revolution in unit 10.8, ask them to summarise their findings. What were its successes?

3   Choose a student to be in the hot seat. Another student asks him or her a question about farming in LEDCs. Then nominate two different students (4-6 pairs in total). There's one golden rule – questions cannot be repeated.

4   Do an alphabet run from A-Z with a word or phrase to do with farming for each letter.

Further class and homework activities

1   Visit the Intermediate Technology website and find out if you think this is the way forward. Research this and produce a wall display.

Answers to the Activities

1 a   Small plots of land. Tenant farmers. Low yields. Pests and diseases. Natural disasters. High levels of malnutrition. Long distance to markets.

 c   Not all of the problems are natural. The actions of people in many cases makes the situation worse.

2   It is not always appropriate to their needs. It may be too expensive, or rely heavily upon the input of pesticides and fertilisers. It is often only a small number of large farms that benefit.

3   By consolidating land owned into one plot, and by working against systems such as primogeniture, and consequently ensuring a more equitable distribution of land.

4   It is not always appropriate, as it may be too expensive, too large in scale, and/or environmentally damaging.

5   Answers will in some part depend upon students' research, but should build upon previous answers. The Green Revolution did help farming in the developing world, but to a large extent the larger and more wealthy farmers.

Industry

chapter overview

The big picture

These are the key ideas behind this chapter:

◆ Industry and employment is classified as primary, secondary, tertiary and quaternary.

◆ Industry, or a factory, is a system, with inputs, processes and outputs.

◆ As industry changes different location factors become more important, so industry locates in different places, and employment structures change.

◆ Some areas of traditional heavy industry, such as South Wales and the Ruhr, have gone through a cycle of decline, followed by a cycle of growth. They have attracted new industries and jobs.

◆ Industry is global – TNCs often have their headquarters and main factory in an MEDC with smaller factories and offices in LEDCs.

◆ The NICs of east Asia have industrialised very quickly.

Note that the students' version of the big picture is given in the students' chapter opener.

Chapter outline

Use this, and the students' chapter opener, to give students a mental roadmap for the chapter.

Objectives and outcomes for this chapter

Objectives	Unit	Outcomes
Most students will understand:		Most students will be able to:
• That industry and employment are classified as primary, secondary, tertiary and quaternary.	11.1	• Give examples of primary, secondary, tertiary and quaternary industry.
• That industry is a system.	11.1	• Describe a system and give examples of inputs, outputs and processes.
• That there are a range of factors which affect where an industry locates, and that as industry changes location factors change.	11.2, 11.3, 11.4, 11.5, 11.6	• List the factors affecting industrial location; give an example of one industry and say what factors were important in its location; explain why the location of industry has changed in the UK.
• Why areas of traditional heavy industry have declined, and the effect this has on the area.	11.3	• Give an example of an area of traditional heavy industry and explain why the industry declined; describe the effect that the decline of industry had on people.
• That high-tech and footloose industries can choose where to locate.	11.4	• List the factors important for the location of footloose industries; explain why these factors are important; give examples of the types of places footloose industries can locate; give an example of a business park and describe and explain its location.
• That TNCs can bring advantages and disadvantages.	11.5, 11.6	• Explain what TNCs are and where they operate; give examples of the advantages and disadvantages they can bring to LEDCs; give one example of a TNC in an LEDC; explain why it located there and whether it benefits the economy of the LEDC.
• How industry has changed in the UK, and how declining areas have turned around.	11.2, 11.4, 11.7, 11.8	• Define deindustrialisation; draw pie charts to show changing employment structures in the UK from 1800 onwards; explain how and why governments help areas in decline; describe how a declining area has changed.
• That there is a link between employment structures and levels of development.	11.9	• Draw pie charts of employment structures of countries at different stages of development and explain the differences.
• That NICs are countries that rapidly developed large manufacturing industries, and that this has created some problems.	11.10	• Give examples of NICs and name the four Tiger economies; describe how one NIC developed its industry so rapidly; describe the problems that rapid industrialisation causes.

These tie in with 'Your goals for this chapter' in the students' chapter opener, and with the opening lines in each unit, which give the purpose of the unit in a student-friendly style.

Using the chapter starter

The photo on page 212 of the *geog.GCSE* students' book shows a factory worker in Malaysia inspecting latex surgical gloves that have been manufactured. The gloves will be exported to countries around the world.

Latex is a type of rubber made from the sap of rubber trees found in Malaysia and other countries including Indonesia, Thailand, and Brazil.

A number of companies in Malaysia manufacture and export latex gloves for use in the medical profession – and Malaysia is currently the world's leading exporter of surgical gloves.

The Malaysian government is encouraging the growth of the medical device industry. It is currently concentrated on rubber-based products, but more companies are starting to manufacture products made from plastics, silicone, and metal alloys.

Industry, jobs and systems

The unit in brief

This unit introduces industry. It is about how industry is classified, and how it works as a system. In the Activities, students come up with a list of jobs and classify them as primary, secondary etc. They compare the number in each sector with national UK figures. They also look at the links between different industries.

Key ideas

◆ Industry provides employment.

◆ Industry can be classified into primary, secondary, tertiary and quaternary industry.

◆ Industries aren't separate – they are linked together.

◆ An industry, or a factory, is a system with inputs, processes and outputs. There may be some feedback, e.g. where profits are put back into the system.

◆ Inputs (factors) affect where an industry, or factory, will locate.

Key vocabulary

employment, classifying, primary, secondary, tertiary, quaternary, raw materials, manufacture, service, system, inputs (physical, human and economic), processes, outputs, feedback, factors, waste

Skills practised in the Activities

◆ Numeracy skills: comparing numbers of jobs with UK figures

◆ Thinking skills: listing and classifying jobs; explaining links between industries

Unit outcomes

By the end of this unit, most students should be able to:

◆ define or explain the terms given in 'Key vocabulary' above;

◆ understand that industry provides employment (jobs);

◆ classify jobs into primary, secondary, tertiary and quaternary sectors;

◆ use examples to explain how industries are linked together;

◆ understand that industry, or a factory, is a system with inputs, processes and outputs;

◆ understand that inputs (factors) affect where an industry, or factory, will locate.

Ideas for a starter

1   Provide students with job advertisements from the local newspaper. Ask them to classify jobs under the headings Primary, Secondary, Tertiary and Quaternary. Compare the local pattern with the national picture (2% in primary, 28% in secondary, and 70% in tertiary in 2000).

2   Quiz students about parents/family employers and classify jobs using the same headings as in **1** above.

3   Discuss job aspirations with the class and classify these under the headings given in **1** above. Consider what a similar group of young people would have aspired to 150 years ago.

4   Give a systems model (inputs/processes/outputs) to the class and ask them to work in pairs and add as much information as possible about a firm or industry they have studied before. Ask one group to work on the interactive whiteboard to present to the rest of the class.

Ideas for plenaries

1   Ask students to classify the following jobs into primary, secondary, tertiary, and quaternary:

IT consultant	Deep sea fisherman	Nurse
Financial consultant	Printer	Journalist
Football professional	Garage Mechanic	Baker
Stock market broker	Headhunter	Personal Trainer

Make sure the students understand what each of the jobs entails.

2   Give students the percentages of people working in the various sectors in the UK. How will this compare with employment structures in LEDCs?

3   How has employment structure in the UK changed in the past? How is it likely to change in the future?

4   Use Activity 2 as a plenary. Use the board to draw/write the answer and ask students to come and add links to other factories/businesses.

5   Provide students with a photo of a factory. Ask students to annotate the photo showing how it affects the environment.

6   Ask your neighbour to name three physical inputs and three human and economic inputs into the industry system. Ask for examples of two processes and two outputs.

7   Tell me the three key things you have learned today. Now tell me another three things you have learned.

Further class and homework activities

Research using the internet and other resources a local factory or firm to develop the input/process/output model.

Answers to the Activities

1   The answers provided here will depend upon students' choice of jobs.

2   The car factory is an assembly plant, building from many already manufactured components. If the factory closes, the suppliers will also lose out. There are many examples, including the manufacture of engines, windscreens, and tyres.

Industry–deciding where to put it

The unit in brief

This unit is about industrial location factors, and uses the Toyota plant at Burnaston in Derbyshire as a real-life example of how decisions are made about where to locate an industry or factory. It also looks at how industry has changed and how this has been matched by changes in locations. In the Activities, students describe the distribution of industry and explain why location has changed. They give reasons for the decline in coal mining and textiles; explain the change in importance of different location factors; and think about whether Toyota would have located in the UK without government help.

Key ideas

◆ There are a range of physical and human and economic factors which people have to think about when deciding where to locate an industry or factory.

◆ As industry changes, different location factors become more important.
   - Many of the old traditional UK industries needed raw materials and energy provided by coal, so they located near coalfields or ports.
   - New industries have developed with different locational requirements.

◆ Changes to the type or location of industry can mean factories or businesses close and people lose their jobs.

Key vocabulary

locate, factors, raw materials, site and land, energy supply, labour (workers), transport, capital (money), markets, government policy, environment

Skills practised in the Activities

◆ Geography skills: describing the distribution of industry

◆ Thinking skills: explaining the change in the location of industry and the changing importance of location factors; giving reasons for the closure of industries; thinking and giving reasons for answers

Unit outcomes

By the end of this unit, most students should be able to:

◆ define or explain the terms given in 'Key vocabulary' above;

◆ name the physical and human factors which affect the location of industry;

◆ explain why the importance of various location factors has changed;

◆ understand that changes to the type or location of industry can mean factories or businesses closing and people losing their jobs.

Ideas for a starter

1 Brainstorm to identify as many factors as possible which could affect the location of a factory. Write them in two columns on the board and ask students what the two columns are (physical inputs/factors and human and economic inputs/factors).

2 Use the photograph of the Toyota car plant at Burnaston on page 216 and the text boxes to recap the previous lesson.

3 Use an industrial simulation/game to demonstrate how changing factors may lead to changes in location.

Ideas for plenaries

1 Provide students with a resource such as that found at http://news.bbc.co.uk/1/hi/programmes/working_lunch/education/1804227.stm and get them to draw a spider diagram summarising the information about the siting of the car plant.

2 Why might companies decide not to move even when their factors of location have changed? Discuss in pairs and then open up to the whole class.

3 A quick test. Call out a students name and term: primary industry; secondary industry; tertiary industry; quaternary industry; classification; inputs; outputs; processes; feedback; location etc. The student has 10 seconds to give you a definition.

4 Look at the two maps on page 217. Close your book. Describe the patterns before 1970 and today to your neighbour. Your neighbour can tell you why industrial location has changed.

5 Question time! Think back over the lesson and write down three questions related to what you have learned. The teacher will ask a member of the class to try to answer.

6 Research the traditional industry of South Wales and/or the Ruhr in preparation for the next lesson.

Further class and homework activities

Go to the Toyota website www.toyotauk.com and find out more about the company. This may come in useful when working on transnational companies.

Answers to the Activities

1 Most industry was concentrated in the northern and western parts of the UK; London was the principal exception to this.

2 There has been a decline in some traditional industrial areas, such as mining and shipbuilding in North-east England. There has also been a growth in high-tech industry in areas such as the M4 corridor, due to good transport links and a trained workforce.

3 The decline has been due to factors such as the exhaustion of raw materials, cheaper foreign production, and the substitution in some cases of alternative products (such as gas for coal).

4 Many industries in the past were based around raw materials – heavy industries. As such, physical factors were important. More modern industries are more footloose, and depend much less upon the natural environment – more upon human factors such as the location of markets and suitably qualified workers.

5 This depends upon students' opinions, but it is important to stress the role played by government incentives that attract foreign investment.

Industry – traditional and heavy

The unit in brief

This unit includes two case studies of traditional heavy industry – South Wales and the Ruhr in Germany. In the Activities, students think about why the steelworks at Port Talbot and Llanwern remained open while others closed, and the reasons for Llanwern's eventual closure. They draw a consequences map to show how people are affected by the closure of industries; and look at the similarities and differences between the examples of South Wales and the Ruhr.

Key ideas

◆ In the nineteenth century South Wales had supplies of all the raw materials for making iron and steel.

◆ By the 1990s all the steelworks had closed except for Port Talbot and Llanwern (both integrated steelworks). All local raw materials had run out (only Tower Colliery remained working).

◆ Llanwern closed in 2001 with the loss of 3000 jobs.

◆ The Ruhr iron and steel industries developed as there were huge amounts of coal and local supplies of iron ore.

◆ Other industries were attracted to the Ruhr.

◆ Since the 1970s, coalmines, steelworks and other heavy industries have closed in the Ruhr with massive job losses.

◆ Unemployment is far higher in the Ruhr than in the rest of Germany, and the environment has been ruined.

Key vocabulary

integrated steelworks

Skills practised in the Activities

◆ Thinking skills: identifying disadvantages; suggesting reasons; thinking about reasons for Llanwern's closure; drawing a consequences map; identifying similarities and differences between South Wales and the Ruhr

Unit outcomes

By the end of this unit, most students should be able to:

◆ explain the term given in 'Key vocabulary' above;

◆ explain why iron and steel industries developed in South Wales and the Ruhr;

◆ explain why other industries were attracted to the Ruhr;

◆ explain why coalmines, steelworks and other heavy industries closed in South Wales and the Ruhr;

◆ describe the effect of the decline of traditional heavy industry on people in South Wales and the Ruhr.

Ideas for a starter

1 Ask students to brainstorm in groups – either about South Wales or the Ruhr – to find out what they know about the area's industrial past, and how things are changing (in preparation for unit 11.8). When students have finished, produce a concept map for each area which shows the links between different ideas.

2 Show students a map extract of an area with a traditional industrial past. Ask them to draw a sketch map of the area and label the main features of the industry and associated features such as spoil heaps and housing. This could be done on an interactive whiteboard.

Ideas for plenaries

1 Ask students to draw a cycle of decline showing how an area can become run-down following the closure of the main industry. Ask them to add facts and figures to their cycle. Share the best ones with the class.

2 Students work in twos and threes to produce either a storyboard for a video or a script for a TV/radio programme developing the theme of industrial decline. These should include an interview with someone who has lived in the area for a long time.

3 Use Activity 6 as a plenary.

4 Close your books. Draw a sketch map to show either South Wales or the Ruhr. Annotate your map to show why industry developed there and what has happened since the decline of heavy industry.

5 Make 10-15 statements about industry based on what students have learned so far, some true, some false. Students hold up *True* or *False* cards. Where statements are false, ask students to correct them.

Answers to the Activities

1 The area is inaccessible – it is very hilly with steep valleys.

2 Combination of factors, relating to accessibility – via motorway, large area of flat land, proximity of workforce.

3 Imports of steel could be cheaper from countries where the costs of extracting raw materials is cheaper, or where the labour costs are lower.

4 Students' consequence maps should include loss of income, less money to spend, purchasing of fewer 'luxury' goods, decline in other local industries, particularly sevices, decline in social facilities.

5 Cheaper costs of production in other countries. Costs of industry caused by pollution. People moving away from the area to better environments.

6 Similarities include reasons for growth and development of the areas – such as presence of raw materials, and the decline in the traditional industries. Differences include the scale, as the Ruhr is much larger, and the range of industries being greater in the Ruhr e.g. the chemical industries.

Industry – footloose (and fancy free)

The unit in brief

This unit is about the location of high-tech and footloose industries, and includes Aztec West as an example of a business park. In the Activities, students find out where high-tech products are made; choose important location factors for a high-tech company; explain why some industries are footloose and others are tied to particular locations; identify what problems footloose industries could cause the UK economy.

Key ideas

◆ The new industries that have developed and begun to replace the traditional heavy industries are often high-tech.

◆ Industries which can choose where to locate are called footloose.

◆ Footloose industries need: cheap land with large sites to expand; good transport links; workers with special skills nearby; other industries nearby to swap ideas and information.

◆ Footloose industries are often found on science parks, business parks and industrial estates.

◆ Areas where footloose industries have located include the M4 corridor, Silicon Glen in central Scotland, Silicon Valley in California.

Key vocabulary

high-tech, footloose, science parks, business parks, industrial estates

Skills practised in the Activities

◆ Geography skills: finding out where products are made

◆ Thinking skills: choosing factors and justifying choices; explaining why some industries are footloose and others aren't; identifying the problems of footloose industries; identifying similarities and differences in location choices

Unit outcomes

By the end of this unit, most students should be able to:

◆ define or explain the terms given in 'Key vocabulary' above;

◆ understand that the new industries that have developed and begun to replace traditional heavy industries are often high-tech;

◆ know that industries which can choose where to locate are called footloose;

◆ describe what footloose industries look for when deciding where to locate;

◆ explain the differences between science parks, business parks and industrial estates;

◆ name three areas where footloose industries have located.

Ideas for a starter

1 Recap: where industry traditionally located and where industry is located now.

2 Students work in pairs to decide what they would want from an area if they worked for a hi-tech company. Try to draw out behavioural factors. 'What facilities would you want to be close to?'

3 Provide students with catalogues of high-tech products. Ask students to define high-tech products, and decide what would be the most important factors in the location of factories producing them.

Ideas for plenaries

1 Give students an odd-one-out exercise. Give them four words, three are obviously linked and the fourth one is not. They have to discuss and give reasons for rejecting the fourth word, e.g. Labour, Raw Materials, Energy, Footloose (Answer = Footloose because all the others are factors of production).

2 Provide students with photos of a traditional industrial area and a Science Park. Ask them to produce a table comparing the environments shown in the photos.

3 Write a letter to an unemployed miner living in a traditional industrial area describing the benefits of retraining and working in an area of footloose industries.

4 Consider some of the reasons why the miner might not want, or be able, to move.

5 Provide students with advertisements from newspapers and magazines advertising new industrial location opportunities. Ask students what type of industry would locate in these places, and why.

6 Quick-fire test. Close your books. Ask your neighbour how many location factors they can come up with for footloose industry in 15 seconds.

7 What is the difference between science parks, business parks, and industrial estates?

8 Make a graffiti wall of what students have learned today.

Further class and homework activities

1 Investigate other science parks such as the Cambridge Science Park http://www.cambridge-science-park.com/home.htm and produce an annotated map of the park including location features.

2 Research a local business park or industrial estate and display findings on a map as a wall display.

Answers to the Activities

1 This will depend upon students' own choices, but will probably include products related to computing and electronics, for example the latest in game products, telephones and other communication devices.

2 This will depend upon students' choices. Ensure that choices are justified.

3 There are many industries that have a freedom of choice of location. Examples include many types of communication industries, telephone and internet sales, etc. Industries tied to a particular location will include those dependent upon raw materials, and to a certain extent those dependent upon a certain type or size of market.

4 An increase in competition from companies making use of the advantages of locating abroad, such as cheaper labour, and importing their products cheaply into the UK - thus costing UK jobs.

5 This will depend upon students' choices.

The unit in brief

This unit looks at transnational corporations and considers their advantages and disadvantages. In the Activities, students look at why TNCs have their headquarters in MEDCs and their factories in LEDCs. They identify the advantages and disadvantages for a country of having a branch of a TNC located there; and think about whether the arguments for and against TNCs are the same for the UK having a Toyota factory in Derbyshire, as for an LEDC. They also give their opinions on the increasing trend towards globalisation.

Key ideas

- Britain is part of a global market.
- Transnational corporations (TNCs) have offices and factories around the world.
- The revenue of some TNCs is larger than the total GDP of some countries.
- Some of the first businesses to become TNCs were car manufacturers.
- TNCs can have advantages and disadvantages for the countries they locate in.

Key vocabulary

global market, transnational corporation (TNC)

Skills practised in the Activities

- Thinking skills: explaining the location of TNC headquarters and factories; identifying the advantages and disadvantages of TNCs; giving opinions

Unit outcomes

By the end of this unit, most students should be able to:

- define or explain the terms given in 'Key vocabulary' above;
- understand that Britain is part of a global market;
- explain what a TNC is and why they manufacture products in LEDCs;
- describe how the revenue of some TNCs is larger than the total GDP of some countries;
- give six examples of TNCs;
- identify the advantages and disadvantages for an LEDC of having a TNC factory located there.

Ideas for a starter

1 Ask students: what are transnational corporations? Then brainstorm to find out how many transnational corporations they can come up with.

2 Brainstorm the range of products made by the transnational corporations listed in **1**.

3 Ask students to guess the names of the largest companies in the world and then look at the figure on page 223. You could also look up the current rich list on the internet.

4 Ask students which items at home are likely to have been manufactured by TNCs? Which country are they likely to have been made in? You could plot the countries on a blank world map.

Ideas for plenaries

1 Activities question 3 could be used as a plenary.

2 Prepare a speech given by the head of a TNC outlining the reasons for opening a new factory in an LEDC.

3 What is globalisation? What are the arguments for and against globalisation?

4 Read Chen Ernu's story. Put yourself in her shoes. Write a letter from her to the boss of the company she works for. She's worried that she can't feed her family on the amount she earns and that her job isn't safe. Now write a reply from the boss.

5 Write an email from the head of the TNC which Chen Ernu's garment factory supplies. Tell the boss of the company that the factory must produce more goods, more cheaply, or else they will get the garments elsewhere.

6 Sum up what you have learned today in 35 words.

Further class and homework activities

Investigate examples of TNCs. Try to put together a fact file showing where they have their head office, where Research and Development is located, and what they manufacture.

Answers to the Activities

1 The capital needed to invest in and develop these industries is in MEDCs. The initial market for the products is in MEDCs. The infrastructure, knowledge and management expertise required to run a TNC is generally in MEDCs.

2 Cheaper labour costs, often cheaper other costs of production. Regulations may be less strict regarding labour rights, pollution, etc.

3 a Costs will include foreign ownership, most benefits going abroad, most management jobs being occupied by people from the HQ country. Benefits will include the creation of jobs, probably including hi-tech, possible improvements to the country's infrastructure to support the development of industry, economic growth.

b The evaluation will be a matter of judgement.

4 a This will depend upon students' opinions – ensure that they are justified. Costs and benefits will be similar to those outlined for question 3.

b There will be differences related to matters such as pollution and labour controls, which will be stricter in MEDCs. Arguably, MEDCs will gain more from having a TNC than will LEDCs.

5 This will depend upon students' opinions, which need to be justified.

The unit in brief

This unit is a case study of one TNC in an LEDC – the Ford Motor Company in India. In the Activities, students explain why Ford decided to locate in India; give their opinions about statements to do with Ford in India; and consider whether Ford has benefited the Indian economy. They also look at how far Ford has tried to make its car manufacturing in India sustainable.

Key ideas

- ◆ The Ford Motor Company is the world's second largest car manufacturer.
- ◆ In 1995 Ford went into partnership with Mahindra and Mahindra Limited in India and opened a high-tech manufacturing plant at Maraimalai Nagar.
- ◆ Ford chose to locate in India because of its huge population, high-earning middle class and cheap labour costs.
- ◆ Ford India pays its workers more than others in similar industries in India, and all are offered training.
- ◆ Ford India is working towards the sustainable use of resources in its production processes.

Key vocabulary

There is no key vocabulary in this unit.

Skills practised in the Activities

- ◆ Thinking skills: explaining why Ford located in India; giving opinions; thinking about benefits to the Indian economy and sustainable manufacturing; explaining answer

Unit outcomes

By the end of this unit, most students should be able to:

- ◆ explain why Ford chose to locate in India;
- ◆ describe how far Ford has benefited the Indian economy and identify any disadvantages of Ford locating in India;
- ◆ explain how far Ford India has tried to make its car manufacturing sustainable.

Ideas for a starter

1 Recap: the advantages and disadvantages that a TNC brings to an LEDC.

2 Ask: What do you know about the Ford Motor Company? Write the answers on the board as a spider diagram. Then ask: What has Ford got to do with geography? You can return to this for plenary 1.

3 Show students a photo of a very old Ford car; a Jaguar, Land Rover or Aston Martin; and a map of India. Ask: What's the connection between these three images?

Ideas for plenaries

1 Draw up a table which compares the benefits that Ford locating in India brings to India, and the benefits that it brings to Ford. How much does India benefit?

2 How could the development of the car plant boost the local area? Draw a diagram to show this.

3 Use Activities question 3 as a plenary. Discuss the notion of sustainability and see how it could be applied to a car plant.

4 If you used starter 2, ask students to return to the spider diagram and add to, or modify, it.

5 Create an acrostic. Write 'transnational corporations' down one side of a page. Make each letter the first letter of a word, phrase, or sentence about TNCs.

Answers to the Activities

1 Large market – over 1 billion people. Despite being an LEDC, India has a large middle class and is therefore a relatively prosperous car buying country. Labour is cheaper than in MEDCs.

2 Answers will depend upon students' opinions.

3 Most components come from the local area. It is trying to bring in a more sustainable use of resources. Reuse of waste products. Cars are being designed so that the components may be re-cycled.

All change for industry

The unit in brief

This unit is about how industry has changed in the UK. It looks at deindustrialisation, what the government has done to help, and where the new jobs are. In the Activities, students look back at the list of jobs they wrote in Unit 11.1 to find evidence of deindustrialiastion, and explain why it has happened in the UK. They compare the maps showing the changing location of industry in Unit 11.2 with the pie charts of employment structure to see the relationship between them, and suggest why the government should help industries that are in decline or struggling.

Key ideas

◆ Deindustrialisation is the decline in manufacturing (secondary) industry, and the growth in tertiary and quaternary industry.

◆ The Industrial Revolution in the 19th century changed the jobs people did. In the 20th century there was a shift to service industries (and then quaternary).

◆ 'New' jobs are in high-tech and footloose industries, often located on the edges of towns and cities.

◆ The government has tried to help areas in decline by providing grants and subsidies to create new jobs and to protect existing ones.

◆ The Environment Agency is responsible for maintaining and improving water quality in England and Wales, and has a major role in monitoring air quality.

Key vocabulary

deindustrialisation, productivity, rural-urban fringe

Skills practised in the Activities

◆ Geography skills: comparing maps and pie charts

◆ Thinking skills: identifying evidence of deindustrialisation and explaining why it has happened; identifying positive impacts; thinking of reasons

Unit outcomes

By the end of this unit, most students should be able to:

◆ define or explain the terms given in 'Key vocabulary' above;

◆ explain how industry and employment in the UK has changed since 1800;

◆ describe the consequences of industry locating at the rural-urban fringe;

◆ describe how the government has tried to help areas in decline;

◆ identify how industry affects the environment and who is responsible for maintaining air and water quality.

Ideas for a starter

1 Recap: Industrial changes in the UK over the last 200 years:

◆ Heavy industry on coalfield locations

◆ Footloose Industries – the development of Science Parks etc.

2 How has Government influenced the location of industry? Refer back to the work on South Wales.

3 What changes are happening locally to industry and employment structure? Are factories closing down and new businesses starting up? Are these in different locations in and around the town? What types of industries are closing? What types of businesses are starting up?

Ideas for plenaries

1 Do you think there are problems in changing jobs from one industry to another? Would the skills in steel making transfer to the IT industry?

2 How might the government help the transition from one industry to another?

3 Activities question 5 could be used as a plenary.

4 Close your book. Describe how employment structure has changed in the UK since 1800. Draw pie charts to show the employment structure in 1800, 1900, and 2000.

5 Close your book. Why does industry locate at the rural-urban fringe? What are the consequences of this?

6 A quick-fire test. Call out a student's name and the definition of a term related to changes in industry in the UK. The student has 5 seconds to give you the term.

Further class and homework activities

Collect information about South Wales. Write to the South Wales Development Agency and find out what is new in the area.

Answers to the Activities

1 This will depend upon students' choice from 11.1, but it is likely that most of the chosen jobs will have come from the tertiary sector, supporting the argument that deindustrialisation is taking place.

2 Partly due to increased competition from industries abroad, which are often able to offer products at a cheaper price. Also due to increased efficiency in the UK, which means that fewer jobs are needed in industry. Also an increased demand for tertiary and quarternary industries.

3 The growth areas on the map are principally those areas where there has been the greatest growth in service industries.

4 Increased wealth to the local area, creation of new jobs. Less congestion than if located further into urban areas.

5 To support the local economy by sustaining jobs. Saving jobs has the knock-on effect of preserving other local industries. Products may still be needed, they may be too expensive – government help may make them economical.

The unit in brief

This unit looks again at the two case study areas included in Unit 11.3 – South Wales and the Ruhr – to see how these two declining areas have changed. In the Activities, students explain whether new industries would have located in South Wales without government help, and why most of them are from outside the UK. They consider the advantages and disadvantages of foreign companies locating in South Wales, and compare the changes in South Wales and the Ruhr.

Key ideas

◆ New industry was attracted to Wales through the setting up of the Welsh Development Agency and Urban Development Corporations. The region also became a Development Area and had help from the EU.

◆ New industries (particularly tertiary) were attracted to South Wales, including a lot from overseas.

◆ South Wales and the Ruhr have been through a cycle of decline and are now in a cycle of growth.

◆ In the 1960s the state and central government wanted to encourage new types of employment and improve the environment in the Ruhr. Now 65% of the Ruhr's workers are in the tertiary sector.

◆ New universities and colleges were set up, business parks developed and the environment cleaned up.

Key vocabulary

There is no key vocabulary in this unit.

Skills practised in the Activities

◆ Geography skills: comparing South Wales and the Ruhr; finding out about another area in the UK where new industries have located

◆ Thinking skills: thinking of reasons; explaining answer; identifying advantages and disadvantages; identifying similarities and differences

Unit outcomes

By the end of this unit, most students should be able to:

◆ compare the changes that have taken place in South Wales and the Ruhr, and identify the similarities and differences;

◆ draw a diagram to show a cycle of decline and a cycle of growth for either South Wales or the Ruhr;

◆ describe how one place in South Wales has changed;

◆ give one example of how the environment has been improved in the Ruhr.

Ideas for a starter

1 Ask: Who can remind me about traditional heavy industry in South Wales? And who can remind me about the Ruhr?

2 Draw a map of South Wales showing iron and steel production.

3 Show 'before' and 'after' photos of either South Wales or the Ruhr (photos of traditional heavy industry and modern industry). Ask: Is this the same place? How has it changed?

Ideas for plenaries

1 Write an email to a friend describing the changes in South Wales or the Ruhr over the last 40 years.

2 Ask students to draw a cycle of growth showing how an area can be regenerated.

3 Give two examples of new industry attracted to South Wales. Where did the companies come from?

4 Activities question 4 could be used as a plenary.

5 Take two minutes with a partner and think up one interesting question about how South Wales and the Ruhr have changed that we have not covered today.

Further class and homework activities

1 Produce a wall display of all information collected on South Wales (and/or the Ruhr if possible).

2 Investigate the TNCs which have moved to Wales. Where have they located and what do they manufacture? Have they all stayed or have some of them moved away?

3 Look at other areas in the UK, as suggested in Activities question 5.

Answers to the Activities

1 This will depend upon students' opinions – ensure that they are justified. Considerable government help has been given to regenerate industries in the area.

2 Government incentives and grants. Wanting to get a foothold in the UK / European markets. Larger scale multi-nationals. There may be some reluctance by UK firms to invest in an area of economic and industrial decline.

3 Advantages would include more jobs, positive impact on other industries in the local area. Disadvantages would include that many of the best-paid jobs will go to foreign workers, many are not well paid or with good career development prospects.

4 Similarities are many, including references to the role of the government. The Ruhr is a larger-scale system, and one difference is the creation of the Emscher Landscape Park, the largest in Europe.

5 Answers will depend upon the example chosen by students.

Industry and LEDCs

The unit in brief

This unit is about industry in LEDCs, the problems that industrialisation causes and the need for sustainable development. In the Activities, students use the map of employment structures to describe the differences shown. They predict what the employment structure of some countries might look like in the future; and think about whether it's fair that countries like India and China are criticised for the pollution they are creating in their drive to industrialise.

Key ideas

- There is a difference in the employment structures of MEDCs and LEDCs.
- The employment structures of LEDCs change as they develop.
- China and India are industrialising, but in doing so are causing massive pollution.
- Sustainable development means improving people's lives without wasting resources or harming the environment.
- The Jua Kali workshops in Kenya are one example of a sustainable development project.

Key vocabulary

employment structure, sustainable development

Skills practised in the Activities

- Geography skills: using a map to describe differences in employment structures
- Thinking skills: giving reasons for differences; explaining answer; predicting and explaining changes in employment structures; considering whether LEDCs should be criticised for the pollution they're creating

Unit outcomes

By the end of this unit, most students should be able to:

- define the terms given in 'Key vocabulary' above;
- describe and explain the differences in the employment structures of MEDCs and LEDCs;
- understand that the employment structures of LEDCs change as they develop;
- describe the problems caused as countries industrialise;
- give one example of a sustainable development project.

Ideas for a starter

1 Recap: changing employment structure of the UK (1800, 1900, 2000). Ask students: What would you expect the employment structure of an LEDC to look like?

2 Draw the employment structure pie charts of an MEDC, e.g. the UK, and an LEDC, e.g. Kenya, on the board. Add that for Brazil – a country becoming more developed. Ask for comments from students.

3 Brainstorm to find out what students know about countries such as India and China. What is changing in terms of their industry and employment?

Ideas for plenaries

1 How do you think the LEDCs employment structure will change in the next few years?

2 What is 'sustainable development'? Are the TNCs helping sustainable development? (Look up examples on the internet to help your argument.)

3 Have a debate arguing the pros and cons of the industrial development in LEDCs:

This house believes that the best route for sustainable development is by working alongside the TNCs.

4 Use Activities question 1 as a plenary.

5 Draw the employment structures for two MEDCs and two LEDCs from memory.

6 Make a graffiti wall of what students have learned today.

Further class and homework activities

Research intermediate technology. Is this the way that certain LEDCs should be developing, or should they be working with the TNCs?

Answers to the Activities

1 a MEDCs are dominated by tertiary activities, LEDCs mostly by primary. Brazil is an example of a country where the occupational structure is rapidly changing.

b Increased mechanisation and efficiency in primary and secondary industries in MEDCs, increased demand for tertiary industries. Generally more people are employed in agriculture in LEDCs, although the situation is changing rapidly in some countries, for example Brazil.

2 a Russia has the lowest proportion in tertiary, and the highest in primary. UK and US have the lowest in primary.

b Brazil is the obvious exception in the LEDCs, having by far the highest in tertiary. Kenya has the highest proportion in primary.

3 Differences between MEDCs and LEDCs are generally greater than those within the categories, but this division is diminishing. This is because of the rapid development of countries such as Brazil and other NICs.

4 a Very much more like those of MEDCs – smaller proportion in primary, large in tertiary.

b Same reasons as for growth of MEDCs – increased efficiency, wealth, and growth in demand for services.

5 This will depend upon students' opinions, which should be justified. On one hand the MEDCs may have made their wealth at least in part by polluting the environment and therefore have no place to criticise. On the other hand, knowledge of pollution and the means to combat it are greater than ever before, and so arguably LEDCs should take pollution control into account.

The unit in brief

This unit is about the newly industrialised countries (NICs) of eastern Asia, and includes a case study of South Korea. In the Activities, students explain why the economies of the NICs grew so quickly, and suggest why they developed so much faster than the European economies in the 19th century. They also explain some of the problems caused by rapid industrialisation in NICs.

Key ideas

◆ Newly industrialised countries (NICs) are countries that have developed large manufacturing industries very quickly.

◆ The four countries whose economy has grown the fastest are the Tiger economies of South Korea, Taiwan, Singapore and Hong Kong.

◆ The NICs developed quickly for reasons to do with labour, government, transport and markets.

◆ In South Korea the government planned a series of five-year economic plans and the country developed in three stages.

◆ In South Korea people's standard of living has improved but rapid industrialisation has caused problems.

Key vocabulary

newly industrialised countries (NICs), industrialisation

Skills practised in the Activities

◆ Thinking skills: explaining and suggesting reasons for rapid economic growth, and the problems caused by it

Unit outcomes

By the end of this unit, most students should be able to:

◆ define the terms given in 'Key vocabulary' above;

◆ understand that NICs are countries that have developed large manufacturing industries very quickly;

◆ name the four Tiger economies;

◆ suggest why the NICs economies developed more rapidly than those of European countries in the nineteenth century;

◆ explain how the South Korean economy grew so quickly;

◆ list the problems that rapid industrialisation has caused in South Korea.

Ideas for a starter

1 Show students a large image of a tiger (like that on page 232), but the more fierce/powerful it looks the better. Ask: What has this got to do with geography? Use it to introduce the idea of NICs and the tiger economies.

2 Ask students: What are your impressions of industry in LEDC countries? Brainstorm a list of characteristics.

3 Develop a model on the board consisting of linked boxes to show how developing industry can lead to the economic development of a country.

Ideas for plenaries

1 What are NICs? Name the four tiger economies.

2 Many countries are changing as their industry changes/develops. Make a list of the problems facing the world today from its industrial sector.

3 Review your list of characteristics of industry in LEDC countries (starter 2). How many of your impressions were correct? What can you now add to your list?

4 What are the implications for the EU of increased manufacturing in the NIC countries and the emergence of China as an industrial superpower? Discuss with a partner and be ready to participate in a full class discussion.

5 Write 'Industry' in the middle of the board. Create a mind map around the word. How many ideas can students come up with to do with any of the work they have done on this topic?

Further class and homework activities

1 Investigate one of the tiger economies and try to work out why it has been so successful. Make a list of the companies which are now TNCs. Try to find out why they managed to grow so quickly.

2 Do a survey of your own possessions and find out how many come from one of the NIC counties of East Asia.

Answers to the Activities

1 Cheap labour, government planning, effective shipping transport and goods being produced for a global market.

2 Production for a global market, cheap and large scale production, large-scale government investment.

3 In part, as governments have invested in long-term planning. Other factors, already mentioned in the answers above, also play a part.

4 Pollution, rapid urbanisation, growing demand for higher-paid jobs and services, corruption and industrial disputes.

Managing resources

chapter overview

The big picture

These are the key ideas behind this chapter:

◆ A resource is anything – natural or made by people – which humans can use.

◆ As population grows, and as countries develop economically, there is an increased demand for energy and other resources.

◆ Increasing demands for resources affect the environment. Burning fossil fuels leads to increased global warming.

◆ We need to tackle global warming, and find alternative sustainable sources of energy.

◆ Tourism has grown dramatically in the last 25 years, and tourists have a major (often negative) impact on holiday destinations.

◆ Tourism can be sustainable and help to preserve the environment.

Note that the students' version of the big picture is given in the students' chapter opener.

Chapter outline

Use this, and the students' chapter opener, to give students a mental roadmap for the chapter.

12   Managing resources As the students' chapter opener, this unit is an important part of the chapter; see page 11 of this book for notes about using chapter openers

12.1   The rate of resource use How population growth and economic development leads to increased resource use

12.2   Resource use and new technology How resource use changes with developments in technology

12.3   Changing resource use in an LEDC: China The huge increases in energy production in China, and the impacts this is having

12.4   Global warming The greenhouse effect, evidence for global warming, and the possible effects of global warming

12.5   What can I do about global warming? What we can do to tackle global warming on an individual and national level

12.6   Wind power in the UK The example of North Hoyle Wind Farm, and how opinion is divided over wind power

12.7   Going anywhere nice on your holidays? Tourism has grown dramatically in the last twenty-five years, and people now travel much further

12.8   The impacts of tourism Case study looking at the effect of tourism on Ibiza, and how things might change

12.9   Tourism in the UK Case study looking at the effects of tourism on the Pennine Way National Trail, and a restoration project

12.10 Tourism in an LEDC: Phuket, Thailand Case study looking at the impact of tourism on an LEDC destination

12.11 Green tourism How tourism can help to preserve the environment – Antalya in Turkey

Objectives and outcomes for this chapter

Objectives	Unit	Outcomes
Most students will understand:		Most students will be able to:
● How population growth increases resource use.	12.1	● Describe how population growth puts pressure on resources.
● How resource use changes with new technology, and the effects of this.	12.2	● Draw a timeline to show changing technology and the development of energy resources; describe the effect of the closure of coal mines and declining use of coal on people.
● How as countries develop economically there is an increased demand for energy and other resources, but that this can create problems.	12.1, 12.3	● Describe the increase in energy production in China from burning coal and the problems this causes; describe the Three Gorges Dam project and list the impacts on people and the environment.
● What causes global warming; that there is conflicting evidence for global warming; the possible effects of global warming.	12.4	● Explain the greenhouse effect and how burning fossil fuels creates greenhouse gases; give evidence for and against global warming; list the possible effects of global warming.
● That individuals can do something about global warming as well as governments.	12.5	● List how individuals could reduce their energy use; say what the Kyoto protocol is and how the UK government plans to reduce greenhouse gas emissions by developing alternative energy.
● That wind power is being developed as an alternative source of energy in the UK, but that opinions are divided over it.	12.6	● Give an example of a wind farm in the UK, describe its location and the amount of energy it produces; explain why some people dislike wind farms on land.
● Why tourism has increased in the last 25 years; that tourists travel much further now than 50 years ago and that different people want different things on a holiday.	12.7	● Give reasons why tourism has increased and people travel further; explain that different people want to do different things on holiday and so will visit different places.
● That tourism develops in different environments.	12.8, 12.9, 12.10	● List the attractions of a tourist area in an MEDC and an LEDC; classify the attractions as physical and human.
● That tourism has an impact on all holiday destinations.	12.8, 12.9, 12.10	● List the advantages and disadvantages of tourism in an MEDC and an LEDC destination.
● Why, and how, Ibiza is trying to change its image.	12.8	● Explain why the government is trying to attract different tourists to Ibiza and what it plans to do.
● How tourism can be made more sustainable (green tourism).	12.11	● Define green tourism; give an example of a resort which has changed to sustainable tourism; list the changes the resort has made; assess whether the resort is really sustainable.

These tie in with 'Your goals for this chapter' in the students' chapter opener, and with the opening lines in each unit, which give the purpose of the unit in a student-friendly style.

Using the chapter starter

The photo on page 234 of *geog.GCSE* students' book shows an engineer inspecting copper-bearing rock fragments at the Chuquicamata copper mine in Chile'. Copper is used as a conductor of electricity, as a building material, and in various alloys. It's a non-renewable resource, though it can be recycled.

The town of Chuquicamata became so polluted people could no longer live there. In 2003 the residents were relocated to Calama, 17 km away; Chuquicamata is being buried under a giant slag heap.

The rate of resource use

The unit in brief

In this unit students learn why resource use is growing at an increasingly faster rate. It looks at population increase and economic development as the drivers for increased resource use. In the Activities, students complete a flow diagram to show the effect which population increase can have on the environment. They draw a bar chart of China's earnings (per head) and explain the connection between what the bar chart shows and China's increased fuel use. They also describe how economic development leads to increased resource use.

Key ideas

◆ A resource is anything – natural or man-made – which people can use.

◆ Population growth puts pressure on soil and water resources.

◆ In places like Burkina Faso, trying to feed growing populations has led to overcultivation and overgrazing. Declining rainfall and droughts exacerbate the problems.

◆ As countries become richer, resource use increases.

◆ LEDCs want to improve standards of living through economic development. As they develop, energy use increases.

Key vocabulary

overcultivation, overgrazing, evapotranspiration, drought, materialism, economic development

Skills practised in the Activities

◆ Geography skills: explaining the term 'overcultivation'; describing how economic development leads to increased resource use

◆ Numeracy skills: drawing a bar chart of earnings

◆ Thinking skills: completing a flow diagram to show how population increase can damage the environment; explaining a bar chart and making a connection between earnings and fuel use

Unit outcomes

By the end of this unit, most students should be able to:

◆ define the terms given in 'Key vocabulary' above;

◆ understand that a resource is anything which people can use;

◆ explain how population growth puts pressure on soil and water resources;

◆ describe how, as countries develop and become richer, resource use increases.

Ideas for a starter

1 Ask students: What do you understand by the term resources? Make a list of all the resources you can think of.

2 What resources do you use as a family? Make a spider diagram of the resources your family uses.

3 Write the dictionary definition of resources on the board. Ask students to develop it for Geography.

4 Show photos of a range of resources – food, water, fuel, soil, etc. Ask students what these things have in common.

Ideas for plenaries

1 What is the relationship between economic development and resource use?

2 Are the amounts of resources finite? Can you think of situations and factors that may lead to more of a resource being available? Think of a resource such as oil. Make a list and discuss it with the rest of the class.

3 Investigate energy resources in the UK. How is our energy produced? What issues do we face in terms of energy use and production? Prepare a short presentation of your findings.

4 What do you think are the five resources which would help a country to develop?

5 Take two minutes with a partner and think up one interesting question about resource use that we have not covered today.

Further class and homework activities

How does the relationship between sustained economic development and resource use operate. You might like to look up information on *ecological footprints*. There are a number of websites to visit. Some will help you calculate your ecological footprint.

Answers to the Activities

1 Overcultivation means growing too much; usually this means not letting the soil revive between sowings, so that there is no time for the soil to recover the nutrients lost.

2 upper box, middle: overgrazing; lower box, middle: overcultivation; end box: soil erosion

3 a Bar graph of China's earnings per head showing earnings generally rising, but a dip for 1986. Ensure that scales are appropriate, and check that both axes are labelled and graph has a title!

b This is a good exercise in stressing that numbers should be extracted from the table. The answer would identify rises and falls; for example:

In 1981, China's earnings per head were $275. This fell by $10 in 5 years, but improved to $351 by 1991. After that earnings per head rose steadily to $921, and were forecast to reach $1553 in 2006.

c Total energy demand, million tonnes coal equivalent is:

◆ 1981 1100
◆ 1986 1700
◆ 1991 1750
◆ 1996 1770
◆ 2001 1800
◆ 2006 2500

But answers will vary, according to the accuracy of graph-reading.

To look at possible correlations, students could **either** draw a scattergraph – this makes a nice plot, with only 1986 as an anomaly – **or** rank the data:

year	energy demand million tonnes coal equivalent	rank energy demand, highest ranked 1	earnings per head, $US	rank earnings per head
1981	1100	6	285	5
1986	1700	5	275	6
1991	1750	4	351	4
1996	1770	3	667	3
2001	1800	2	921	2
2006	2500	1	1553	1

. . . this shows that in four out of the six years energy demand and earnings have the same rank.

4 Economic development leads to increased resource use because:

◆ as we get richer we buy more things – like computers, plasma televisions, or play stations; all these use up resources

◆ many of the things we buy need energy, like electric toothbrushes or four-wheel drive vehicles

◆ as our living standards rise, we live longer, so use more resources.

The unit in brief

This unit is about how our use of energy changes with developments in technology, and looks at the effects that closing coal mines had on miners. In the Activities, students complete a paragraph on the development of energy and answer questions based on the graph of energy use in the UK. They also write an interview with a coal miner in the 1980s when mines began to close. They make up questions to ask and suggest the answers the miner might give.

Key ideas

◆ New technologies have been developed to increase energy production and meet our increasing needs.

◆ In the UK our use of coal has declined, but the use of other sources of energy has increased.

◆ Coal mining in the UK used to be subsidised by the government, but coal could be imported more cheaply from abroad.

◆ From the 1980s onwards, coal mines began to be closed and thousands of miners lost their jobs.

Key vocabulary

subsidies, deindustrialisation

Skills practised in the Activities

◆ Geography skills: describing and explaining the fall in the use of coal

◆ Numeracy skills: reading information from a graph of energy use

◆ Literacy skills: completing a paragraph on the development of energy; writing an interview with a miner

◆ Thinking skills: giving reasons for the decline in the numbers of coal mines and why people protested against these closures

Unit outcomes

By the end of this unit, most students should be able to:

◆ define the terms given in 'Key vocabulary' above;

◆ describe how new technologies have been developed to increase energy production and meet our increasing needs;

◆ describe the changing use of energy in the UK;

◆ explain why coal mines began to be closed from the 1980s and the effects this had on miners.

Ideas for a starter

1 Recap: the definition of resources developed in Unit 12.1.

2 Ask several students to present their report on energy resources in the UK. What are the major issues we face in terms of energy use and production?

3 Develop a timeline on the board with students' input to show the development of energy resources (like the one on p. 238).

Ideas for plenaries

1 Consider all the different types of energy used to generate power in the UK. Try to think of one negative and one positive impact on the environment for each fuel. Discuss with the class.

2 Do you think that modern types of energy production are better for the environment?

3 Do you have a policy at school about recycling? Do you recycle packaging and other products at home? What is the relationship between resource management and recycling? Can you make a difference?

4 Find out about energy use in an LEDC such as China or India. How is energy use increasing and why? Prepare a short presentation.

5 Do we have coal, oil or natural gas in the UK? Ask students to find an energy map for the UK in an atlas. They should note down at least six geographical facts about these fuels. Ask selected students to call out their facts. Other students comment.

6 Why does the UK have coal, if it was formed in warm, steamy, tropical swamps? (Think back to planet movements!)

7 Sum up what you have learned today in 35 words.

Further class and homework activities

1 Run a survey of energy use in your home. How often are electrical appliances plugged in? How long is the central heating on for? How often is the car in use? How much petrol is consumed per week? What methods have the family got for conserving energy? Try to analyse the data and present it as a presentation or a wall display.

2 Investigate the international issue of acid rain and visit the websites of organisations such as Greenpeace to find out about the relationship of thermal power stations and acid rain. Report back to the class.

Answers to the Activities

1 Humans probably worked out how to make fire in 500 000 BC. Watermills were developed by the Romans, around 20 BC. Windmills were developed around 500 AD, but steam power only began in the 19th century. Electricity stations burning coal, gas or oil were built in the 20th century. The UK started to use nuclear power around 1965, and natural gas around 1970.

2 a Oil first became an important energy source for the UK in 1980.

   b Natural gas can be piped to most houses in the UK, and it's cheap to transport. You don't need a storage tank to store gas in, and it's a 'cleaner' fuel.

   c Coal use has fallen every year; from 120 15 million tonnes in 1950 to 15 million tonnes in 2000. At first, it fell slowly, but the biggest fall was 35 million tonnes between 1960 and 1965. It also fell quickly between 1990 and 1995.

   d ◆ Coal is dirty.
      ◆ Coal is expensive to transport.
      ◆ When coal is burnt, it gives off sulphur dioxide – which causes acid rain – and carbon dioxide – which is a greenhouse gas.

3 a ◆ British coal was subsidised, so cost the taxpayers a lot.
      ◆ Other countries could produce coal more cheaply.
      ◆ Other sources of energy were being used: natural gas, oil, and hydroelectric power.

   b ◆ The miners lost their jobs.
      ◆ Unemployment is expensive! Without a job, people claim benefits, which cost money.
      ◆ If a lot of people have lost their jobs, they don't have as much money to spend in shops and on entertainment.

   c There are many possible questions and answers. They could be based on:
      ◆ the attractions of mining – well-paid job, local work
      ◆ problems for younger men when the pits closed
      ◆ problems for the older men when the pits closed
      ◆ psychological effects of losing jobs
      ◆ effects on the whole village of losing jobs
      ◆ why, when there is coal in the ground, were the pits closed?

Changing resource use in an LEDC:China

The unit in brief

This unit is about the huge increases in energy production in China, and the impacts that this is having. It investigates the Three Gorges Dam. In the Activities, students design a poster to protest about air pollution caused by a coke plant, and write a reply to the protest from the Chinese government. They suggest arguments which could be used in favour of increased resource use. They then look at the Three Gorges Dam and consider the advantages and disadvantages of the project and whether it should have been allowed to go ahead.

Key ideas

◆ China's coal consumption has more than doubled since 1980. About two-thirds of its power comes from coal and coal-products – the cheapest and dirtiest forms of energy.

◆ Burning coal causes air pollution, including acid rain and greenhouse gas emissions, and causes health problems.

◆ The Three Gorges Dam will provide a clean source of energy (from HEP), and will manage flooding on the Yangtze River.

◆ The Three Gorges Dam will cause other problems including relocating over 1 million people and concerns that the lake behind the dam will become a dumping ground for waste produced by the 15 million people living nearby.

Key vocabulary

There is no key vocabulary in this unit.

Skills practised in the Activities

◆ Geography skills: designing a poster to protest about air pollution;

◆ Literacy skills: writing a reply to protests about air pollution

◆ Thinking skills: explaining why people develop new ways of creating energy; identifying arguments in favour of increased resource use; giving advantages and disadvantages of the Three Gorges Dam

Unit outcomes

By the end of this unit, most students should be able to:

◆ describe where most of China's energy comes from;

◆ suggest reasons for the increasing use of energy in China;

◆ explain the problems caused by burning coal;

◆ list the advantages and disadvantages of the Three Gorges Dam.

Ideas for a starter

1 Ask students to give their presentations on resource use in an LEDC. What have they discovered about how and why resource use is increasing?

2 LECDs are trying to develop as quickly as possible. MEDCs are concerned about sustainable development. Brainstorm to find out what issues and conflicts this raises.

3 Ask students to find China in an atlas. Can they locate the Three Gorges Dam? What do they know about the Three Gorges Dam so far?

Ideas for plenaries

1 China is going to be the next major force in industrial development. But it could also become a major source of global pollution. How could the MEDCs help China to develop more sustainably? What could the UK do to help China without selling polluting technologies?

2 Use Activity 3 as a plenary. Then write a letter to the Chinese government pointing out your point of view about the Three Gorges Dam project.

3 Investigate global warming. You need to distinguish between the normal greenhouse effect which protects the planet and the enhanced greenhouse effect which is responsible for global warming. Prepare a 3 minute PowerPoint presentation.

4 Draw 2 cartoon heads. One is Liu Hongkui (leader of the retired workers in Tangshan). The other is a Chinese government minister. Draw 2 speech bubbles by the heads and write their conversation. Liu Hongkui is concerned about pollution from the coke plant near houses, the government minister is explaining why China needs to develop energy resources.

5 Make 10-15 statements based on what students have learned so far about resource use, some true, some false. Students hold up True or False cards. Where statements are false, ask students to correct them.

Further class and homework activities

Try to find out more about industrial development in China. Try to use other reference books and web articles to draw a map of China showing the centres of industry.

Answers to the Activities

1 a People invented new ways of creating energy to:
   - improve their diet – fire
   - do things faster and with less effort – windmills, watermills, factories
   - improve their standard of living – electrification.

b 'Necessity is the mother of invention' means that when people need something new, or more, they invent a new technology. The Agricultural Revolution in the UK, or the Green Revolution are good examples.

2 a Mr Liu's protest poster might refer to the link between air pollution and:
   - diseases of the lung and heart
   - acid rain
   - greenhouse gases.

b The Chinese government would stress that China is going through very rapid economic development, and economic development will improve the living standards of the nation. In time, it will be possible to improve health and safety standards, but at present China has to produce goods at a lower price than the other exporting nations if its economy is to grow.

c Increased resource use can:
   - stop undernourishment and malnutrition
   - improve people's standards of living
   - increase trade, giving people and nations the opportunity to buy globally.

3 Advantages of the Three Gorges Scheme:
   - It will generate 11% of China's electricity – at the moment, China is experiencing shortages of power.
   - HEP generation doesn't release greenhouses gases.
   - Large ships can sail 2000 km into the interior of China; cheaper transport will help China compete economically.
   - On average, 3000 people a year are killed by flooding of the Yangtze; the dam will control floods.

   Disadvantages of the Three Gorges Scheme:
   - Over 1 million people will have to relocate. They will have to pay some of the costs themselves; farmers will not get as much, or as good, land; people will lose their vegetable gardens which provided a lot of their food.
   - The reservoir could become a dumping ground for industrial and domestic waste, and sewage. It could become highly toxic.
   - Many of China's most historic sites will disappear under water.

The unit in brief

This unit looks at the evidence for global warming, and the possible effects it might have. In the Activities students, match heads and tails of sentences to show their understanding of the greenhouse effect, and use a graph of global temperatures to describe the changes shown. They sort the effects of global warming listed in the text into positive and negative, and identify evidence which shows that global warming may not be happening everywhere.

Key ideas

◆ Most scientists agree that human activities are contributing to global warming.

◆ The main source of greenhouse gases is the burning of fossil fuels.

◆ Deforestation also contributes to global warming.

◆ Most scientists predict that global temperatures will rise between 2.5 °C and 10.5 °C over the next 100 years.

◆ Some of the possible consequences of global warming are likely to be negative, some may be positive.

◆ Not all the evidence points to a rise in temperature, some scientists believe that Antarctica is getting cooler.

Key vocabulary

fossil fuels, greenhouse gas, greenhouse effect, global warming,

Skills practised in the Activities

◆ Geography skills: describing changes in global temperatures

◆ Numeracy skills: reading a graph of global temperatures

◆ Thinking skills: matching heads and tails of sentences about the greenhouse effect; sorting the effects of global warming into positive and negative; identifying evidence

Unit outcomes

By the end of this unit, most students should be able to:

◆ define the terms given in 'Key vocabulary' above;

◆ explain the causes of global warming;

◆ draw a diagram to show the greenhouse effect;

◆ sort the possible consequences of global warming into negative and positive effects;

◆ identify evidence that global warming may not be happening everywhere.

Ideas for a starter

1 Ask a few students to give their PowerPoint presentation on global warming. Ask: How does a greenhouse work?

2 Draw a diagram on the board of a greenhouse to show a 'normal' greenhouse effect. Apply these principles to the planet and produce a model of the normal greenhouse effect.

3 Brainstorm the major problems affecting our planet. Which is the major one? Is global warming a greater threat than terrorism?

Ideas for plenaries

1 What is the main source of greenhouse gases?

2 Divide students into small groups. Give each group 10 minutes to find out information on the effects of global warming on one of the following:

◆ sea level

◆ agriculture

◆ climates

◆ coral reefs and islands

◆ population distribution

3 Discuss the effects of global warming as a class. Some countries, for example the USA, do not accept the idea of the enhanced greenhouse effect. What do you think their argument is?

4 Draw a diagram showing the greenhouse effect. Annotate it to show how human activity enhances the greenhouse effect. Tell students you will use some of their diagrams at the beginning of the next lesson.

5 Draw 2 speech bubbles on the board. One says: We're helping to cause global warming by burning so much fossil fuel. The other says: Global warming is a natural change and nothing to do with us. Should we:

◆ cut down on using fossil fuels?

◆ carry on as we are?

Point out to students that most experts now agree we are either causing global warming, or greatly accelerating a natural trend.

Further class and homework activities

Investigate the various summit meetings that have taken place to try to get some agreement on the action to be taken internationally – the Kyoto Protocol, the Montreal summit, etc.

Answers to the Activities

1 The sun's radiation passes through the atmosphere.

Some of this solar radiation is reflected by the Earth and its atmosphere.

But most solar radiation is absorbed by the Earth.

The Earth then begins to send out long-wave, infra-red radiation.

Some of this radiation is trapped by greenhouse gases, which warm the atmosphere.

2 a Overall, the average global temperature has risen since 1860; having identified this general upwards trend, it should be noted that the average global temperature fell 1870-1875, 1880-1895, 1900-1905, 1945-1950, 1960-1965.

b The average global temperature has risen about 1°C since 1860.

3 Positive

◆ In many parts of the world, warmer weather should mean a longer growing season.

◆ More carbon dioxide (CO_2) in the atmosphere should make plants grow more energetically. Experts reckon that the extra CO_2 would improve food output by 17%.

◆ People like warm climates; heating bills are lower and clothing costs are reduced.

Negative

◆ Sea level will rise between 9 and 88 cm (3.5 and 34.6 inches).

◆ If sea level rises, there will be more coastal erosion.

◆ If sea level rises, there will be more flooding, and vital, fertile land, as in Bangladesh, will be lost.

◆ Many natural ecosystems will be lost – perhaps for ever.

◆ There will be greater threats to human health as mosquitoes and other disease-carrying insects spread infection over much more of the earth.

◆ Loss of vital land due to sea-level rise in low-lying areas like Bangladesh or the Mississippi delta.

4 Although the average air temperature at the Earth's surface has increased during the 20th century, US scientists have found that Antarctica got cooler between 1966 and 2000.

The unit in brief

This unit is about how we can tackle global warming, both from an individual's and from a government's point of view. In the Activities, students produce a table to show their activities that day and the resources used, and suggest how the resources could be used more carefully. They rank the methods suggested for reducing energy consumption, and identify which resources in their own homes are recycled. They also list the renewable energy resources being developed by the UK and think about their positive and negative impacts.

Key ideas

◆ Most scientists believe that our increasing output of greenhouse gases is causing global warming.

◆ Individuals can help to tackle global warming by using less energy based on fossil fuels.

◆ In 1997 over 160 nations signed the Kyoto Protocol – an international agreement on climate change.

◆ Countries signing the Protocol have decided to reduce their emissions of greenhouse gases.

◆ The UK intends to increase production of energy from renewable sources – mainly using wind power.

Key vocabulary

Kyoto Protocol

Skills practised in the Activities

◆ Geography skills: making a table of activities and the resources used; listing the renewable resources being developed by the UK

◆ Numeracy skills: ranking methods of energy saving

◆ Thinking skills: suggesting ways of using resources more carefully; identifying items which are recycled in their own home; thinking about the positive and negative impacts of renewable energy resources; explaining offshore windfarms

Unit outcomes

By the end of this unit, most students should be able to:

◆ explain the term given in 'Key vocabulary' above;

◆ suggest how individuals (including themselves) can help to tackle global warming;

◆ explain the purpose of the Kyoto Protocol;

◆ say how the UK intends to increase the production of energy from renewable sources; and identify the negative and positive impacts of these methods.

Ideas for a starter

1 Recap: What is the natural greenhouse effect and why is this necessary for life on Earth? What is the enhanced greenhouse effect?

2 Show some of the best diagrams from Plenary 4 in Unit 12.4 to remind students about how human activity increases global warming.

3 Ask: Can individuals act to tackle global warming, or is it just something governments set targets about? Can you think of any examples of when individual actions made governments and TNCs adapt or change their policies?

Ideas for plenaries

1 Why is international agreement necessary for the reduction of greenhouse gases? Why is it sometimes difficult to get governments to agree targets for greenhouse gas emissions? Why don't they always meet their targets?

2 Use Activity 5 as a plenary.

3 Provide students with information on alternative energy, such as the article at: www.guardian.co.uk/renewable/0,2759,180749,00.html. Ask them to read it and make the case for having more alternative forms of energy in the UK.

4 Create an acrostic. Write GLOBAL WARMING down one side of a page. Make each letter the first letter of a word, phrase or sentence about global warming.

Further class and homework activities

1 Many governments from MEDCs are thinking about redeveloping plans to build more nuclear power stations. How would this help to reduce global warming? Collect information from Greenpeace and Friends of the Earth. See what their view is.

2 Investigate advice that is given to householders from the British government and fuel supply companies about cutting down on the use of fuel and improving insulation in the home. Make a wall display of the findings. Find out what is done in school to try to reduce the consumption of energy.

Answers to the Activities

1 Answers will depend on student activities and lifestyle.

2 The texts might include:
- ◆ don't use your mobile alarm; it costs more than using a wind-up clock
- ◆ recycle batteries
- ◆ use a short flush for a 'shorter visit'
- ◆ only boil as much water as you need – not the whole kettle
- ◆ don't clean your teeth over a running tap
- ◆ walk/cycle to school, if possible
- ◆ recycle cans; get drinks in recyclable plastic
- ◆ leaving your computer/TV on stand-by uses a lot of electricity.

'Text-speak', e.g. 'U cn', would be OK in this answer!

3 a & b

	cost £	saving £	balance after 1 yr	balance after 25 yrs
loft insulation	220	92	-128	2080
lowering the thermostat by 2°C	0	86	86	2150
1 low energy light bulb	3	10	7	250-7.5*
turning off un-necessary lights	0	8	8	200
turning TV off	0	3.29	3.29	82.25

* assuming bulbs last 10 years

4 a & b Answers will depend on student/family lifestyle and local council policy and initiatives.

5 Judgements should be based on criteria such as those below :

renewable resource	advantage	disadvantage
wind	can be located offshore – out of sight	Some people think that onshore wind farms are ugly and noisy
biomass	Good use of waste products – like straw, or even sewage!	Burning biomass will give off greenhouse gases
solar cells	No greenhouse gas emissions	Use a lot of resources to make; the UK isn't very sunny
waves	No greenhouse gas emissions	Expensive to set up and difficult to repair
tides	No greenhouse gas emissions	Will flood large areas of mudflats – for example, the planned Severn barrier

6 A series of turbines located in the sea, on tall pillars. When the wind blows, the turbines turn, generating electricity. [If you've got one of your own, you can sell your surplus energy to a power-generating company.]

The unit in brief

This unit is about the development of wind power in the UK, with the North Hoyle Wind Farm used as an example. It also looks at how opinions are divided over wind power. In the Activities, students try to convince people that windfarms are the future; use text and photo evidence to explain why some people don't like windfarms on land, and think about the advantages of offshore windfarms. They also consider whether the use of fossil fuels is unavoidable at the moment.

Key ideas

- ◆ North Hoyle is the UK's first important offshore wind farm.
- ◆ North Hoyle is made up of 30 wind turbines and produces enough clean 'green' electricity to power about 40 000 homes a year.
- ◆ The electricity produced by North Hoyle will offset the emission of about 160 000 tonnes of carbon dioxide every year.
- ◆ Opinions are divided over wind power. Some people think the turbines are too noisy.

Key vocabulary

offshore

Skills practised in the Activities

- ◆ Numeracy skills: reading a graph of fuel use
- ◆ Thinking skills: using arguments and evidence to persuade people that windfarms are the future; using text and photo evidence to explain why some people dislike windfarms on land; identifying the advantages of offshore windfarms; considering whether they agree or disagree with a statement and justifying their answer

Unit outcomes

By the end of this unit, most students should be able to:

- ◆ explain the term given in 'Key vocabulary' above;
- ◆ know that North Hoyle is the UK's first important offshore wind farm;
- ◆ understand how much power North Hoyle produces and the benefits of producing energy from windfarms;
- ◆ describe the advantages and disadvantages of windfarms (on land and offshore).

Ideas for a starter

1 Ask: Who can remind me about the main sources of energy used in the UK? How much of it comes from renewable sources?

2 Brainstorm: What are renewable resources and non-renewable resources? Make a list on the board of examples of each.

3 Show a range of images of wind turbines/wind farms. Ask: Why do we need to cut down on our use of fossil fuels for making electricity? What renewable alternatives do we have in the UK? Why do we have more potential for using wind power than anywhere else in Europe?

Ideas for plenaries

1 Summarise the argument given in the unit for and against wind farms. What other advantages and disadvantages can you think of?

2 Work with a partner. One of you is to write an email to your local newspaper arguing against the development of a wind farm. The other one is to write in favour of the wind farm. Read your emails to the class. How many different arguments can you come up with?

3 Invite someone in to speak to the class from an alternative power company. Prepare students in advance to make notes and be ready to ask questions.

4 Sketch a simple wind turbine. On the blades write down the 3 key things you have learned today about wind power in the UK.

Answers to the Activities

1 The percentage share of primary electricity fell from about 10% to about 8% between 2000 and 2004. Stress that this is percentage use. [This is a good opportunity to revise reading cumulative graphs, and you can do a lot more with this graph.]

2 Wind farms don't give off any carbon dioxide, which is a greenhouse gas, so they are a clean, renewable energy source. If the UK is to reach its targets in greenhouse gas reduction, wind energy is an environmentally-friendly form of energy. We try to site our turbines at least 300 m away, so noise shouldn't be a problem.

3 Some people don't like wind farms because they think the turbines are ugly. Others don't like wind farms because, they say, they are noisy. Others say they're a hazard to birds.

4 Offshore wind farms produce more electricity because they are not sheltered from the wind. They are far enough away from the shore to be out of sight, and there are no neighbours to complain about the noise.

5 The use of fossil fuel is unavoidable at the moment, because, in 2004 for example, only 3.6% of the UK's electricity supply came from all sources of renewable energy.

help at a glance

The unit in brief

In this unit students learn about how the holidays people take have changed, and the reasons for the growth in tourism. In the Activities, they identify different types of tourist attractions and classify them as physical or human. They think about the effect which different holidays have on the environment and people, and classify them according to their level of impact. They also use a graph to describe and explain the increase in the number of foreign trips made by UK residents between 1980 and 2000.

Key ideas

◆ Different people want different things on holiday and so will visit different places.

◆ Tourism has grown rapidly in the last twenty five years.

◆ Reasons for the growth in tourism include the fact that people have more leisure time and more disposable income, plus technology allows people to travel further and more cheaply than ever.

Key vocabulary

There is no key vocabulary in this unit.

Skills practised in the Activities

◆ Geography skills: describing and explaining the changes in the number of foreign trips made by UK residents over a period of time

◆ Thinking skills: identifying different types of tourist attractions and classifying them into physical and human; classifying holidays in terms of their impact on the environment and people; explaining likely future holidays

Unit outcomes

By the end of this unit, most students should be able to:

◆ identify and classify different types of tourist attractions;

◆ explain why tourism has grown rapidly in the last twenty five years;

◆ describe the impact of different types of holiday on the environment and people.

Ideas for a starter

1 Ask students where they have been on holiday. Record answers on the board. Try to group answers by location, duration, frequency, transport mode, accommodation and activities.

2 Show a set of photos of tourist attractions – in the UK and abroad. Ask students to try to name them quickly.

3 Brainstorm: Why do you think tourism has grown rapidly in the last 25 years?

Ideas for plenaries

1 Summarise the changes that have taken place in holidays over the last 40 years in terms of location, frequency and activities.

2 Why do people like going on holiday? Brainstorm the reasons and record the answers on a spider diagram.

3 Why do countries like to see tourists arriving? Brainstorm the reasons and record the answers on a spider diagram.

4 Activity 3 can be used as a plenary.

5 What impact can tourists have on the destination areas?

6 Write down as many words as you can relating to today's work.

Answers to the Activities

1a

climate	suntan
sight-seeing photographs	
social life	girs/boys
culture	meeting the natives; ancient ruins; away from fellow-Brits
sports	extreme sports; hill-walking
like home	no foreign food; satellite TV; a rep to stop you getting lost
cost	cheap is best

b

physical	human
sunny climate	sports
hills	social life
beach/sea	just like home, but sunny
	a rep to help you out
	museums and archaeology
	sample local culture
	cost

2 a You will want to talk here about the nature of the impact – environmental or cultural. Answers could include:

low impact	high impact
A Blackpool – within the UK; short distance	B Spain – airline CO_2 emissions, increased extraction of water C Florida – high CO_2 emissions during transatlantic flight D Thailand (x 3) – travel costs, plus the possibility of offending/changing local culture, for example sex tourism

b Answer will depend on student opinion/attitude and, perhaps, imagination.

3 a The number of foreign trips went up – from about 17 million in 1980 to about 57 million in 2000.

b Travel – especially air travel – has got cheaper; people in the UK have more leisure time and more disposable income; pensioners are richer and more active and therefore more likely to travel than they used to be; booking holidays has got easier.

The unit in brief

This unit is about the impact of tourism on holiday destinations, using Ibiza as a case study. In the Activities, students write a postcard describing a holiday in Ibiza, and use the photo diary and text to list the advantages and disadvantages of tourism for the island. They describe the balancing act that the local government has to pull off in terms of controlling existing tourism while attracting a different type of tourist in the future, and explain why tourists and Ibiza are interdependent.

Key ideas

◆ All tourists have an impact on their holiday destination.

◆ Two million tourists visit Ibiza every year – 700 000 of them from Britain. Many go to party.

◆ The local government wants to cut down on noise pollution and limit the number of people in the clubs.

◆ Ibiza needs the money tourists bring ($939 million p.a.) but wants to attract tourists who are interested in culture and wildlife, not just those who want to party.

Key vocabulary

There is no key vocabulary in this unit.

Skills practised in the Activities

◆ Geography skills: describe what the local government in Ibiza needs to do to keep tourists coming

◆ Literacy skills: writing a postcard describing a holiday in Ibiza

◆ Thinking skills: sorting the effects of tourism into advantages and disadvantages; explaining why tourists and Ibiza are interdependent

Unit outcomes

By the end of this unit, most students should be able to:

◆ describe the advantages and disadvantages of tourism for Ibiza;

◆ explain why so many people visit Ibiza every year;

◆ describe what the local government in Ibiza is trying to do to control existing tourism; and what type of tourist they want to encourage in the future.

Ideas for a starter

1 Ask students to produce a spider diagram showing all the possible impacts tourists could have. If they did plenary 5 in Unit 12.7, ask them to work with a partner to add the impacts they have already come up with.

2 Brainstorm to find out what students know about Ibiza. Where is it? Why do tourists go there?

3 Give out tourist brochures which include holidays in Ibiza. What kind of holidays are on offer? Does this agree with the answers students came up with in starter 2?

Ideas for plenaries

1 Give students holiday brochures for holidays in Europe. They need to look at different locations and types of holiday. Ask them to complete a table of advantages and disadvantages of tourism for the holiday destination.

2 Work with a neighbour. You both live in the same holiday destination. One of you writes a letter to the planning committee in favour of a new tourist development. Your partner writes a letter against it. Read your letters out to the rest of the class.

3 Now you are the planning committee so you need to be in small groups. Consider the letters for and against the tourist development. Will you want to let it go ahead? Try to agree and read your conclusions out to the rest of the class.

4 Investigate one of the tourist attractions in the UK from the beginning of Unit 12.9. Be ready to give a short talk about the attraction at the beginning of the next lesson.

5 Tell your neighbour the 2 key things you learned today.

Answers to the Activities

1 Jules might mention:
- lots of different clubs
- clubs open all night
- cheap drinks
- lots of young people.

2 Advantages of tourism for Ibiza
- Money – Ibiza makes $93 million a year
- Jobs – for example, as maids, drivers, gardeners and bar staff

Disadvantages of tourism for Ibiza
- Local culture disappearing
- Noise pollution
- Bad behaviour: drugs, drinking
- Tourists provide a bad example for Ibiza's children

3 It will be difficult to lessen the tourist impact – for example, by limiting numbers at any given club, reducing the legal noise limit, or cracking down on anti-social behaviour – without destroying lots of the things that young people come to Ibiza for.

4 Ibiza needs tourists as a central part of its economy; tourists won't find that special Ibiza 'vibe' anywhere else.

The unit in brief

This unit looks at the impact of tourism on one of the UK's National Trails – the Pennine Way, and asks whether it can be managed sustainably. In the Activities, students look at the attractions of the Pennine Way, consider how the causes of erosion could be reduced and whether making a harder wearing footpath will solve the problems of over-use. They also design an information board to inform walkers about the sustainable use of the Pennine Way.

Key ideas

◆ The Pennine Way became the UK's first National Trail in 1965. It runs for 429km (268 miles).

◆ Erosion is caused by summer fires that destroy vegetation, and overgrazing by sheep.

◆ The greatest cause of erosion on and around the Pennine Way is the thousands of walkers crossing the moorland every year. A restoration project has been set up to:
   - protect and restore the fragile soil and vegetation;
   - provide a long-lasting walking surface;
   - make sure that all the work is in harmony with the landscape.

Key vocabulary

people pressure, restoration project

Skills practised in the Activities

◆ Geography skills: designing an information board about the sustainable use of the Pennine Way

◆ Thinking skills: choosing tourist attractions and explaining why students would like to see them; listing the attractions of Pennine Way; thinking of ways in which erosion could be reduced; justifying an answer

Unit outcomes

By the end of this unit, most students should be able to:

◆ explain the terms given in 'Key vocabulary' above;

◆ describe the attractions of the Pennine Way;

◆ identify the causes of erosion on the Pennine Way;

◆ list the consequences of thousands of people using the Pennine Way each year;

◆ say how the Pennine Way can be managed sustainably.

Ideas for a starter

1 Recap: the impacts of tourism.

2 Take a quick class survey. Choose some of the attractions listed in box the at the top of page 252. Ask who would like to visit them.

3 Ask a couple of students to give a short talk about the attractions listed in the box at the top of page 252.

4 Look at the attractions listed in the box at the top of page 252. On a blank map of the UK locate as many as you can. For something like ' locations' choose a suitable place to locate the attraction.

Ideas for plenaries

1 Would you like to walk the Pennine Way or part of it? Explain why, or why not. What else would you want to know about it before you walked it? What type of people would want to walk the Pennine Way? Why?

2 What problems do tourists cause the Pennine Way? How can the problems be managed?

3 Consider the amount and type of employment generated by the tourist industry. Make a list of the number of types of jobs generated by opening up one small theme park.

4 Is this employment going to be long lasting and is it all year? Does it produce skills which are going to be transferable and, in the long run, is it sustainable? Consider these questions as a whole class. How could the jobs created in the tourist industry be more sustainable?

5 Investigate holidays in Thailand and be ready to talk about them at the beginning of the next lesson.

6 Make up 10-15 statements about tourism based on what students have learned so far, some true, some false. Students hold up True or False cards. Where statements are false, ask students to correct them.

Further class and homework activities

Look up the following website and investigate tourism in the UK. Try to find out the number of people visiting attractions and information about the attractions themselves. Start with attractions you have been to yourself and then add others. www.staruk.org.uk/

Answers to the Activities

1 Individual answers will vary, of course, but reasons given might include:
   ◆ strenuous/relaxing
   ◆ family/individual
   ◆ scenic/cultural

2 Look for three from:
   ◆ some of the best landscape features in Britain: Malham Cove, High Force, and High Cup Nick
   ◆ entirely off-road, using old miners' tracks, packhorse routes, and drove road
   ◆ clearly signposted
   ◆ east access by public transports
   ◆ you can book in advance

3
causes of erosion	solutions
Summer fires	Rapid-response fire-control unit
Overgrazing by sheep	Reduce sheep numbers

Trampling	Provide a long-lasting, paved surface; signs saying 'Stick to the Path'; add fertiliser to the ground each side of the path to restore the vegetation; limit the numbers doing fun runs

4 It will help, but, at busy times particularly, people will stray from the path. Some people will ignore the notices to stick to the path.

5 The information board might include:
   ◆ 'We want this footpath to be used by your grandchildren – please use it carefully.'
   ◆ 'Protect the vegetation/Pennine Way: Keep to the path.'
   ◆ 'Trampling crushes the moorland: keep to the path, please.'
   ◆ 'Take your cigarette ends with you!'
   ◆ 'Take nothing except pictures; leave only your footprints on the path.'

Tourism in an LEDC: Phuket, Thailand

help at a glance

The unit in brief

This unit includes a case study of the impact of tourism on an LEDC. It looks at Phuket in Thailand. In the Activities, students use the photos and text on Phuket to list the attractions of the island and classify them into physical and human attractions. They think about which type of attractions are most important to the tourist business, and whether increased numbers of tourists might be harmful in the long term. They also write a letter to a local Phuket newspaper explaining why they are either for, or against, the development of Phuket Bay International City.

Key ideas

◆ Phuket is one of Asia's top beach destinations.

◆ It offers warm seas, great beaches and lively nightlife.

◆ It has a population of 250 000 but gets 4 million tourists a year.

◆ Smuggling and the illegal trade in exotic plants and animals has become a multi-billion dollar business.

◆ There are plans to build a new mini-city (Phuket Bay International City) on reclaimed land in the bay off Saphan Hin. It would include hotels, a convention centre, sports facilities and a casino.

Key vocabulary

There is no key vocabulary in this unit.

Skills practised in the Activities

◆ Literacy skills: writing a letter to a Phuket local paper

◆ Thinking skills: listing the attractions of Phuket and classifying them into physical and human; explaining which attractions are most important to Phuket; explaining why increased numbers of tourists might be harmful in the long term; explaining whether local people benefit from tourism

Unit outcomes

By the end of this unit, most students should be able to:

◆ identify where Phuket is;

◆ list Phuket's attractions and classify them as either physical or human;

◆ explain why increased numbers of tourists might be a problem in the long term;

◆ describe the planned new development of Phuket Bay International City.

Ideas for a starter

1 Recap: the impacts of tourism in The UK. Do you need to add anything for the impacts of tourism on an LEDC country?

2 Ask students what they found out about holidays in Thailand (planary 5 in Unit 12.9). Has anyone been to Thailand? What type of holiday did they go on? What did they see and do?

3 Show photos of Thailand. Ask: who wants to go to Thailand? What impacts of tourism can you see in the photos?

4 How could tourism help LEDCs? Ask: What is an LEDC?

Ideas for plenaries

1 Produce a table showing the advantages and the problems with the planned Phuket Bay international City (the new tourist development in Thailand). Give each entry a score (plus or minus). Add up the scores when you have finished your table. What is the result?

2 How sustainable is this planned new development?

3 What would happen if many countries in the area established new tourist facilities? What would be the impact on the environment? What impact would the increased number of flights have on the global environment?

4 If Phuket falls out of favour with tourists, what would happen to the local economy?

5 Think of a more sustainable type of tourist development which would still help the economic development of the area. Try to make a model.

6 Investigate ecotourism (also known as green tourism or sustainable tourism). Start by looking at a site such as www.coralcay.org/index.php, but use a search engine to help locate others.

7 Question time! Think back over the lesson and write down 3 questions related to what you have learned on the impact of tourism on holiday destinations. The teacher will ask a member of the class to try and answer.

Answers to the Activities

1 a & b

physical/natural attractions

- sandy, white beaches
- warm seas
- elephants and other tropical fauna
- lush vegetation, palm trees
- beautiful landscapes

human/cultural attractions

- snorkelling
- the location of 'The Beach'
- accommodation ranging from deluxe to back-packer
- good nightlife
- water-jets, bog motorbikes, or four-wheel drives available to rent
- beautiful temples
- local festivals and religious traditions, great street markets
- colourful, lively atmosphere.

c You could argue that Phuket's natural resources are the basis for sunny, tropical tourism, local settlement, and thus to all the traditional culture. Some people might come just for the local culture, but the beaches are the main 'pull'. [In fact, as a revision aid for migration, you could develop 'pushes' from the UK: cold, grey, familiar, dull and dreary, and the 'pulls' of Phuket.]

2 Increased visitor numbers would increase the income and jobs created from tourism. However, if visitor numbers continue to rise, the resort will become more crowded. The problems of smuggling (including drugs) and 'biopiracy' will surely increase.

3 The Royal Meridian offer only mentions jobs for staff from MEDCs: French chef, British reps. Presumably the cooking and cleaning staff will be local, but their jobs will be less well paid. This is good for the Europeans, who get to work in a beautiful location, and offers less skilled jobs to the locals, but doesn't provide skilled work experience for them.

4
Dear Editor,

I am writing to protest against the proposed Phuket Bay International City project:

- a 2000-room hotel is too big to blend in
- so is the lotus-shaped marina
- spaceship-shaped structures will not blend in with the traditional architecture
- casinos are tacky
- increased visitor numbers will surely increase the problems of crime and drugs
- the project will benefit the Japanese (and maybe the Chinese) much more than it will the locals
- more traffic – more pollution

Dear Editor,

I am writing in support of the proposed Phuket Bay International City project:

- the project will provide hundreds of jobs, and boost the local economy, including agriculture
- the conference centre will make us less dependent on tourism (diversification)
- with increased office space, Phuket will attract businesses
- the marina will attract cruise passengers and yachtsmen
- Phuket suffered as a result of the 2004 tsunami; this project will protect us against another one

The unit in brief

This unit looks at how tourism can help to preserve the environment and investigates hotels in Ibiza and the resort of Antalya in Turkey. In the Activities, students choose a hotel for a holiday and explain their choice. They complete a checklist on sustainable tourism for the hotels included in this unit, and think about whether Antalya is truly sustainable.

Key ideas

◆ Green tourism has developed to try to limit the negative impacts of our holidays.

◆ Green tourism is also known as ecotourism, or sustainable tourism.

◆ Green tourism includes agro-tourism and cultural tourism.

◆ Even hotels which aim to be green are not always truly sustainable.

◆ The resort of Antalya on Turkey's Mediterranean coast has switched from mass tourism to sustainable tourism.

◆ Changes at Antalya include: no more hotel building; all hotels are connected to wastewater purification plants; all waste is composted; plans to preserve or increase the biodiversity of the area.

Key vocabulary

green tourism, ecotourism, sustainable tourism, agro-tourism, cultural tourism

Skills practised in the Activities

◆ Thinking skills: explaining a choice of hotel options; thinking about whether holidays are sustainable; completing a sustainable tourism checklist and explaining findings; thinking about whether Antalya is sustainable; explaining and answering a question

Unit outcomes

By the end of this unit, most students should be able to:

◆ define the terms given in 'Key vocabulary' above;

◆ describe the aims of green tourism;

◆ explain how even hotels which aim to be green are not always truly sustainable;

◆ describe the changes made at Antalya to switch from mass tourism to sustainable tourism;

◆ identify other ways in which Antalya could be made more sustainable.

Ideas for a starter

1 Remind students this chapter is about managing resources. Ask: Who can remind me what resources are? How does this include tourism?

2 Brainstorm: why should tourism be sustainable?

3 Ask students what they have discovered about ecotourism (plenary 6 unit 12.10). produce a spider diagram on the board of their findings

Ideas for plenaries

1 Produce a table of the advantages and disadvantages of sustainable tourism.

2 How should this type of holiday be marketed? Produce a poster, or a script, for a TV holiday programme to show how this type of holiday could be marketed.

3 Close your book. Test your neighbour. Ask: What is green tourism? What does it aim to do?

4 How would students manage and develop an island in the Pacific Ocean which has some resources and a small population? Give the students a basic map and factfile and ask them to produce a plan for developing the island. They need to think about how the resources are used and the impact of any developments.

5 A quick fire test: call out a student's name and definition of one of the key terms from this chapter. The student has 5 seconds to give you the term. Or, play a pairs matching game to check that students know the key terms and definitions from the chapter.

6 Play 'Just a minute'. the topic is 'Managing resources'. Students have the chance to talk for a minute on the topic without repitition or hesitation. As soon as a student repeats an idea, or hesitates, the next student takes over until the minute is up.

Further class and homework activities

Try to find other examples of ecotourism or green tourism and make a wall display of the findings. Who will these holidays appeal to?

Answers to the Activities

1 a & b

The focus here would be on the quality and consistency of the answers, as students focus on natural/local advantages or on mod cons and high-tech attractions.

c Answer will depend on student holiday and experience. The sustainable tourism checklist can be used for students' holidays (as well as for questions 2 and 3).

2 As guidelines …

Can Zangamanga	comments
Develops good relations between tourists and locals	little contact with locals
Supports learning of other cultures	Zangamanga is self contained, providing spa treatments and satellite TV; no mention of trips to places of interest
Mixes land use for varied habitats	access to pine forest and almond trees, but beaches seem to be out of walking distance
Uses local materials and local businesses	difficult to tell
Minimises water use	jacuzzis, hydro-massagers, swimming pool
Minimises electricity use	air conditioning
Provides worthwhile jobs in tourism	difficult to tell
Minimises pollution from motor exhausts	car hire, boat hire

Note: 'Zangamanga' is Spanish for a fold, a wrinkle, or a scam!

Finca Agricultor	comments
Develops good relations between tourists and locals	the farm labourers will be locals
Supports learning of other cultures	organised trips to places of interest are available
Mixes land use for varied habitats	latest environmentally-friendly methods to provide guests with fresh natural food; farms own fruit and vegetables and uses produce in cooking
Uses local materials and local businesses	local olives, plums, apricots, table and wine grapes, satsumas, tangerines, oranges and lemons, nectarines and apricots, avocados, figs, cherries, pomegranates, almonds and walnuts,

	wheat, and beans are farmed using environmentally-friendly methods
Minimises water use	no pools or jacuzzis
Minimises electricity use	wood fires when nights are cold
Provides worthwhile jobs in tourism	difficult to tell
Minimises pollution from motor exhausts	country walks, horseback and bike riding, scuba-diving, and sailing are non-motorised

3 a Again, using the sustainable tourism checklist:

Develops good relations between tourists and locals, supports learning of other cultures, uses local materials and local businesses	again, a self-contained resort, so there is little contact with the local people; fresh food probably comes from local farms – some of the purified waste water is used for irrigation; environmental protection by fire services
Mixes land use for varied habitats	golf courses are not varied habitats, but there are plans to preserve or increase biodiversity; pesticides used to eradicate insects
Minimises water use	huge water use for the golf course; wastewater purification plants release some water for irrigation and the rest is released back into nature; water available for fire fighting
Minimises electricity use	low energy light bulbs; plan to use wastes as biofuel
Provides worthwhile jobs in tourism	The ecology jobs look interesting
Minimises pollution from motor exhausts	difficult to tell, but no obviously motorised activity

4 Basically, the more a resort attracts tourists, the more it will be a victim of its own success. A good answer would refer to increasing tourist numbers using the graph in 12.6. Units 12.8 (Ibiza) and 12.10 (Phuket) summarise a lot of tourism-related problems. Ask the students how often they have heard people say 'I liked X, but it was full of tourists', not acknowledging the fact that they are tourists themselves.

(13) Development

The big picture

These are the key ideas behind this chapter:

◆ Countries around the world are at different stages of development. There is a huge gap between the most and least developed countries.

◆ Development can be measured using a variety of indicators. The UN Human Development Index measures quality of life.

◆ Huge numbers of people in LEDCs don't have access to the basics – clean water, or sufficient food.

◆ There's a global imbalance in trade with the MEDCs taking the lion's share. So the rich North gets richer, and the poor South gets poorer.

◆ LEDCs need aid for a variety of reasons, but different types of aid have advantages and disadvantages.

◆ Fairer trade and more effective aid can help countries develop.

Note that the students' version of the big picture is given in the students' chapter opener.

Chapter outline

Use this, and the students' chapter opener, to give students a mental roadmap for the chapter.

13   Development As the students' chapter opener, this unit is an important part of the chapter; see page 11 of this book of this book for notes about using chapter openers

13.1   Development – a world of two halves What development means, and how it can be measured

13.2   Mind the gap Why some countries are more developed than others, and measuring development using the Human Development Index

13.3   Water – a matter of life and death The difference in the availability and use of clean water in MEDCs and LEDCs

13.4   Water – increasing supply A large-scale scheme – the High Aswan Dam in Egypt, and a small-scale scheme – a well and pump in Ghana

13.5   Food Millions of people don't have enough food to eat

13.6   Development and trade What trade is, and patterns of trade

13.7   Trade – problems and partners LEDCs trade problems, and trading partners

13.8   Trade – it's not fair Free trade, tariffs and quotas; trading blocs; the WTO; and Fair Trade

13.9   Aid – closing the gap? What aid is, different types of aid, and why it is needed

13.10 Aid – is it all good news? Advantages and disadvantages of aid, and other ways to help LEDCs develop

Using the chapter starter

The photo on page 258 of *geog.GCSE* students' book shows a container ship leaving the port of Seattle, USA. It could be sailing for anywhere in the world.

Container ships carry most of the world's 'dry' cargo – this means manufactured goods. (Cargoes like metal ores, coal, and wheat are carried in bulk carriers.) They can carry up to 10 000 containers. The biggest are over 300 metres long – only oil tankers are bigger.

Objectives and outcomes for this chapter

Objectives	Unit	Outcomes
Most students will understand:		Most students will be able to:
● That different aspects of development can be measured.	13.1	● Give at least six examples of development indicators including GDP per capita (PPP).
● That the UN's Human Development index combines three aspects of human development to measure quality of life.	13.2	● State which aspects of human development the HDI measures.
● Why some countries are more developed than others.	13.2	● Give at least four reasons why there is a gap in development between the LEDCs and MEDCs; name at least three MEDCs and three LEDCs.
● That there is a difference in access to clean water in MEDCs and LEDCs.	13.3	● Explain: why water supplies and access to clean water vary globally; why countries need water to develop; what can be done to improve water supply and access to safe water.
● That water supply can be increased through large scale schemes (but these can have benefits and disadvantages), and small scale schemes.	13.4	● Give an example of a large scale scheme to increase water supply in an LEDC and list the benefits and disadvantages; give an example of a small scale scheme in an LEDC and say why it is an example of appropriate technology and sustainable development.
● Where people are suffering from malnutrition; why, and what can be done about it.	13.5	● Describe where in the world people are suffering from malnutrition; explain why people are malnourished and what can be done.
● What trade is, and patterns of trade.	13.6	● Define imports, exports, trade balance, trade surplus, trade deficit; describe the pattern of trade between MEDCs and LEDCs.
● That LEDCs face a number of problems when it comes to trade.	13.6, 13.7, 13.8	● Describe and explain the problems facing LEDCs eg the export of primary products, reliance on one or two export products, free trade, tariffs, quotas, trading blocs etc.
● That MEDCs and LEDCs have different trading patterns and partners.	13.6, 13.7	● Describe the exports, imports and trading partners of Kenya and Japan.
● That it is possible to improve people's lives with Fair Trade.	13.8	● Explain how Fair Trade helps to improve people's lives in LEDCs.
● What aid is, why it is needed, and that there are different types of aid.	13.9	● Define aid; explain why LEDCs need aid; describe different types of aid (government – bilateral, international organisations – multilateral, and voluntary); explain that aid can be short-term/emergency or long-term/sustainable.
● That different types of aid have advantages and disadvantages.	13.10	● List the advantages and disadvantages of different types of aid.
● What else can be done to help LEDCs develop their economy and reduce poverty.	13.10	● Give at least four examples of other things which can help LEDCs develop their economies and reduce poverty.

These tie in with 'Your goals for this chapter' in the students' chapter opener, and with the opening lines in each unit, which give the purpose of the unit in a student-friendly style.

Using the chapter starter   continued

Larger container ships are being built – they will be able to service a line of lorries over 60 miles long.

Containerisation made the shipping of products around the world cheaper. Consequently it has been said that without the container, there would be no globalisation.

Development – a world of two halves

The unit in brief

This unit introduces students to development. It explains what development means and shows students how it can be measured using a variety of indicators. In the Activities, students use the map of GDP per capita to describe the distribution of wealth and analyse a table of development indicators.

Key ideas

◆ Development is about improving people's lives.

◆ Development can be measured.

◆ GDP per capita (PPP) is one of the easiest ways of measuring development.

◆ Social indicators (population and health) can be used to measure development, as well as other things.

Key vocabulary

development, more economically developed countries (MEDCs), less economically developed countries (LEDCs), GDP (Gross Domestic Product), GDP per capita, PPP (purchasing power parity), social indicators

Skills practised in the Activities

◆ Geography skills: describing the distribution of wealth shown on a GDP map; describing differences between countries

◆ Numeracy skills: analysing a table of development data

◆ Thinking skills: explaining anomalies; suggesting reasons; identifying indicators; explaining choices, explaining differences

Unit outcomes

By the end of this unit, most students should be able to:

◆ define or explain the terms given in 'Key vocabulary' above;

◆ understand that development is about improving people's lives;

◆ understand how development can be measured;

◆ describe the world distribution of GDP per capita (PPP);

◆ explain which indicators are good measures of development.

Ideas for a starter

1 What are the aspects of your home environment that you value - clean water, comfortable housing, employment, leisure, good diet, safety etc? Brainstorm to find out what students value, and use these to come up with a definition of what development is about.

2 Ask students to look at a list of development indicators in an atlas. Which indicators do they think will give the best definition of development?

3 Ask students: do you consider that you live in a developed part of the world? What is it that makes the UK developed?

4 Use the two photos and speech bubbles at the top of page 260 as a starter. What do they tell students about development?

Ideas for plenaries

1 Why do we need to know how developed or less developed certain countries are?

2 The Brandt report initially divided the world into 'north' and 'south'. Is this a useful way of describing the levels of development in the world?

3 Continue the conversation between the two teenagers at the top of page 260. remember, the boy is from a MEDC and the girl is from an LEDC.

4 What is sustainable development? Try to come up with your own definition. Look at the different resources to try to refine your definition. You could try these websites:

www.worldbank.org/depweb/ (click on What is sustainable development?)

www.sustainable-development.gov.uk/

www.johannesburgsummit.org/

news.bbc.co.uk/hi/english/static/in_depth/world/2002/disposable_planet/

5 It was the Brandt report that started us thinking of the world in terms of north and south. Is this a useful way of describing the levels of development in the world?

6 Investigate two LEDCs. Why are these countries so poorly developed?

7 Make a graffiti wall of what students have learned today.

Further class and homework activities

Use data from the following sources to put together indicators of development – remember you will have to sample countries say take 20 maximum:

www.cyberschoolbus.un.org/

http://web.worldbank.org/WBSITE/EXTERNAL/DATASTATISTICS/0,,menuPK:232599~page PK:64133170~piPK:64133498~theSitePK:239419,00.html

Answers to the Activities

1 Richer countries are mostly the MEDCs, which are in the north. Obvious exceptions to this simple geographical pattern include Australia and South Africa. The division becomes increasingly indistinct when considering countries such as India and China, one above and one below the 'Brandt' line. There are also some countries that are developing very quickly, such as Brazil.

2 This is the currency that is most widely used for global trading purposes, and so is the most easy to use for comparisons.

3 This will depend upon students' choices – ensure that reasons are given.

4 a Students describe the figures for Kenya and the UK – the reasons for the differences are those that distinguish LEDCs and MEDCs, such as better health care and education, diet, etc.

b Students describe the figures for Japan and China. Although many differences are like those between the UK and Kenya, they are generally not as great.

5 Although it is possible to broadly divide the countries, it is quite difficult to give exact definitions because there are several measures used, and not all countries fit neatly into the 'rich' or 'poor' category for all of the indicators.

Mind the gap

The unit in brief

In this unit students find out why some countries are more developed than others. The unit also introduces the HDI – the UN measure of quality of life. In the Activities, students describe the pattern of development on the map showing HDI and compare it with the GDP map in Unit 13.1; think about whether the HDI is a better measure of development than other indicators; and consider how the HDI rankings of countries will change in the future.

Key ideas

◆ There is a gap in levels of development between LEDCs and MEDCs.

◆ The gap in development has been caused by a variety of factors, including history, politics, industry, debt, environment and hazards.

◆ The UN produces the HDI which measures quality of life, not just wealth.

◆ The HDI for countries around the world is improving except for the new countries of central Asia and sub-Saharan Africa.

Key vocabulary

Human Development Index (HDI), quality of life

Skills practised in the Activities

◆ Geography skills: describing the pattern of development shown on the HDI map; comparing patterns on maps and explaining differences

◆ Thinking skills: explaining reasons; thinking; suggesting reasons

Unit outcomes

By the end of this unit, most students should be able to:

◆ define the terms given in 'Key vocabulary' above;

◆ recognise that there is a gap in levels of development between LEDCs and MEDCs;

◆ understand what has caused the gap in development;

◆ describe the pattern of development shown by the HDI;

◆ understand why the HDI for certain countries is getting worse.

Ideas for a starter

1 Ask students to report back from their investigation into why some LEDCs are so poorly developed (plenary 5 unit 13.1).

2 Brainstorm to find out what students know about why there's a gap in levels of development between MEDCs and LEDCs. Produce a spider diagram of students' responses.

3 Recap: the definition of development from unit 13.1. Does it contain an element of sustainability in it?

4 Ask students: How do you think the world's development is viewed from one of the poorer LEDCs? Put yourself in their shoes. Tell me why they are so poorly developed.

Ideas for plenaries

1 Work in groups of 3. Role play an interview between one person representing an LEDC and one person representing a MEDC. The interview is about the reasons for differences in levels of development. (The third person is the interviewer).

2 Go back to the spider diagram you produced in starter 2. Ask students to modify it if necessary.

3 Choose one: History, Industry, Environment and Hazards, and Politics. Draw a consequence map to show how it had held back development in the LEDCs.

4 Did you find anything difficult about the work in this Unit? What? Why? What would help to make it less difficult?

Further class and homework activities

1 Go to the Human Development Index website and collect your own data. (hdr.undp.org/) Compare this definition of development with the original one you came up with.

2 At this website you can select countries and also download data in an Excel spreadsheet for further manipulation hdr.undp.org/hd/default.cfm

3 Use this information to produce a wall display showing the level of development in a representative sample of countries. Add pictures and flags to make your display more memorable.

Answers to the Activities

1 In many ways this is similar to the rich / poor divide usually seen on LEDC / MEDC maps – Western Europe, Australia / New Zealand, and North America have the highest figures. Typically, it is the LEDCs that have the lower figures. An exception to this is the southern part of South America, where Argentina and Chile have high HDI figures.

2 Africa is the continent that comes out poorest in both maps. North America and Western Europe are high on both, as is Australia. There are some differences, for example parts of South America – where the HDI is relatively high, and variations in Asia.

3 Before industrialisation and globalisation. MEDCs grew rapidly and became wealthy very quickly. Part of this growth was at the expense of colonies of these countries – many of today's LEDCs – which became poorer as a result of poor trade relations and increasing dependence on a small number of products for export.

4 The HDI gives a composite measure, and so is likely to be more accurate than just one measure such as GDP. It is meant to give a broader picture of quality of life. GDP does not really do this, particularly as it does not give an indication of real wealth within a country.

5 One possibility is that it will not change much – actual figures may change as countries develop, but the ranking may not. Alternatively, some of the LEDCs may move up the rankings as their quality of life improves – perhaps, for example, Brazil.

The unit in brief

This unit is about the availability of clean water in MEDCs and LEDCs. It considers what can be done to increase the supply of, or access to, safe, clean water. In the Activities, students study a map showing access to safe water to describe the pattern shown and compare this with a map of population distribution; contrast the way water is used in individual countries; and look at some of the solutions to water shortages.

Key ideas

◆ The supply of water is finite.

◆ The amount of water available varies spatially and temporally.

◆ One billion people don't have access to safe clean water.

◆ As countries develop and population increases, so does the demand for water.

◆ Solutions to the water supply problem range from UN initiatives to countries doing deals for water.

Key vocabulary

There is no key vocabulary in this unit.

Skills practised in the Activities

◆ Geography skills: describing the pattern of access to safe water shown by a map; comparing patterns on maps; contrasting water use

◆ Thinking skills: suggesting reasons and explaining them

Unit outcomes

By the end of this unit, most students should be able to:

◆ recognise that the supply of water is finite;

◆ understand that the amount of water available varies spatially and temporally;

◆ describe the global pattern of access to safe clean water;

◆ understand why the demand for water is increasing;

◆ suggest whether the solutions to the water supply problem are more suitable for LEDCs or MEDCs.

Ideas for a starter

1 Brainstorm to find out what students think are the basic necessities of life. Try to come up with an agreed list.

2 Hold up a bottle of muddyish (river) water. Ask: How would you like to drink this? Explain that over 1 billion people don't have access to clean piped water.

3 Recap: the water cycle. Draw it on the board and label it. Use it to explain why there is a crisis when water is in a closed system.

4 Use this article to discuss the water problem – Crisis? What crisis?

news.bbc.co.uk/hi/english/static/in_depth/world/2000/world_water_crisis/default.st

Ideas for plenaries

1 Compare the map on page 264 showing the percentage of population with access to safe water with the map on page 260. What does it tell you?

2 Write a letter from the United Nations to member states urging them to provide more support for water aid projects. Explain the importance of water supply to them.

3 It is 2015. Has the UN been successful in halving the number of people without access to safe drinking water and basic sanitation?

4 How will water use change around the world in the future? How can we make water supplies go further?

5 Find out about the different types of irrigation in Egypt. Be ready to give a short report at the beginning of the next lesson.

6 Tell me the 3 main things you have learned today. Now tell me another 3 things which are interesting but less important.

Further class and homework activities

1 Investigate the local supply of water. Which company provides water for your home? Are there any local issues such as hose pipe bans? Write to the company and find out what the local situation is.

2 Use the information in this section and from additional websites to collect more information to write a short essay outlining the problems of access to water:

news.bbc.co.uk/1/hi/world/1887451.stm

www.wateraid.org/uk/

3 Do a survey on how much water is used by the family over the course of a week. Are there suggestions you could make to reduce the amount of water used?

4 Contact the local water supply company and see if they have suggestions on how water supply could be better used.

Answers to the Activities

1 Generally best in MEDCs, and also those countries where the HDI is relatively high, for example Argentina and Chile.

2 Some of the areas of greatest population density are those with lowest access to safe water, for example Bangladesh. Problems of increased diseases due to unclean water, particularly where population is increasing. Possibility of disputes and conflicts over future water supplies.

3 In MEDCs – UK and USA – greatest amount of water usage is for industry. In LEDCs it is for agriculture. The exception is Brazil, where there has been rapid industrial growth.

4 'Use less' is often cited as a means by which MEDCs may solve the problems of water shortages, although arguably this applies increasingly to LEDCs as well. 'Get technical' is usually more appropriate for MEDCs, and the others for MEDCs.

The unit in brief

In this unit students find out about two different approaches to increasing water supply. The examples included are the High Aswan Dam in Egypt (a large-scale project) and the provision of wells and pumps in Ghana (a small-scale example of appropriate technology). In the Activities, students complete a cost-benefit table for the High Aswan Dam and compare the advantages of large-scale projects like this with those of the small-scale scheme in Ghana.

Key ideas

◆ Water supply can be increased using both large and small-scale projects.

◆ The High Aswan dam brought both benefits and disadvantages.

◆ The provision of wells and pumps for rural communities in LEDCs are examples of appropriate technology and sustainable development.

Key vocabulary

non-governmental organisation (NGO), appropriate technology, sustainable development

Skills practised in the Activities

◆ Geography skills: completing a cost-benefit table for the High Aswan Dam and evaluating its impact; comparing schemes

◆ Thinking skills: explaining; identifying benefits and disadvantages; thinking

Unit outcomes

By the end of this unit, most students should be able to:

◆ define the terms given in 'Key vocabulary' above;

◆ understand that water supply can be increased using both large and small-scale projects;

◆ give examples of the benefits and disadvantages of the High Aswan Dam;

◆ explain why the provision of wells and pumps for rural communities in LEDCs are examples of appropriate technology and sustainable development.

Ideas for a starter

1 Ask students to report back on irrigation in Egypt. How efficient are the different types of irrigation? Draw up a table showing the advantages and problems associated with each type of irrigation. Use photographs to help the debate.

2 Read out the first paragraph under the heading 'Or is small beautiful' on page 267. then read the first two paragraphs of Apoyanga's story. Ask students to complete the story. What happened next? How did Apoyanga and her family's life improve? Who helped and how?

3 The expression 'small is beautiful' was first used by an economist called E.F. Schumacher. Ask students what they think it means. (He believed the best results in LEDCs came from small projects involving local people, as opposed to large projects controlled by international organisations which may exploit people and be unsustainable.)

Ideas for plenaries

1 Try to produce a model of linked boxes showing the positive effects of the High Aswan Dam. Be ready to draw yours on the board and discuss it with the class.

2 Why have people in Apoyanga's village not built a well themselves, ages ago? (Lack of knowledge/expensive, lack of tools and materials, no spare money.)

3 Large scale development schemes can bring a great deal of prestige to a country and can bring rapid economic development, while small scale schemes may bring lasting sustainable development. Discuss this amongst the class, and come to a conclusion.

4 Activity 4 could be used as a plenary.

5 Create an acrostic. Write WATER SUPPLY down the side of a page. make each letter the first letter of a word, phrase or sentence about water supply.

Further class and homework activities

Investigate the workings of one the NGOs. Try to find some specific projects they are involved with.

Answers to the Activities

1 The majority of Egypt is a desert, and so therefore lacking in a reliable supply of water. The Nile provided that only source.

2 Benefits include those to agriculture, HEP from the dam and economic growth. Disadvantages include lack of silt downstream affecting soil fertility, increased pollution through the use of fertilisers for agriculture, and the re-settlement of people due to the creation of Lake Nasser.

3 Suitable for the people who use it – it is not expensive, complicated, or reliant upon input from other people.

4 This will depend upon students' opinions – ensure that they are justified.

The unit in brief

This unit is about food – how much and what type we need, what happens if you don't have enough, who's suffering from malnutrition and why. In the Activities, students identify the causes of the 2005 food crisis in Niger and the possible long-term problems that giving food aid to countries such as Niger might cause. They also consider whether poverty and hunger are problems for Africa or all LEDCs.

Key ideas

◆ The dietary energy supply is the number of calories each person needs.

◆ A balanced diet is necessary to maintain health.

◆ People with insufficient food suffer from malnutrition.

◆ The percentage of people suffering from malnutrition has fallen everywhere since 1970, except for sub-Saharan Africa, but the number of people affected has risen.

◆ Helping countries to develop and making trade fairer are two ways of increasing food for LEDCs.

Key vocabulary

malnutrition, dietary energy supply (DES), marasmus, kwashiorkor

Skills practised in the Activities

◆ Thinking skills: identifying causes; identifying problems; thinking; explaining reasons for agreeing or disagreeing with a statement

Unit outcomes

By the end of this unit, most students should be able to:

◆ define or explain the terms given in 'Key vocabulary' above;

◆ understand that a balanced diet is necessary to maintain health;

◆ explain what happens if you don't have enough food;

◆ explain what has happened to the percentage and number of people suffering from malnutrition since 1970;

◆ say what can be done to increase food supply in LEDCs.

Ideas for a starter

1 Ask students: What do you eat in an 'average' day? How much food do we need? (In MEDCs at least 2600 calories. Our average intake in the UK is 3317 calories.)

2 What do we mean by a 'balanced diet'? Is your diet balanced? What problems might people in MEDCs have by eating an unbalanced diet? What problems might people in LECDs have by eating an unbalanced diet? (Things like rickets, blindness.)

3 Use photographs and video clips from the news to highlight the problem of starvation and poverty. Contrast this with photographs from the affluent west to highlight the problem of distribution rather than production.

Ideas for plenaries

1 Draw a consequence map to show how providing huge amounts of food aid can result in low prices for local farmers and an eventual reduction in the number of farmers and locally produced food.

2 Should rich farmland in LEDCs be used to grow cash crops for export or food crops for the local market? Cash crops bring in money from abroad. Food crops will be consumed locally and produce a better nourished population. What is more important? Prepare a 3 minute speech to the rest of the class on this issue.

3 Draw a basic cycle of poverty and give to students. Ask them to annotate the cycle. Where would they break the cycle? Whose responsibility is it to break the cycle? Who can help?

4 Look at the map on page 269 showing the percentage of the population which is malnurished. Close your book and describe the pattern shown on the map to your neighbour.

5 In preparation for the next Unit do a survey at home to find out which countries food products come from. How many come from LEDCs and how many from MEDCs?

6 Make 10-15 statements based on what students have learned so far, some true, some false. Students hold up True or False cards. Where statements are false, ask students to correct them.

Answers to the Activities

1 Repeated drought made worse by destruction of crops by plagues of locusts.

2 Dependency upon foreign aid, lack of sustainability of own agricultural systems.

3 This will depend upon students' opinions, which should be justified.

4 This will depend upon students' opinions, but it is true that the situation in Africa is worse than other developing parts of the world – there is little change in many African nations, while many other LEDCs are developing rapidly.

Development and trade

The unit in brief

This unit introduces trade. Using Japan and Kenya as examples, it investigates what trade is, and patterns and imbalances of trade. In the Activities, students look at the differences in Japan and Kenya's exports; identify the problems caused by trade deficits; look at the effect of price fluctuations on countries exporting primary products; and think about the trade imbalance.

Key ideas

◆ Trade consists of imports and exports.

◆ The difference between imports and exports is the trade balance.

◆ Where the value of exports is higher than the value of imports then a country has a trade surplus.

◆ Where the value of imports is higher than the value of exports then a country has a trade deficit.

◆ Generally, MEDCs export manufactured goods and import primary products, while LEDCs export primary products and import manufactured goods.

◆ There is an imbalance in trade.

Key vocabulary

trade, imports, exports, trade balance, trade surplus, trade deficit, interdependent

Skills practised in the Activities

◆ Thinking skills: explaining differences; identifying problems; thinking

Unit outcomes

By the end of this unit, most students should be able to:

◆ define or explain the terms given in 'Key vocabulary' above;

◆ understand that trade consists of imports and exports and that the difference between imports and exports is the trade balance;

◆ give examples of countries with a trade surplus and a trade deficit, and identify the problems caused by a trade deficit;

◆ identify the problems caused for people in LEDCs which export primary products;

◆ say why the imbalance in trade doesn't appear to be improving.

Ideas for a starter

1 Ask students to report back where their food comes from (plenary 5 Unit 13.5). Mark the origin of the food on a blank map of the world. What pattern does this show?

2 Go to the World Trade Organisation website (www.wto.org/). Download the 10 advantages they give for world trading arrangements. Put these up on the board for the class. Do students agree with them?

3 Read the paragraph 'Trouble brewing' to the class, omitting the last sentence. Ask students: How are your lives linked to Elizabeth and Ibrahim's? This can lead to a discussion of 'what is trade', 'how does it work', etc.

Ideas for plenaries

1 Produce a flow map using the figures at the top of page 271 to show Kenya and Japan's imports and exports.

2 Work with a partner. Try to come up with a set of principles which could give the LEDCs a better and fairer trade deal. Try to build in the principles of sustainability as well.

3 Write 'development and trade' in the middle of your page. Create a concept map around the phrase. How many ideas can you come up with?

4 Test your partner! Ask your partner to close their book. Test them to see if they know the definitions of the key words in this unit (the ones in bold).

5 Investigate the various trading organisations around the world and be ready to report back next time.

Further class and homework activities

1 Investigate the trade patterns of other LEDCs and see if they are similar to those shown for Kenya.

2 Investigate the prices of a selection of primary products over the last few years and compare these with the prices for manufactured items.

Answers to the Activities

1 Most of Japan's exports are manufactured goods – many hi-tech – and those from Kenya are primary.

2 Many countries, particularly LEDCs, rely heavily upon manufactured imports to balance their export of primary products – and so are likely to have a trade deficit.

3 More money leaving than entering the country, reliance on imports.

4 Variable demand, as some products may go in and out of fashion. In times of high production, prices may fall – as they may rise when production is limited. Prices may also change as alternative / substitute products become available.

5 It is in the interests of MEDCs to preserve the imbalance. Many LEDCs owe so much in interest charges on debt that it will be a long time before they are able to make progress. Exports of primary products, typically from LEDCs, are of lesser value than manufactured goods and services, predominantly from MEDCs.

The unit in brief

This unit looks at some of the other trading problems LEDCs have, and at trade partners – again using Japan and Kenya as examples. In the Activities, students look at the problems of LEDCs which rely on a small number of export products; suggest why the price of primary products fluctuates; classify statements about trade and describe and explain the pattern of trading partners for Japan and Kenya.

Key ideas

◆ Many LEDCs rely on the export of one or two goods.

◆ Trade creates winners and losers.

◆ All countries have trading partners.

◆ Japan imports most from China, and exports most to the USA.

◆ Kenya imports most from UAE and Saudi Arabia, and exports most to Uganda.

Key vocabulary

trading partners

Skills practised in the Activities

◆ Geography skills: describing and explaining the pattern of import and export partners

◆ Thinking skills: identifying and explaining problems; suggesting reasons; classifying statements

Unit outcomes

By the end of this unit, most students should be able to:

◆ explain the term given in 'Key vocabulary' above;

◆ explain the problems for LEDCs which rely on a small number of export products;

◆ understand that trade creates winners and losers;

◆ describe and explain the pattern of trading partners for Japan and Kenya.

Ideas for a starter

1 Recap: the problems of trade for LEDCs covered in Unit 13.6.

2 Show photos of certain ships, freight planes, lorries, freight trains, etc. Ask: What are these vehicles doing? Where have they come from? Where are they going to? Introduce the idea of trading partners.

Ideas for plenaries

Investigate the World Trade Organisation and trading blocs. Be ready to report back at the beginning of the next lesson.

Answers to the Activities

1 There could be a fall in prices and a reduction in earnings for the economy if there is a reduced demand for a product, a substitute comes on to the market, or there is surplus production.

2 Due to much greater fluctuation in demand, possible loss of crops due to natural hazards or diseases.

3 Political factors are dominant, with environmental factors being of greater weight in LEDCs.

4 Japan is closely linked to Asian neighbours, and the USA. Kenya has some links with Africa, then some European nations and some links with Asia.

Trade – it's not fair

The unit in brief

This unit explains some of the reasons why trade isn't fair. It looks at free trade, tariffs and quotas, trading blocs and the WTO. It also looks at Fair trade as a way of making trade fairer. In the Activities, students explain why countries introduce tariffs and quotas; why they form trading blocs; consider free trade and think about Fair trade products.

Key ideas

◆ Countries control trade with tariffs and quotas.

◆ Countries group together to form trading blocs to improve their trade balance.

◆ The WTO polices and promotes free trade, settles trade disputes and organises trade negotiations.

◆ Fair trade is where producers in developing countries get a guaranteed price for their product.

Key vocabulary

tariffs, quotas, free trade, trading blocs, World Trade Organisation (WTO), Fair trade

Skills practised in the Activities

◆ Thinking skills: explaining; identifying products; expressing opinions; giving reasons

Unit outcomes

By the end of this unit, most students should be able to:

◆ define or explain the terms given in 'Key vocabulary' above;

◆ understand that countries control trade with tariffs and quotas;

◆ understand why countries group together to form trading blocs;

◆ explain the role of the WTO;

◆ explain how Fair trade works.

Ideas for a starter

1   Ask students what they have found out about the World Trade Organisation and trading blocs.

2   Bring in some Fair Trade products and try them with the class. Compare them with other products – the chocolate is particularly nice!

3   Trade benefits MEDCs at the expense of LEDCs. Ask: How could the situation be changed to make it fairer to LEDCs? Would students be prepared to pay more for goods from LEDCs to make trade fairer for them?

Ideas for plenaries

1   What is to stop LEDCs grouping together to form their own trading group? Discuss this possibility with the class.

2   Should we in the UK try to eliminate trading blocs over time? How could this be done? Would it benefit the LEDCs?

3   Write to your local supermarket. Ask them what their policies are on stocking more produce from a fair trade source. Will they increase their fair trade produce?

4   Remember Elizabeth and Ibrahim on page 270? How could fair trade help them?

5   Write a short essay entitled *How can we make International Trade fairer for all?*

6   Find out: what is aid? Who gives it? How do NGOs help LEDCs?

7   Choose a student to be in the hot seat. Another student asks him or her a question about trade. Then nominate two different students (4-6 pairs in total). There's one golden rule – questions cannot be repeated.

Further class and homework activities

1   Investigate the Fair Trade organisation. Survey your local supermarket and try to identify the products that are traded under the Fair Trade brand.

2   Go to some of the NGO websites and try to find information about schemes which have been set up with farmers selling their produce through fair trading organisations

Answers to the Activities

1   To protect their own products by making those from other countries more expensive, or limiting the number allowed to enter the country.

2   Any country may set tariffs and quotas. Typically, an MEDC will set a tariff or quota to protect its industries from cheaper goods from abroad – although often from other MEDCs, these increasingly may come from other parts of the world such as the NICs.

3   To gain greater strength in protection than is possible for individual countries.

4   This will depend upon students' opinions, which need to be justified.

5   Russia has not met the agreed rules of the WTO. This matters due to the size, power and influence of Russia.

6   This depends upon students' own opinions.

The unit in brief

This unit is about aid, with Niger and Zimbabwe used as examples. It looks at different types of aid, why aid is needed, what exactly aid is and how much aid we give. In the Activities, students identify when it is best to give short-term and long-term aid; look at the similarities and differences between the aid given to Niger and Zimbabwe and consider 'tied' aid and how much MEDCs should give in aid.

Key ideas

◆ Aid is when one country or organisation gives resources to another country.

◆ Aid can be provided by governments (bilateral aid), international organisations (multilateral aid) or voluntary organisations (NGOs like Oxfam).

◆ Aid can be short-term/emergency or long-term/sustainable.

◆ LEDCs need aid because of imbalances in trade, differences in levels of development and to recover from hazards.

◆ The UN's target is that MEDCs should give 0.7% of their income in aid to LEDCs.

Key vocabulary

aid, government (bilateral), international organisations (multilateral), voluntary, short-term/emergency, long-term/sustainable, donor, recipient

Skills practised in the Activities

◆ Thinking skills: thinking and giving examples; identifying similarities and differences; justifying opinions

Unit outcomes

By the end of this unit, most students should be able to:

◆ define or explain the terms given in 'Key vocabulary' above;

◆ understand that aid is when one country or organisation gives resources to another country;

◆ explain different types of aid;

◆ know that aid can be short-term/emergency or long-term/sustainable;

◆ understand why aid is needed;

◆ say whether MEDCs should give more or less than the UN's target of 0.7% of their income as aid.

Ideas for a starter

1 Review what students found out about aid in plenary 6 (Unit 13.8). Check that students are clear about what aid is, and what types of aid there are.

2 Brainstorm to find out if students knew why aid is needed. Who needs aid? Do MEDCs ever need aid?

3 Do students or their families give money to help people in LEDCs? E.g. do they contribute to Children in Need or did their family purchase one of the *Feed the World* singles? Should aid be something that individuals give or should it be up to governments to provide it?

4 Recap: the cycle of poverty used in plenary 3 Unit 13.5. How can aid help to break the cycle?

Ideas for plenaries

1 Draw up a table showing the advantages and disadvantages of different types of development aid – bilateral aid, multilateral aid and voluntary aid from NGOs.

2 Think of situations when aid from the different sources would be most appropriate.

3 Consider the following schemes for LEDCs and prioritise them. Bear in mind that any developments you make need to be sustainable.

- A gift of tractors and other farm machinery
- Electrical pumps for providing irrigation water
- Toilets built by a volunteer organisation such as World Challenge
- Two school teachers and school text books from UK
- Two places for teacher training at a UK university for two local people
- Irrigation equipment
- Supplies of grain
- A communal meeting house
- A medical centre and medical equipment
- A doctor funded for 12 months.

Present your findings to the rest of the class and be ready to discuss the outcomes.

4 Draft an email to the American and UK governments. Tell them why you think they should give more money in aid than they did in 2003 (be polite!). Say how much they should give and what it could be spent on.

5 Sum up what you have learned today in 35 words.

Answers to the Activities

1 a In the case of an emergency situation to provide immediate help.

b For the longer-term benefit and development of a country.

2 Both are LEDCs receiving aid. Niger was in danger of becoming reliant on short-term food aid. Zimbabwe was being provided with longer-term techniques and tools to promote sustainable development.

3 a Aid that has to be spent on a particular purpose.

b Lack of opportunity to use the money for other purposes, or to respond to changing needs.

4 This will depend upon students' opinions, which should be justified.

Aid – is it all good news?

The unit in brief

This unit looks at the advantages and disadvantages of different types of aid and asks students to think about whether aid is the best way to help LEDCs develop. In the Activities, students pull together what they have learnt about aid in units 13.9 and 13.10; think about debt cancellation and consider whether trade and not aid is what LEDCs need to develop.

Key ideas

◆ Different types of aid have advantages and disadvantages.

◆ Aid has a role in helping LEDCs develop.

◆ There are many other things which can be done to help LEDCs develop.

◆ Many people think that trade, not aid, is the key to economic development.

Key vocabulary

government (bilateral), international organisations (multilateral), voluntary, short-term/emergency, long-term/sustainable,

Skills practised in the Activities

◆ Literacy skills: summarising information on aid

◆ Thinking skills: identifying benefits of aid; thinking; justifying opinions

Unit outcomes

By the end of this unit, most students should be able to:

◆ define or explain the terms given in 'Key vocabulary' above;

◆ identify the advantages and disadvantages of different types of aid;

◆ understand that while aid has a role in helping LEDCs to develop, there are many other things which can be done to help them;

◆ say whether they think that trade, not aid, is what is needed to help LEDCs to develop.

Ideas for a starter

1 Produce a word search for students. Include the following terms – trade, imports, exports, interdependence, trading bloc, WTO, tariffs, quotas, aid, donor, recipient. Once students have found the words ask them to write definitions for them.

2 Who can remind me what aid is? And who can remind me what different types of aid there are?

3 Brainstorm to find out how many ideas students can come up with of different ways of helping LEDCs develop their economies and reduce poverty. Record students' ideas on a spider diagram.

Ideas for plenaries

1 LEDCs have often borrowed lots of money to try to develop. the money has to be repaid – with interest. Should MEDCs cancel all the debts of the LEDCs? Do you think this is the best way to help LEDCs develop?

2 If students completed plenary 1 Unit 13.9, ask them to look back at the table of advantages and disadvantages of different types of aid they drew up. Ask them to modify their table if necessary.

3 Activity 4 could be used as a plenary.

4 If plenary 3 Unit 13.6, ask them to look back at the concept map they created. Now ask them to write 'Development, Trade and Aid' in the middle of their page and create a concept map around the phrase. How many other ideas can they add?

5 Do an alphabet run from A-Z, with a word or phrase to do with development for each letter.

Further class and homework activities

1 Collect information about the G8 summit and Live8. Do you think these initiatives were successful?

2 Make a list of the major case studies. These will help you in your preparation for examinations. Remember case studies for Development will be found in other parts of the book such as Industry and Agriculture.

Answers to the Activities

1 This will depend upon students' own learning. Government aid is often tied, so it has to be spent on particular projects. International aid is not usually tied, so it can be more flexible. Voluntary aid is useful, but is dependent upon how much people give. Short-term aid can provide help for emergencies, while long-term aid aims to be sustainable.

2 Poorer regions of the EU receive help from the EU, so strictly speaking they are receiving aid. It is a matter of opinion as to whether all aid to should go to the poorest nations, or some should be spent in MEDCs.

3 This will depend upon students' opinions, which should be justified.

4 Students should refer to the imbalance of trade between LEDCs and MEDCs, and it is clear that a more equitable system of trading would be in the long-term interest of LEDCs.

Glossary

A

abrasion – the scratching and scraping of a river bed and banks by the stones and sand in the river

afforestation – the replanting of trees

agribusiness – large-scale capital-intensive farming

agri-environment scheme – schemes which combine farming with looking after, and improving, the environment, such as Tir Gofal in Wales and Environmental Stewardship in England

agro-tourist – someone who spends their holiday on a farm

air pressure – the weight of air pressing down on the Earth's surface. Low pressure means warm air is rising, so rain is on the way. (The rising air cools and its water vapour condenses.)

appropriate technology – meets the needs of local people and the environment they live in

arch – a hole right through a headland. It is made by waves eroding through caves in the headland

arête – a sharp ridge between two corries (see corrie)

ash cloud – a cloud of volcanic ash occurring during and after a volcanic eruption; may be carried a long way and can cause damage and death

B

biome – a very large ecosystem. The rainforests are one biome. Hot deserts are another

birth rate – the number of live births in a country in a year, per 1000 people

blow-hole – formed when a cave is eroded upwards by hydraulic action

C

CAP – Common Agricultural Policy set up by the EU and which subsidised farmers

caves – erosion by waves enlarges joints and faults in rocks to form caves

CBD – central business district. It's the area at the centre of a town or city where you find the main shops and offices

cliffs – high rock faces that run along the coast

cloud cover – how much of the sky is hidden by cloud. It is given in eighths (oktas).

cloud type – there are five main types of cloud: stratus, cumulus, nimbus, cumulonimbus and cirrus

collision margin – where two tectonic plates (continental plates) are colliding

commercial farming – outputs from the farm are sold to make a profit

composite volcano – a steep-sided cone-shaped volcano, made from sticky acidic lava

conservative margin – where two tectonic plates are moving past each other

constructive margin – where two tectonic plates are moving apart and new crust is constructed

consumers – living things that eat other living things for food. For example zebra consume grass

continental crust – the part of the Earth's crust that makes the continents; it's between 25 km and 100 km thick

corrie – a circular, armchair-shaped hollow cut into rock by ice during glaciation

counter-urbanisation – the movement of people out of cities to smaller towns and villages

crater – the hollow at the mouth of a volcano. Rain falling into craters may form lakes

crevasse – a vertical or wedge-shaped crack in a glacier

D

death rate – the number of deaths in a country in a year, per 1000 people

decomposers – organisms that break down dead and waste material in an ecosystem. Bacteria and fungi are examples

deforestation – clearing forest for another use. For example cutting down rainforest to make way for a motorway or cattle ranches

deindustrialisation – the decline in manufacturing (secondary) industry, and the growth in tertiary and quaternary industry

delta – a flat area at the mouth of a river, made of sediment deposited by the river

desertification – when soil in a savanna region gets worn out, dusty and useless

destructive margin – where two tectonic plates are moving together and oceanic crust is destroyed by subduction

dietary energy supply – the number of calories per person available each day

distributaries – if sediment blocks a river it has to divide into small channels called distributaries

drumlin – a smooth hill shaped by glaciers

E

economic migrants – people who move voluntarily for jobs and higher wages

ecosystem – a unit made up of living things and their non-living environment. For example a pond, a forest, a desert

employment structure – what % of workers are in the primary, secondary and tertiary sectors of the economy

epicentre – the point on the ground directly above the focus (centre) of an earthquake

esker – a long ridge of material deposited from streams flowing under glaciers

estuary – the mouth of a large river, which is affected by the tides. As the tide rises, sea water flows up into the estuary and mixes with the river water

extensive farming – has smaller inputs of labour, money or technology than intensive farming. Extensive farms are usually larger than intensive farms

F

factors – things which affect where industry, agriculture, settlements etc will locate

favela – name for a shanty town in a South American city

feedback – things are put back into the system – like profits which may be reinvested

fertility rate – the number of children, on average, a woman will have in her lifetime

floodplain – flat land around a river that gets flooded when the river overflows

focus – the centre of an earthquake. It is the exact point where rock moved, setting off the quake. It could be far below the ground

food chain – a chain of names linked by arrows, showing what species feed on. It always starts with a plant

food web – a network of food chains, showing how they link together

footloose – an industry which is not tied to raw materials and so can choose where to locate

fossil fuels – coal, oil and natural gas. They are called fossil fuels because they are the remains of plants and animals that lived millions of years ago

free trade – when goods and services can flow freely from country to country, without any taxes

freeze-thaw weathering – the weathering (breakdown) of rock by the action of water getting into cracks in the rock, freezing and thawing

G

GDP per capita (PPP) – GDP is gross domestic product. It is the total value of the goods and services produced in a country in a year. GDP per capita means the GDP divided by the population. PPP means purchasing power parity. GDP is adjusted because a dollar buys more in some countries than others

glacial trough – a steep-sided U-shaped valley caused by glaciers

global warming – the way temperatures around the world are rising. Scientists think we have made this happen by burning too much fossil fuel

green belt – an area of open land around a city, which is protected from development. This is to stop the city spreading further

Green Revolution – the introduction of high-yielding varieties of cereals such as rice and wheat into LEDCs

green tourism – aims to limit the negative impact of tourism. It is also known as ecotourism or sustainable tourism

greenhouse gases – gases like carbon dioxide and methane that trap heat around the Earth, leading to global warming

groundwater flow – the flow of groundwater through saturated rock or soil

H

hanging valley – a high-level tributary valley with a sharp fall to the main valley; a feature of glacial erosion

high-tech industry – an industry that develops and produces new and advanced products. For example new kinds of mobile phones or medical drugs

hot spot – where volcanoes occur away from plate margins; probably due to strong upward currents in the mantle

humidity – the % of water vapour in the air

I

impermeable – doesn't let water through

infant mortality – the number of babies out of every 1000 born alive, who die before their first birthday

infiltration – the soaking of rainwater into the ground

inputs – things that go into a system. They can be physical, or human and economic.

intensive farming – has large inputs of labour, money or technology to produce high outputs. Farms are usually quite small

interception – the capture of rainwater by leaves. Some evaporates again and the rest trickles to the ground

interlocking spurs – hills that stick out on alternate sides of a V-shaped valley like the teeth of a zip

irrigation – artificial watering of land and crops

K

kame – a mound or heap of material dropped from a glacier

L

lava – melted rock that erupts from a volcano

levees – embankments built up on either side of a river channel

life expectancy – how many years a new baby can expect to live, on average. Life expectancy is higher for females than for males

M

magma – melted rock below the Earth's surface. When it reaches the surface it is called lava

materialism – wanting only belongings or comfort, and having no interest in morals

meander – a bend in a river

misfit stream – a small stream in the bottom of glacial trough

moraine – material carried by a glacier

mouth – the end point of a river, where it enters the sea or a lake

mudflow (lahar) – a river of mud formed when ash and other material from an erupting volcano mixes with water or ice. It can drown towns and villages

N

natural increase – the birth rate minus the death rate for a place. It is always given as a % of the total population

NGO – non-governmental organisation. NGOs work to make life better, especially for the poor. Oxfam, the Red Cross and Greenpeace are all NGOs

O

oceanic crust – the part of the Earth's crust which is under the oceans; it's made of basalt and is between 5 km and 10 km thick

outputs – things that come out of the system (products)

ox-bow lake – a lake formed when a loop in a river is cut off by floods

P

percolation – the movement of water downwards through rock

plates – the Earth's surface is broken into large pieces, like a cracked eggshell. The pieces are called tectonic plates, or just plates

plucking – when ice freezes on to rock, moves, and so plucks the rock away

plug – a rock plug that may be left in the crater of a volcano after an eruption; may be blown off in a future eruption

population density – the average number of people per square kilometre

population growth rate – the number of people added to a population each year due to natural increase and net migration. It is given as a %

porous – lets water soak through

precipitation – water falling from the sky. It could fall as rain, hail, sleet or snow.

primary industry – people extract raw materials from the land or sea. For example farming, fishing and mining

processes – things that happen in the middle of the system to turn inputs into outputs

producers – plants are called producers because they make their own food from carbon dioxide and water

pyramidal peak – the peak formed when three or more corries form round a mountain (see corrie)

pyroclastic flow – a scorching hot avalanche of gas, ash, cinders and rocks that rushes down the slopes of a volcano after an explosive eruption

Q

quaternary industry – people are employed in industries providing information and expert help. For example IT consultants and researchers

quota – a limit on the amount of goods produced or purchased

R

refugee – a person who is forced to flee from danger (for example war or an earthquake) and seek refuge in another country

river channel – the bed and sides of a river form a river channel

river terraces – areas of flatter land above the floodplain

rural-urban fringe – the area where a town or city meets the countryside

S

salinisation – soil becomes increasingly salty (saline) and plants die. Irrigation can cause salinisation

secondary industry – people make, or manufacture, things. For example turning iron ore into steel, making cars and building houses

set-aside land – land which isn't used for growing crops or keeping animals on; farmers are paid for this

shanty town – areas of poor quality housing lacking facilities which develop in unfavourable sites in, and around, cities in LEDCs

shield volcano – a low flat volcano, like an upturned shield, made from runny basic lava

slumping – a mass movement of rock and soil down a slope

solution – the dissolving of minerals from rocks, by water

source – the starting point of a river

sphere of influence – area around a settlement (or shop, or other service) where its effect is felt. London has a very large sphere of influence

SPS – Single Payment System, part of the CAP reform. Farmers now get one single payment a year instead of several different subsidy payments

stack – a pillar of rock left standing in the sea when the top of an arch collapses

striation – scratches in rock caused by abrasion in a glacier

stump – the remains of a stack which the sea has eroded away

subsistence farming – where farmers grow food to feed their families, rather than to sell

surface run-off – rainwater that runs across the surface of the ground and drains into the river

sustainable – can be carried on without doing any harm (to people, or other living things, or the environment)

sustainable development – development that will not lower our quality of life or harm the environment

sustainable management – meeting the needs of people now and in the future, and limiting harm to the environment

system – has inputs, processes and outputs. Industry and agriculture can be described as systems

T

tariff – a tax that a country places on goods being imported or exported

temperature – how hot or cold something is, usually measured in degrees Centigrade

tertiary industry – people are employed in providing a service. For example the health service (doctors, nurses, dentists) and education (teachers)

through-flow – the flow of rainwater sideways through the soil, towards the river

till – jumbled, unsorted material dropped by glaciers

trade balance – the difference between the value of imports and exports of a country

trade deficit – a country spends more on imports than it earns from exports

trade surplus – a country earns more money from exports than it spends on imports

trading bloc – a group of countries that have joined together to improve trade

truncated spurs – where a glacier has eroded and cut off inter locking spurs

U

urban model – a simplified diagram of the way land is used in a city

urban redevelopment – clearance and rebuilding of old inner city areas

urban renewal – improving (without knocking down and clearing) old inner city areas

urban zones – areas of different land use in an urban area

urbanisation – an increase in the percentage of people living in towns and cities

U-shaped valley – see glacial trough

V

visibility – the greatest distance you can see, in km or m. On a foggy day it could be just 1 or 2 metres

V-shaped valley – a valley shaped like the letter V, carved out by a river

W

waterfall – where a river or stream flows over a steep drop

wave-cut platform – the flat rocky area left behind when waves erode a cliff away

wind direction – the direction the wind blows from

wind strength (speed) – how fast the wind blows

World Trade Organisation – a body set up to help trade between countries